METHOD AND RESULTS

ESSAYS

BY

THOMAS H. HUXLEY

NEW YORK
D. APPLETON AND COMPANY
1898

Authorized Edition.

PREFACE

THE fourth of the "Collected Essays" in the volume now published gives an account of the indispensable conditions of scientific assent, as they are defined by the author of the famous "Discours de la Méthode."

The other eight set forth the results which, in my judgment, are attained by the application of the "Method" of Descartes to the investigation of problems of widely various kinds; in the right solution of which we are all deeply interested. Hence I have given the volume the title of "Method and Results."

Written, for the most part, in the scant leisure of pressing occupations, or in the intervals of ill-health, these essays are free neither from superfluities in the way of repetition, nor from deficiencies which, I doubt not, will be even more conspicuous to other eyes than they are to my own. But so far as their substance goes, I find nothing to alter in them,—though the oldest bears the date of 1866. Whether that is evidence of the soundness of my opinions, or of my having made no progress in wisdom for the last quarter of a century, must be left to the courteous reader to decide.

T. H. H.

HODESLEA, EASTBOURNE,
January 16th, 1893.

CONTENTS

CONTENTS

AUTOBIOGRAPHY

AND when I consider, in one view, the many things . . . . . .
which I have upon my hands, I feel the burlesque of being
employed in this manner at my time of life. But, in another
view, and taking in all circumstances, these things, as trifling as
they may appear, no less than things of greater importance, seem
to be put upon me to do. . . . . . —*Bishop Butler to the Duchess
of Somerset.*

THE " many things " to which the Duchess's
correspondent here refers are the repairs and
improvements of the episcopal seat at Auckland.
I doubt if the great apologist, greater in nothing
than in the simple dignity of his character, would
have considered the writing an account of himself
as a thing which could be put upon him to do
whatever circumstances might be taken in. But
the good bishop lived in an age when a man
might write books and yet be permitted to keep
his private existence to himself; in the pre-
Boswellian epoch, when the germ of the photo-
grapher lay in the womb of the distant future, and

the interviewer who pervades our age was an unforeseen, indeed unimaginable, birth of time.

At present, the most convinced believer in the aphorism "Bene qui latuit, bene vixit," is not always able to act up to it. An importunate person informs him that his portrait is about to be published and will be accompanied by a biography which the importunate person proposes to write. The sufferer knows what that means; either he undertakes to revise the "biography" or he does not. In the former case, he makes himself responsible; in the latter, he allows the publication of a mass of more or less fulsome inaccuracies for which he will be held responsible by those who are familiar with the prevalent art of self-advertisement. On the whole, it may be better to get over the "burlesque of being employed in this manner" and do the thing himself.

It was by reflections of this kind that, some years ago, I was led to write and permit the publication of the subjoined sketch.

I was born about eight o'clock in the morning on the 4th of May, 1825, at Ealing, which was, at that time, as quiet a little country village as could be found within half-a-dozen miles of Hyde Park Corner. Now it is a suburb of London with, I believe, 30,000 inhabitants. My father was one of the masters in a large semi-public school which at one time had a high reputation. I am not aware that any portents preceded my arrival in this world, but, in my childhood, I remember hearing a traditional account of the manner in which I lost the chance of an endowment of great practical value. The windows of my mother's room were open, in consequence of the unusual warmth of the weather. For the same reason, probably, a neighbouring beehive had swarmed, and the new colony, pitching on the window-sill, was making its way into the room when the horrified nurse shut down the sash. If that well-meaning woman had only abstained from her ill-timed interference, the swarm might have settled on my lips, and I should have been endowed with that mellifluous eloquence which, in this country, leads far more surely than worth, capacity, or honest work, to the highest places in Church and State. But the opportunity was lost, and I have been obliged to content myself through life with saying what I mean in the plainest of plain language, than which, I suppose, there is no habit more ruinous to a man's prospects of advancement.

Why I was christened Thomas Henry I do not know; but it is a curious chance that my parents should have fixed for my usual denomination upon the name of that particular Apostle with whom I have always felt most sympathy. Physically and mentally I am the son of my mother so completely —even down to peculiar movements of the hands, which made their appearance in me as I reached the age she had when I noticed them—that I can hardly find any trace of my father in myself, except an inborn faculty for drawing, which unfortunately, in my case, has never been cultivated, a hot temper, and that amount of tenacity of purpose which unfriendly observers sometimes call obstinacy.

My mother was a slender brunette, of an emotional and energetic temperament, and possessed of the most piercing black eyes I ever saw in a woman's head. With no more education than other women of the middle classes in her day, she had an excellent mental capacity. Her most distinguishing characteristic, however, was rapidity of thought. If one ventured to suggest she had not taken much time to arrive at any conclusion, she would say, " I cannot help it, things flash across me." That peculiarity has been passed on to me in full strength ; it has often stood me in good stead ; it has sometimes played me sad tricks, and it has always been a danger. But, after all, if my time were to come over again, there is nothing I would less willingly part with than my inheritance of mother wit.

I have next to nothing to say about my childhood. In later years my mother, looking at me almost reproachfully, would sometimes say, " Ah ! you were such a pretty boy ! " whence I had no difficulty in concluding that I had not

fulfilled my early promise in the matter of looks.
In fact, I have a distinct recollection of certain
curls of which I was vain, and of a conviction that
I closely resembled that handsome, courtly gentleman, Sir Herbert Oakley, who was vicar of our
parish, and who was as a god to us country folk,
because he was occasionally visited by the then
Prince George of Cambridge. I remember turning
my pinafore wrong side forwards in order to represent a surplice, and preaching to my mother's maids
in the kitchen as nearly as possible in Sir Herbert's manner one Sunday morning when the rest
of the family were at church. That is the earliest
indication I can call to mind of the strong clerical
affinities which my friend Mr. Herbert Spencer
has always ascribed to me, though I fancy they
have for the most part remained in a latent
state.

My regular school training was of the briefest,
perhaps fortunately, for though my way of life has
made me acquainted with all sorts and conditions of
men, from the highest to the lowest, I deliberately
affirm that the society I fell into at school was the
worst I have ever known. We boys were average
lads, with much the same inherent capacity for
good and evil as any others; but the people who
were set over us cared about as much for our
intellectual and moral welfare as if they were
baby-farmers. We were left to the operation of
the struggle for existence among ourselves, and

bullying was the least of the ill practices current among us. Almost the only cheerful reminiscence in connection with the place which arises in my mind is that of a battle I had with one of my classmates, who had bullied me until I could stand it no longer. I was a very slight lad, but there was a wild-cat element in me which, when roused, made up for lack of weight, and I licked my adversary effectually. However, one of my first experiences of the extremely rough-and-ready nature of justice, as exhibited by the course of things in general, arose out of the fact that I—the victor—had a black eye, while he—the vanquished —had none, so that I got into disgrace and he did not. We made it up, and thereafter I was unmolested. One of the greatest shocks I ever received in my life was to be told a dozen years afterwards by the groom who brought me my horse in a stable-yard in Sydney that he was my quondam antagonist. He had a long story of family misfortune to account for his position, but at that time it was necessary to deal very cautiously with mysterious strangers in New South Wales, and on inquiry I found that the unfortunate young man had not only been " sent out," but had undergone more than one colonial conviction.

As I grew older, my great desire was to be a mechanical engineer, but the fates were against this and, while very young, I commenced the study of medicine under a medical brother-in-law. But, though the Institute of Mechanical Engineers would certainly not own me, I am not sure that I have not all along been a sort of mechanical engineer *in partibus infidelium*. I am now occasionally horrified to think how very little I ever knew or cared about medicine as the art of healing. The only part of my professional course which really and deeply interested me was physiology, which is the mechanical engineering of living machines; and, notwithstanding that natural science has been my proper business, I am afraid there is very little of the genuine naturalist in me. I never collected anything, and species work was always a burden to me ; what I cared for was the architectural and engineering part of the business, the working out the wonderful unity of plan in the thousands and thousands of diverse living constructions, and the modifications of similar apparatuses to serve diverse ends. The extraordinary attraction I felt towards the study of the intricacies of living structure nearly proved fatal to me at the outset. I was a mere boy—I think between thirteen and fourteen years of age— when I was taken by some older student friends of mine to the first *post-mortem* examination I ever attended. All my life I have been most unfortunately sensitive to the disagreeables which attend anatomical pursuits, but on this occasion my curiosity overpowered all other feelings, and I spent two or three hours in gratifying it. I did not cut myself, and none of the ordinary symptoms of dissection-poison supervened, but poisoned I was somehow, and I remember sinking into a strange state of apathy. By way of a last chance, I was sent to the care of some good, kind people, friends of my father's, who lived in a farmhouse in the heart of Warwickshire. I remember staggering from my bed to the window on the bright spring morning after my arrival, and throwing open the casement. Life seemed to come back on the wings of the breeze, and to this day the faint odour of wood-smoke, like that which floated across the farm-yard in the early morning, is as good to me as the "sweet south upon a bed of violets." I soon recovered, but for years I suffered from occasional paroxysms of internal pain, and from that time my constant friend, hypochondriacal dyspepsia, commenced his half century of co-tenancy of my fleshly tabernacle.

Looking back on my "Lehrjahre," I am sorry to say that I do not think that any account of my doings as a student would tend to edification. In fact, I should distinctly warn ingenuous youth to avoid imitating my example. I worked extremely hard when it pleased me, and when it did not— which was a very frequent case—I was extremely idle (unless making caricatures of one's pastors and masters is to be called a branch of industry), or else wasted my energies in wrong directions. I read everything I could lay hands upon, including novels, and took up all sorts of pursuits to drop them again quite as speedily. No doubt it was very largely my own fault, but the only instruction from which I ever obtained the proper effect of education was that which I received from Mr. Wharton Jones, who was the lecturer on physiology at the Charing Cross School of Medicine. The extent and precision of his knowledge impressed me greatly, and the severe exactness of his method of lecturing was quite to my taste. I do not know that I have ever felt so much respect for anybody as a teacher before or since. I worked hard to obtain his approbation, and he was extremely kind and helpful to the youngster who, I am afraid, took up more of his time than he had any right to do. It was he who suggested the publication of my first scientific paper—a very little one—in the *Medical Gazette* of 1845, and most kindly corrected the literary faults which abounded in it, short as it was; for at that time, and for many years afterwards, I detested the trouble of writing, and would take no pains over it.

It was in the early spring of 1846, that, having finished my obligatory medical studies and passed the first M.B. examination at the London University —though I was still too young to qualify at the College of Surgeons—I was talking to a fellow-student (the present eminent physician, Sir Joseph Fayrer), and wondering what I should do to meet the imperative necessity for earning my own bread,

2

when my friend suggested that I should write to
Sir William Burnett, at that time Director-General
for the Medical Service of the Navy, for an appoint-
ment.   I thought this rather a strong thing to do,
as Sir William was personally unknown to me,
but my cheery friend would not listen to my
scruples, so I went to my lodgings and wrote the
best letter I could devise.   A few days afterwards
I received the usual official circular of acknowledgment, but at the bottom there was written an instruction to call at Somerset House on such a day.
I thought that looked like business, so at the
appointed time I called and sent in my card, while
I waited in Sir William's ante-room.   He was a
tall, shrewd-looking old gentleman, with a broad
Scotch accent—and I think I see him now as he
entered with my card in his hand.   The first
thing he did was to return it, with the frugal
reminder that I should probably find it useful on
some other occasion.   The second was to ask
whether I was an Irishman.   I suppose the air of
modesty about my appeal must have struck him.
I satisfied the Director-General that I was English
to the backbone, and he made some inquiries as
to my student career, finally desiring me to hold
myself ready for examination.   Having passed
this, I was in Her Majesty's Service, and entered
on the books of Nelson's old ship, the *Victory*, for
duty at Haslar Hospital, about a couple of months
after I made my application.

My official chief at Haslar was a very remarkable person, the late Sir John Richardson, an excellent naturalist, and far-famed as an indomitable Arctic traveller. He was a silent, reserved man, outside the circle of his family and intimates; and, having a full share of youthful vanity, I was extremely disgusted to find that "Old John," as we irreverent youngsters called him, took not the slightest notice of my worshipful self either the first time I attended him, as it was my duty to do, or for some weeks afterwards. I am afraid to think of the lengths to which my tongue may have run on the subject of the churlishness of the chief, who was, in truth, one of the kindest-hearted and most considerate of men. But one day, as I was crossing the hospital square, Sir John stopped me, and heaped coals of fire on my head by telling me that he had tried to get me one of the resident appointments, much coveted by the assistant-surgeons, but that the Admiralty had put in another man. "However," said he, "I mean to keep you here till I can get you something you will like," and turned upon his heel without waiting for the thanks I stammered out. That explained how it was I had not been packed off to the West Coast of Africa like some of my juniors, and why, eventually, I remained altogether seven months at Haslar.

After a long interval, during which "Old John" ignored my existence almost as completely as before, he stopped me again as we met in a casual way, and describing the service on which the *Rattlesnake* was likely to be employed, said that Captain Owen Stanley, who was to command the ship, had asked him to recommend an assistant surgeon who knew something of science; would I like that? Of course I jumped at the offer. "Very well, I give you leave; go to London at once and see Captain Stanley." I went, saw my future commander, who was very civil to me, and promised to ask that I should be appointed to his ship, as in due time I was. It is a singular thing that, during the few months of my stay at Haslar, I had among my messmates two future Directors-General of the Medical Service of the Navy (Sir Alexander Armstrong and Sir John Watt-Reid), with the present President of the College of Physicians and my kindest of doctors, Sir Andrew Clark.

Life on board Her Majesty's ships in those days was a very different affair from what it is now, and ours was exceptionally rough, as we were often many months without receiving letters or seeing any civilised people but ourselves. In exchange, we had the interest of being about the last voyagers, I suppose, to whom it could be possible to meet with people who knew nothing of fire-arms—as we did on the south Coast of New Guinea—and of making acquaintance with a variety of interesting savage and semi-civilised people. But, apart from experience of this kind and the opportunities offered for scientific work, to me, personally, the cruise was extremely valuable. It was good for me to live under sharp discipline; to be down on the realities of existence by living on bare necessaries; to find out how extremely well worth living life seemed to be when one woke up from a night's rest on a soft plank, with the sky for canopy and cocoa and weevilly biscuit the sole prospect for breakfast; and, more especially, to learn to work for the sake of what I got for myself out of it, even if it all went to the bottom and I along with it. My brother officers were as good fellows as sailors ought to be and generally are, but, naturally, they neither knew nor cared anything about my pursuits, nor understood why I should be so zealous in pursuit of the objects which my friends, the middies, christened " Buffons," after the title conspicuous on a volume of the " Suites à Buffon," which stood on my shelf in the chart room.

During the four years of our absence, I sent home communication after communication to the " Linnean Society," with the same result as that obtained by Noah when he sent the raven out of his ark. Tired at last of hearing nothing about them, I determined to do or die, and in 1849 I drew up a more elaborate paper and forwarded it to the Royal Society. This was my dove, if I had only known it. But owing to the movements of the ship, I heard nothing of that either until my return to England in the latter end of the year 1850, when I found that it was printed and published, and that a huge packet of separate copies awaited me. When I hear some of my young friends complain of want of sympathy and encouragement, I am inclined to think that my naval life was not the least valuable part of my education.

Three years after my return were occupied by a battle between my scientific friends on the one hand and the Admiralty on the other, as to whether the latter ought, or ought not, to act up to the spirit of a pledge they had given to encourage officers who had done scientific work by contributing to the expense of publishing mine. At last the Admiralty, getting tired, I suppose, cut short the discussion by ordering me to join a ship, which thing I declined to do, and as Rastignac, in the Père Goriot, says to Paris, I said to London "à nous deux." I desired to obtain a Professorship of either Physiology or Comparative Anatomy, and as vacancies occurred I applied, but in vain. My friend, Professor Tyndall, and I were candidates at the same time, he for the Chair of Physics and I for that of Natural History in the University of Toronto, which, fortunately, as it turned out, would not look at either of us. I say fortunately, not from any lack of respect for Toronto, but because I soon made up my mind that London was the place for me, and hence I have steadily declined the inducements to leave it, which have at various times been offered. At last, in 1854, on the translation of my warm friend Edward Forbes, to Edinburgh, Sir Henry De la Beche, the Director-General of the Geological Survey, offered me the post Forbes vacated of Paleontologist and Lecturer on Natural History. I refused the former point blank, and accepted the latter only provisionally, telling Sir Henry that I did not care for fossils, and that I should give up Natural History as soon as I could get a physiological post. But I held the office for thirty-one years, and a large part of my work has been paleontological.

At that time I disliked public speaking, and had a firm conviction that I should break down every time I opened my mouth. I believe I had every fault a speaker could have (except talking at random or indulging in rhetoric), when I spoke to the first important audience I ever addressed, on a Friday evening at the Royal Institution, in 1852. Yet, I must confess to having been guilty, *malgré moi*, of as much public speaking as most of my contemporaries, and for the last ten years it ceased to be so much of a bugbear to me. I used to pity myself for having to go through this training, but I am now more disposed to compassionate the unfortunate audiences, especially my ever-friendly hearers at the Royal Institution, who were the subjects of my oratorical experiments.

The last thing that it would be proper for me

to do would be to speak of the work of my life, or to say at the end of the day whether I think I have earned my wages or not. Men are said to be partial judges of themselves. Young men may be, I doubt if old men are. Life seems terribly foreshortened as they look back, and the mountain they set themselves to climb in youth turns out to be a mere spur of immeasurably higher ranges when, with failing breath, they reach the top. But if I may speak of the objects I have had more or less definitely in view since I began the ascent of my hillock, they are briefly these : To promote the increase of natural knowledge and to forward the application of scientific methods of investigation to all the problems of life to the best of my ability, in the conviction which has grown with my growth and strengthened with my strength, that there is no alleviation for the sufferings of mankind except veracity of thought and of action, and the resolute facing of the world as it is when the garment of make-believe by which pious hands have hidden its uglier features is stripped off.

It is with this intent that I have subordinated any reasonable, or unreasonable, ambition for scientific fame which I may have permitted myself to entertain to other ends ; to the popularisation of science ; to the development and organisation of scientific education ; to the endless series of battles and skirmishes over evolution ; and to untiring opposition to that ecclesiastical spirit, that clericalism, which in England, as everywhere else, and to whatever denomination it may belong, is the deadly enemy of science.

In striving for the attainment of these objects, I have been but one among many, and I shall be well content to be remembered, or even not remembered, as such. Circumstances, among which I am proud to reckon the devoted kindness of many friends, have led to my occupation of various prominent positions, among which the Presidency of the Royal Society is the highest. It would be mock modesty on my part, with these and other scientific honours which have been bestowed upon me, to pretend that I have not succeeded in the career which I have followed, rather because I was driven into it than of my own free will; but I am afraid I should not count even these things as marks of success if I could not hope that I had somewhat helped that movement of opinion which has been called the New Reformation.

I

ON THE ADVISABLENESS OF IMPROVING NATURAL KNOWLEDGE

[1866]

THIS time two hundred years ago — in the beginning of January, 1666—those of our forefathers who inhabited this great and ancient city, took breath between the shocks of two fearful calamities: one not quite past, although its fury had abated; the other to come.

Within a few yards of the very spot on which we are assembled, so the tradition runs, that painful and deadly malady, the plague, appeared in the latter months of 1664; and, though no new visitor, smote the people of England, and especially of her capital, with a violence unknown before, in the course of the following year. The hand of a master has pictured what happened in those dismal months; and in that truest of fictions, "The History of the Plague Year," Defoe shows

death, with every accompaniment of pain and
terror, stalking through the narrow streets of old
London, and changing their busy hum into a silence
broken only by the wailing of the mourners of
fifty thousand dead ; by the woful denunciations
and mad prayers of fanatics ; and by the madder
yells of despairing profligates.

But, about this time in 1666, the death-rate
had sunk to nearly its ordinary amount ; a case of
plague occurred only here and there, and the
richer citizens who had flown from the pest had
returned to their dwellings. The remnant of the
people began to toil at the accustomed round of
duty, or of pleasure ; and the stream of city life
bid fair to flow back along its old bed, with renewed and uninterrupted vigour.

The newly-kindled hope was deceitful. The
great plague, indeed, returned no more ; but what
it had done for the Londoners, the great fire,
which broke out in the autumn of 1666, did for
London ; and, in September of that year, a heap
of ashes and the indestructible energy of the
people were all that remained of the glory of five-
sixths of the city within the walls.

Our forefathers had their own ways of accounting for each of these calamities. They submitted
to the plague in humility and in penitence, for
they believed it to be the judgment of God. But,
towards the fire they were furiously indignant,

interpreting it as the effect of the malice of man, —as the work of the Republicans, or of the Papists, according as their prepossessions ran in favour of loyalty or of Puritanism.

It would, I fancy, have fared but ill with one who, standing where I now stand, in what was then a thickly-peopled and fashionable part of London, should have broached to our ancestors the doctrine which I now propound to you—that all their hypotheses were alike wrong; that the plague was no more, in their sense, Divine judgment, than the fire was the work of any political, or of any religious, sect; but that they were themselves the authors of both plague and fire, and that they must look to themselves to prevent the recurrence of calamities, to all appearance so peculiarly beyond the reach of human control—so evidently the result of the wrath of God, or of the craft and subtlety of an enemy.

And one may picture to one's self how harmoniously the holy cursing of the Puritan of that day would have chimed in with the unholy cursing and the crackling wit of the Rochesters and Sedleys, and with the revilings of the political fanatics, if my imaginary plain dealer had gone on to say that, if the return of such misfortunes were ever rendered impossible, it would not be in virtue of the victory of the faith of Laud, or of that of Milton; and, as little, by the triumph of republicanism, as by that of monarchy. But that the one thing needful for compassing this end was, that the people of England should second the efforts of an insignificant corporation, the establishment of which, a few years before the epoch of the great plague and the great fire, had been as little noticed, as they were conspicuous.

Some twenty years before the outbreak of the plague a few calm and thoughtful students banded themselves together for the purpose, as they phrased it, of "improving natural knowledge." The ends they proposed to attain cannot be stated more clearly than in the words of one of the founders of the organisation :—

" Our business was (precluding matters of theology and state affairs) to discourse and consider of philosophical enquiries, and such as related thereunto:—as Physick, Anatomy, Geometry, Astronomy, Navigation, Staticks, Magneticks, Chymicks, Mechanicks, and Natural Experiments ; with the state of these studies and their cultivation at home and abroad. We then discoursed of the circulation of the blood, the valves in the veins, the venæ lacteæ, the lymphatic vessels, the Copernican hypothesis, the nature of comets and new stars, the satellites of Jupiter, the oval shape (as it then appeared) of Saturn, the spots on the sun and its turning on its own axis, the inequalities and selenography of the moon, the several phases of Venus and Mercury, the im-

provement of telescopes and grinding of glasses
for that purpose, the weight of air, the possibility
or impossibility of vacuities and nature's abhorrence thereof, the Torricellian experiment in
quicksilver, the descent of heavy bodies and the
degree of acceleration therein, with divers other
things of like nature, some of which were then
but new discoveries, and others not so generally
known and embraced as now they are; with other
things appertaining to what hath been called
the New Philosophy, which from the times of
Galileo at Florence, and Sir Francis Bacon (Lord
Verulam) in England, hath been much cultivated
in Italy, France, Germany, and other parts abroad,
as well as with us in England."

The learned Dr. Wallis, writing in 1696,
narrates in these words, what happened half a
century before, or about 1645. The associates
met at Oxford, in the rooms of Dr. Wilkins,
who was destined to become a bishop; and subsequently coming together in London, they attracted the notice of the king. And it is a
strange evidence of the taste for knowledge which
the most obviously worthless of the Stuarts
shared with his father and grandfather, that
Charles the Second was not content with saying
witty things about his philosophers, but did wise
things with regard to them. For he not only bestowed upon them such attention as he could
spare from his poodles and his mistresses, but,

being in his usual state of impecuniosity, begged
for them of the Duke of Ormond ; and, that step
being without effect, gave them Chelsea College,
a charter, and a mace : crowning his favours in the
best way they could be crowned, by burdening
them no further with royal patronage or state
interference.

Thus it was that the half-dozen young men,
studious of the "New Philosophy," who met in
one another's lodgings in Oxford or in London, in
the middle of the seventeenth century, grew in
numerical and in real strength, until, in its latter
part, the "Royal Society for the Improvement of
Natural Knowledge" had already become famous,
and had acquired a claim upon the veneration of
Englishmen, which it has ever since retained, as
the principal focus of scientific activity in our
islands, and the chief champion of the cause it
was formed to support.

It was by the aid of the Royal Society that
Newton published his "Principia." If all the
books in the world, except the "Philosophical
Transactions," were destroyed, it is safe to say that
the foundations of physical science would remain
unshaken, and that the vast intellectual progress
of the last two centuries would be largely, though
incompletely, recorded. Nor have any signs of
halting or of decrepitude manifested themselves
in our own times. As in Dr. Wallis's days, so in
these, " our business is, precluding theology and

state affairs, to discourse and consider of philosophical enquiries." But our "Mathematick" is
one which Newton would have to go to school to
learn; our "Staticks, Mechanicks, Magneticks,
Chymicks, and Natural Experiments" constitute
a mass of physical and chemical knowledge, a
glimpse at which would compensate Galileo for
the doings of a score of inquisitorial cardinals;
our "Physick" and "Anatomy" have embraced
such infinite varieties of being, have laid open such
new worlds in time and space, have grappled, not
unsuccessfully, with such complex problems, that
the eyes of Vesalius and of Harvey might be
dazzled by the sight of the tree that has grown
out of their grain of mustard seed.

The fact is perhaps rather too much, than too
little, forced upon one's notice, nowadays, that
all this marvellous intellectual growth has a
no less wonderful expression in practical life ; and
that, in this respect, if in no other, the movement
symbolised by the progress of the Royal Society
stands without a parallel in the history of
mankind.

A series of volumes as bulky as the "Transactions
of the Royal Society" might possibly be filled
with the subtle speculations of the Schoolmen;
not improbably, the obtaining a mastery over the
products of mediæval thought might necessitate
an even greater expenditure of time and of energy
than the acquirement of the "New Philosophy;"

but though such work engrossed the best intellects of Europe for a longer time than has elapsed since the great fire, its effects were "writ in water," so far as our social state is concerned.

On the other hand, if the noble first President of the Royal Society could revisit the upper air and once more gladden his eyes with a sight of the familiar mace, he would find himself in the midst of a material civilisation more different from that of his day, than that of the seventeenth was from that of the first century. And if Lord Brouncker's native sagacity had not deserted his ghost, he would need no long reflection to discover that all these great ships, these railways, these telegraphs, these factories, these printing-presses, without which the whole fabric of modern English society would collapse into a mass of stagnant and starving pauperism,—that all these pillars of our State are but the ripples and the bubbles upon the surface of that great spiritual stream, the springs of which only, he and his fellows were privileged to see; and seeing, to recognise as that which it behoved them above all things to keep pure and undefiled.

It may not be too great a flight of imagination to conceive our noble *revenant* not forgetful of the great troubles of his own day, and anxious to know how often London had been burned down since his time, and how often the plague had carried off its thousands. He would have to learn that, although London contains tenfold the inflammable matter that it did in 1666; though, not content with filling our rooms with woodwork and light draperies, we must needs lead inflammable and explosive gases into every corner of our streets and houses, we never allow even a street to burn down. And if he asked how this had come about, we should have to explain that the improvement of natural knowledge has furnished us with dozens of machines for throwing water upon fires, any one of which would have furnished the ingenious Mr. Hooke, the first " curator and experimenter " of the Royal Society, with ample materials for discourse before half a dozen meetings of that body; and that, to say truth, except for the progress of natural knowledge, we should not have been able to make even the tools by which these machines are constructed. And, further, it would be necessary to add, that although severe fires sometimes occur and inflict great damage, the loss is very generally compensated by societies, the operations of which have been rendered possible only by the progress of natural knowledge in the direction of mathematics, and the accumulation of wealth in virtue of other natural knowledge.

But the plague ? My Lord Brouncker's observation would not, I fear, lead him to think that Englishmen of the nineteenth century are purer in life, or more fervent in religious faith, than the generation which could produce a Boyle, an Evelyn, and a Milton. He might find the mud of society at the bottom, instead of at the top, but I fear that the sum total would be as deserving of swift judgment as at the time of the Restoration. And it would be our duty to explain once more, and this time not without shame, that we have no reason to believe that it is the improvement of our faith, nor that of our morals, which keeps the plague from our city; but, again, that it is the improvement of our natural knowledge.

We have learned that pestilences will only take up their abode among those who have prepared unswept and ungarnished residences for them. Their cities must have narrow, unwatered streets, foul with accumulated garbage. Their houses must be ill-drained, ill-lighted, ill-ventilated. Their subjects must be ill-washed, ill-fed, ill-clothed. The London of 1665 was such a city. The cities of the East, where plague has an enduring dwelling, are such cities. We, in later times, have learned somewhat of Nature, and partly obey her. Because of this partial improvement of our natural knowledge and of that fractional obedience, we have no plague; because that knowledge is still very imperfect and that obedience yet incomplete, typhoid is our companion and cholera our visitor. But it is not presumptuous to express the belief that, when our knowledge is

more complete and our obedience the expression
of our knowledge, London will count her centuries
of freedom from typhoid and cholera, as she
now gratefully reckons her two hundred years
of ignorance of that plague which swooped upon
her thrice in the first half of the seventeenth
century.

Surely, there is nothing in these explanations
which is not fully borne out by the facts? Surely,
the principles involved in them are now admitted
among the fixed beliefs of all thinking men?
Surely, it is true that our countrymen are less
subject to fire, famine, pestilence, and all the evils
which result from a want of command over and due
anticipation of the course of Nature, than were
the countrymen of Milton; and health, wealth,
and well-being are more abundant with us than
with them? But no less certainly is the difference
due to the improvement of our knowledge of
Nature, and the extent to which that improved
knowledge has been incorporated with the house-
hold words of men, and has supplied the springs
of their daily actions.

Granting for a moment, then, the truth of that
which the depreciators of natural knowledge are
so fond of urging, that its improvement can only
add to the resources of our material civilisation;
admitting it to be possible that the founders of
the Royal Society themselves looked for no other
reward than this, I cannot confess that I was

guilty of exaggeration when I hinted, that to him who had the gift of distinguishing between prominent events and important events, the origin of a combined effort on the part of mankind to improve natural knowledge might have loomed larger than the Plague and have outshone the glare of the Fire; as a something fraught with a wealth of beneficence to mankind, in comparison with which the damage done by those ghastly evils would shrink into insignificance.

It is very certain that for every victim slain by the plague, hundreds of mankind exist and find a fair share of happiness in the world by the aid of the spinning jenny. And the great fire, at its worst, could not have burned the supply of coal, the daily working of which, in the bowels of the earth, made possible by the steam pump, gives rise to an amount of wealth to which the millions lost in old London are but as an old song.

But spinning jenny and steam pump are, after all, but toys, possessing an accidental value; and natural knowledge creates multitudes of more subtle contrivances, the praises of which do not happen to be sung because they are not directly convertible into instruments for creating wealth. When I contemplate natural knowledge squandering such gifts among men, the only appropriate comparison I can find for her is, to liken her to such

a peasant woman as one sees in the Alps, strid-
ing ever upward, heavily burdened, and with mind
bent only on her home; but yet without effort
and without thought, knitting for her children.
Now stockings are good and comfortable things,
and the children will undoubtedly be much the
better for them; but surely it would be short-
sighted, to say the least of it, to depreciate this
toiling mother as a mere stocking-machine—a
mere provider of physical comforts?

However, there are blind leaders of the blind,
and not a few of them, who take this view of natural
knowledge, and can see nothing in the bountiful
mother of humanity but a sort of comfort-grinding
machine.   According to them, the improvement
of natural knowledge always has been, and always
must be, synonymous with no more than the
improvement of the material resources and the
increase of the gratifications of men.

Natural knowledge is, in their eyes, no real
mother of mankind, bringing them up with kindness, and, if need be, with sternness, in the way
they should go, and instructing them in all things
needful for their welfare; but a sort of fairy god-
mother, ready to furnish her pets with shoes of
swiftness, swords of sharpness, and omnipotent
Aladdin's lamps, so that they may have telegraphs
to Saturn, and see the other side of the moon, and
thank God they are better than their benighted
ancestors.

If this talk were true, I, for one, should not greatly care to toil in the service of natural knowledge. I think I would just as soon be quietly chipping my own flint axe, after the manner of my forefathers a few thousand years back, as be troubled with the endless malady of thought which now infests us all, for such reward. But I venture to say that such views are contrary alike to reason and to fact. Those who discourse in such fashion seem to me to be so intent upon trying to see what is above Nature, or what is behind her, that they are blind to what stares them in the face in her.

I should not venture to speak thus strongly if my justification were not to be found in the simplest and most obvious facts,—if it needed more than an appeal to the most notorious truths to justify my assertion, that the improvement of natural knowledge, whatever direction it has taken, and however low the aims of those who may have commenced it—has not only conferred practical benefits on men, but, in so doing, has effected a revolution in their conceptions of the universe and of themselves, and has profoundly altered their modes of thinking and their views of right and wrong. I say that natural knowledge, seeking to satisfy natural wants, has found the ideas which can alone still spiritual cravings. I say that natural knowledge, in desiring to ascertain the laws of comfort, has been driven to discover those of conduct, and to lay the foundations of a new morality.

Let us take these points separately; and first, what great ideas has natural knowledge introduced into men's minds?

I cannot but think that the foundations of all natural knowledge were laid when the reason of man first came face to face with the facts of Nature; when the savage first learned that the fingers of one hand are fewer than those of both; that it is shorter to cross a stream than to head it; that a stone stops where it is unless it be moved, and that it drops from the hand which lets it go; that light and heat come and go with the sun; that sticks burn away in a fire; that plants and animals grow and die; that if he struck his fellow savage a blow he would make him angry, and perhaps get a blow in return, while if he offered him a fruit he would please him, and perhaps receive a fish in exchange. When men had acquired this much knowledge, the outlines, rude though they were, of mathematics, of physics, of chemistry, of biology, of moral, economical, and political science, were sketched. Nor did the germ of religion fail when science began to bud. Listen to words which, though new, are yet three thousand years old :—

> " .   .   . When in heaven the stars about the moon
> Look beautiful, when all the winds are laid,

And every height comes out, and jutting peak
And valley, and the immeasurable heavens
Break open to their highest, and all the stars
Shine, and the shepherd gladdens in his heart." [1]

If the half savage Greek could share our feelings
thus far, it is irrational to doubt that he went
further, to find as we do, that upon that brief
gladness there follows a certain sorrow,—the little
light of awakened human intelligence shines so
mere a spark amidst the abyss of the unknown
and unknowable ; seems so insufficient to do
more than illuminate the imperfections that
cannot be remedied, the aspirations that cannot
be realised, of man's own nature. But in this
sadness, this consciousness of the limitation of man,
this sense of an open secret which he cannot
penetrate, lies the essence of all religion ; and the
attempt to embody it in the forms furnished by
the intellect is the origin of the higher theologies.

Thus it seems impossible to imagine but that
the foundations of all knowledge—secular or
sacred—were laid when intelligence dawned,
though the superstructure remained for long
ages so slight and feeble as to be compatible with
the existence of almost any general view respecting the mode of governance of the universe. No
doubt, from the first, there were certain phænomena which, to the rudest mind, presented a

[1] Need it be said that this is Tennyson's English for Homer's
Greek ?

constancy of occurrence, and suggested that a fixed order ruled, at any rate, among them. I doubt if the grossest of Fetish worshippers ever imagined that a stone must have a god within it to make it fall, or that a fruit had a god within it to make it taste sweet. With regard to such matters as these, it is hardly questionable that mankind from the first took strictly positive and scientific views.

But, with respect to all the less familiar occurrences which present themselves, uncultured man, no doubt, has always taken himself as the standard of comparison, as the centre and measure of the world; nor could he well avoid doing so. And finding that his apparently uncaused will has a powerful effect in giving rise to many occurrences, he naturally enough ascribed other and greater events to other and greater volitions, and came to look upon the world and all that therein is, as the product of the volitions of persons like himself, but stronger, and capable of being appeased or angered, as he himself might be soothed or irritated. Through such conceptions of the plan and working of the universe all mankind have passed, or are passing. And we may now consider what has been the effect of the improvement of natural knowledge on the views of men who have reached this stage, and who have begun to cultivate natural knowledge with no desire but that of "increasing God's honour and bettering man's estate."

For example, what could seem wiser, from a
mere material point of view, more innocent, from
a theological one, to an ancient people, than
that they should learn the exact succession of
the seasons, as warnings for their husbandmen;
or the position of the stars, as guides to their
rude navigators?   But what has grown out of
this search for natural knowledge of so merely
useful a character?   You all know the reply.
Astronomy,—which of all sciences has filled men's
minds with general ideas of a character most
foreign to their daily experience, and has, more
than any other, rendered it impossible for them
to accept the beliefs of their fathers.   Astronomy,
—which tells them that this so vast and seemingly
solid earth is but an atom among atoms, whirling,
no man knows whither, through illimitable space;
which demonstrates that what we call the peaceful
heaven above us, is but that space, filled by an
infinitely subtle matter whose particles are
seething and surging, like the waves of an angry
sea; which opens up to us infinite regions where
nothing is known, or ever seems to have been
known, but matter and force, operating according to rigid rules; which leads us to contemplate phænomena the very nature of which
demonstrates that they must have had a beginning, and that they must have an end, but
the very nature of which also proves that the
beginning was, to our conceptions of time,

infinitely remote, and that the end is as immeasurably distant.

But it is not alone those who pursue astronomy
who ask for bread and receive ideas.   What more
harmless than the attempt to lift and distribute
water by pumping it; what more absolutely and
grossly utilitarian ?   Yet out of pumps grew the
discussions about Nature's abhorrence of a vacuum ;
and then it was discovered that Nature does not
abhor a vacuum, but that air has weight; and
that notion paved the way for the doctrine that
all matter has weight, and that the force
which produces weight is co-extensive with the
universe,—in short, to the theory of universal
gravitation and endless force.   While learning
how to handle gases led to the discovery of
oxygen, and to modern chemistry, and to the
notion of the indestructibility of matter.

Again, what simpler, or more absolutely practical, than the attempt to keep the axle of a
wheel from heating when the wheel turns round
very fast ?   How useful for carters and gig
drivers to know something about this; and how
good were it, if any ingenious person would find
out the cause of such phænomena, and thence
educe a general remedy for them.   Such an
ingenious person was Count Rumford ; and he
and his successors have landed us in the theory of
the persistence, or indestructibility, of force.   And
in the infinitely minute, as in the infinitely great,

the seekers after natural knowledge of the kinds
called physical and chemical, have everywhere
found a· definite order and succession of events
which seem never to be infringed.

And how has it fared with " Physick" and
Anatomy ? Have the anatomist, the physiologist,
or the physician, whose business it has been to
devote themselves assiduously to that eminently
practical and direct end, the alleviation of the
sufferings of mankind,—have they been able to
confine their vision more absolutely to the strictly
useful ? I fear they are the worst offenders of
all. For if the astronomer has set before us the
infinite magnitude of space, and the practical
eternity of the duration of the universe ; if the
physical and chemical philosophers have demonstrated the infinite minuteness of its constituent
parts, and the practical eternity of matter and
of force ; and if both have alike proclaimed the
universality of a definite and predicable order and
succession of events, the workers in biology have
not only accepted all these, but have added more
startling theses of their own. For, as the astronomers discover in the earth no centre of the
universe, but an eccentric speck, so the naturalists
find man to be no centre of the living world, but
one amidst endless modifications of life ; and as
the astronomer observes the mark of practically
endless time set upon the arrangements of the
solar system so the student of life finds the records

of ancient forms of existence peopling the world for ages, which, in relation to human experience, are infinite.

Furthermore, the physiologist finds life to be as dependent for its manifestation on particular molecular arrangements as any physical or chemical phenomenon ; and wherever he extends his researches, fixed order and unchanging causation reveal themselves, as plainly as in the rest of Nature.

Nor can I find that any other fate has awaited the germ of Religion. Arising, like all other kinds of knowledge, out of the action and interaction of man's mind, with that which is not man's mind, it has taken the intellectual coverings of Fetishism or Polytheism ; of Theism or Atheism ; of Superstition or Rationalism. With these, and their relative merits and demerits, I have nothing to do ; but this it is needful for my purpose to say, that if the religion of the present differs from that of the past, it is because the theology of the present has become more scientific than that of the past ; because it has not only renounced idols of wood and idols of stone, but begins to see the necessity of breaking in pieces the idols built up of books and traditions and fine-spun ecclesiastical cobwebs : and of cherishing the noblest and most human of man's emotions, by worship " for the most part of the silent sort " at the altar of the Unknown.

Such are a few of the new conceptions implanted

in our minds by the improvement of natural knowledge. Men have acquired the ideas of the practically infinite extent of the universe and of its practical eternity; they are familiar with the conception that our earth is but an infinitesimal fragment of that part of the universe which can be seen; and that, nevertheless, its duration is, as compared with our standards of time, infinite. They have further acquired the idea that man is but one of innumerable forms of life now existing on the globe, and that the present existences are but the last of an immeasurable series of predecessors. Moreover, every step they have made in natural knowledge has tended to extend and rivet in their minds the conception of a definite order of the universe—which is embodied in what are called, by an unhappy metaphor, the laws of Nature—and to narrow the range and loosen the force of men's belief in spontaneity, or in changes other than such as arise out of that definite order itself.

Whether these ideas are well or ill founded is not the question. No one can deny that they exist, and have been the inevitable outgrowth of the improvement of natural knowledge. And if so, it cannot be doubted that they are changing the form of men's most cherished and most important convictions.

And as regards the second point—the extent to which the improvement of natural knowledge has remodelled and altered what may be termed the intellectual ethics of men,—what are among the moral convictions most fondly held by barbarous and semi-barbarous people.

They are the convictions that authority is the soundest basis of belief; that merit attaches to a readiness to believe ; that the doubting disposition is a bad one, and scepticism a sin ; that when good authority has pronounced what is to be believed, and faith has accepted it, reason has no further duty.   There are many excellent persons who yet hold by these principles, and it is not my present business, or intention, to discuss their views.   All I wish to bring clearly before your minds is the unquestionable fact, that the improvement of natural knowledge is effected by methods which directly give the lie to all these convictions, and assume the exact reverse of each to be true.

The improver of natural knowledge absolutely refuses to acknowledge authority, as such.   For him, scepticism is the highest of duties; blind faith the one unpardonable sin.   And it cannot be otherwise, for every great advance in natural knowledge has involved the absolute rejection of authority, the cherishing of the keenest scepticism, the annihilation of the spirit of blind faith ; and the most ardent votary of science holds his firmest convictions, not because the men he most venerates hold them ; not because their verity is testified by portents and wonders; but because his experience teaches him that whenever he chooses to bring these convictions into contact with their primary source, Nature—whenever he thinks fit to test them by appealing to experiment and to observation—Nature will confirm them. The man of science has learned to believe in justification, not by faith, but by verification.

Thus, without for a moment pretending to despise the practical results of the improvement of natural knowledge, and its beneficial influence on material civilisation, it must, I think, be admitted that the great ideas, some of which I have indicated, and the ethical spirit which I have endeavoured to sketch, in the few moments which remained at my disposal, constitute the real and permanent significance of natural knowledge.

If these ideas be destined, as I believe they are, to be more and more firmly established as the world grows older; if that spirit be fated, as I believe it is, to extend itself into all departments of human thought, and to become co-extensive with the range of knowledge; if, as our race approaches its maturity, it discovers, as I believe it will, that there is but one kind of knowledge and but one method of acquiring it; then we, who are still children, may justly feel it our highest duty to recognise the advisableness of improving natural knowledge, and so to aid ourselves and our successors in our course towards the noble goal which lies before mankind.

4

II

THE PROGRESS OF SCIENCE

1837—1887

[1887]

THE most obvious and the most distinctive feature of the History of Civilisation, during the last fifty years, is the wonderful increase of industrial production by the application of machinery, the improvement of old technical processes and the invention of new ones, accompanied by an even more remarkable development of old and new means of locomotion and intercommunication. By this rapid and vast multiplication of the commodities and conveniences of existence, the general standard of comfort has been raised; the ravages of pestilence and famine have been checked; and the natural obstacles, which time and space offer to mutual intercourse, have been reduced in a manner, and to an extent, unknown to former ages. The diminution or removal of local ignorance and prejudice, the creation of common interests among the most widely separated peoples, and the strengthening of the forces of the organisation of the commonwealth against those of political or social anarchy, thus effected, have exerted an influence on the present and future fortunes of mankind the full significance of which may be divined, but cannot, as yet, be estimated at its full value.

This revolution—for it is nothing less—in the political and social aspects of modern civilisation has been preceded, accompanied, and in great measure caused, by a less obvious, but no less marvellous, increase of natural knowledge, and especially of that part of it which is known as Physical Science, in consequence of the application of scientific method to the investigation of the phenomena of the material world. Not that the growth of physical science is an exclusive prerogative of the Victorian age. Its present strength and volume merely indicate the highest level of a stream which took its rise alongside of the primal founts of Philosophy, Literature, and Art, in ancient Greece ; and, after being dammed up for a thousand years, once more began to flow three centuries ago.

It may be doubted if even-handed justice, as free from fulsome panegyric as from captious depreciation, has ever yet been dealt out to the sages of antiquity who, for eight centuries, from the time of Thales to that of Galen, toiled at the foundations of physical science. But, without entering into the discussion of that large question, it is certain that the labours of these early workers in the field of natural knowledge were brought to a standstill by the decay and disruption of the Roman Empire, the consequent disorganisation of society, and the diversion of men's thoughts from sublunary matters to the problems of the supernatural world suggested by Christian dogma in the Middle Ages. And, notwithstanding sporadic attempts to recall men to the investigation of nature, here and there, it was not until the fifteenth and sixteenth centuries that physical science made a new start, founding itself, at first, altogether upon that which had been done by the Greeks. Indeed, it must be admitted that the men of the Renaissance, though standing on the shoulders of the old philosophers, were a long time before they saw as much as their forerunners had done.

The first serious attempts to carry further the unfinished work of Archimedes, Hipparchus, and Ptolemy, of Aristotle and of Galen, naturally enough arose among the astronomers and the physicians. For the imperious necessity of seeking some remedy for the physical ills of life had insured the preservation of more or less of the wisdom of Hippocrates and his successors; and, by a happy conjunction of circumstances, the Jewish and the Arabian physicians and philosophers escaped many of the influences which, at that time, blighted natural knowledge in the Christian world. On the other hand, the superstitious hopes and fears which afforded countenance to astrology and to alchemy also sheltered astronomy and the germs of chemistry. Whether for this, or for some better reason, the founders of the schools of the Middle Ages included astronomy, along with geometry, arithmetic, and music, as one of the four branches of advanced education; and, in this respect, it is only just to them to observe that they were far in advance of those who sit in their seats. The schoolmen considered no one to be properly educated unless he were acquainted with, at any rate, one branch of physical science. We have not, even yet, reached that stage of enlightenment.

In the early decades of the seventeenth century, the men of the Renaissance could show that they had already put out to good interest the treasure bequeathed to them by the Greeks. They had produced the astronomical system of Copernicus, with Kepler's great additions; the astronomical discoveries and the physical investigations of Galileo; the mechanics of Stevinus and the "De Magnete" of Gilbert; the anatomy of the great French and Italian schools and the physiology of Harvey. In Italy, which had succeeded Greece in the hegemony of the scientific world, the Accademia dei Lyncei and sundry other such associations for the investigation of nature, the models of all subsequent academies and scientific societies, had been founded; while the literary skill and biting wit of Galileo had made the great scientific questions of the day not only intelligible, but attractive, to the general public.

In our own country, Francis Bacon had essayed to sum up the past of physical science, and to indicate the path which it must follow if its great destinies were to be fulfilled. And though the attempt was just such a magnificent failure as might have been expected from a man of great endowments, who was so singularly devoid of scientific insight that he could not understand the value of the work already achieved by the true instaurators of physical science; yet the majestic eloquence and the fervid vaticinations of one who was conspicuous alike by the greatness of his rise and the depth of his fall, drew the attention of all the world to the "new birth of Time."

But it is not easy to discover satisfactory evidence that the "Novum Organum" had any direct beneficial influence on the advancement of natural knowledge. No delusion is greater than the notion that method and industry can make up for lack of motherwit, either in science or in practical life; and it is strange that, with his knowledge of mankind, Bacon should have dreamed that his, or any other, "via inveniendi scientias" would "level men's wits" and leave

little scope for that inborn capacity which is called
génius.   As a matter of fact, Bacon's " via " has
proved   hopelessly   impracticable ; while   the
" anticipation of nature " by the invention of
hypotheses based on incomplete inductions, which
he specially condemns, has proved itself to be a most
efficient, indeed an indispensable, instrument of
scientific progress.   Finally, that transcendental
alchemy—the superinducement of new forms on
matter—which Bacon declares to be the supreme
aim of science, has been wholly ignored by those
who have created the physical knowledge of the
present day.

Even the eloquent advocacy of the Chancellor
brought no unmixed good to physical science.   It
was natural enough that the man who, in his
better moments, took " all knowledge for his patri-
mony," but, in his worse, sold that birthright for
the mess of pottage of Court favour and professional success, for pomp and show, should be led to
attach an undue value to the practical advantages
which he foresaw, as Roger Bacon and, indeed,
Seneca had foreseen, long before his time, must
follow in the train of the advancement of natural
knowledge.   The burden of Bacon's pleadings for
science is the " gathering of fruit "—the importance of winning solid material advantages by the
investigation of Nature and the desirableness of
limiting the application of scientific methods of
inquiry to that field.

Bacon's younger contemporary, Hobbes, casting aside the prudent reserve of his predecessor in regard to those matters about which the Crown or the Church might have something to say, extended scientific methods of inquiry to the phenomena of mind and the problems of social organisation; while, at the same time, he indicated the boundary between the province of real, and that of imaginary, knowledge. The "Principles of Philosophy" and the "Leviathan" embody a coherent system of purely scientific thought in language which is a model of clear and vigorous English style. At the same time, in France, a man of far greater scientific capacity than either Bacon or Hobbes, René Descartes, not only in his immortal "Discours de la Méthode" and elsewhere, went down to the foundations of scientific certainty, but, in his "Principes de Philosophie," indicated where the goal of physical science really lay. However, Descartes was an eminent mathematician, and it would seem that the bent of his mind led him to overestimate the value of deductive reasoning from general principles, as much as Bacon had under-estimated it. The progress of physical science has been effected neither by Baconians nor by Cartesians, as such, but by men like Galileo and Harvey, Boyle and Newton, who would have done their work just as well if neither Bacon nor Descartes had ever propounded their views respecting the manner in which scientific investigation should be pursued.

The progress of science, during the first century after Bacon's death, by no means verified his sanguine prediction of the fruits which it would yield. For, though the revived and renewed study of nature had spread and grown to an extent which surpassed reasonable expectation, the practical results—the "good to men's estate"—were, at first, by no means apparent. Sixty years after Bacon's death, Newton had crowned the long labours of the astronomers and the physicists, by co-ordinating the phenomena of molar motion throughout the visible universe into one vast system ; but the "Principia" helped no man to either wealth or comfort. Descartes, Newton, and Leibnitz had opened up new worlds to the mathematician, but the acquisitions of their genius enriched only man's ideal estate. Descartes had laid the foundations of rational cosmogony and of physiological psychology ; Boyle had produced models of experimentation in various branches of physics and chemistry ; Pascal and Torricelli had weighed the air ; Malpighi and Grew, Ray and Willoughby had done work of no less importance in the biological sciences ; but weaving and spinning were carried on with the old appliances ; nobody could travel faster by sea or by land than at any previous time in the world's history, and King George could send a message from London to York no faster than King John might have done. Metals were worked from their ores by immemorial rule of thumb, and the centre of the iron trade of these islands was still among the oak forests of Sussex. The utmost skill of our mechanicians did not get beyond the production of a coarse watch.

The middle of the eighteenth century is illustrated by a host of great names in science—English, French, German, and Italian—especially in the fields of chemistry, geology, and biology; but this deepening and broadening of natural knowledge produced next to no immediate practical benefits. Even if, at this time, Francis Bacon could have returned to the scene of his greatness and of his littleness, he must have regarded the philosophic world which praised and disregarded his precepts with great disfavour. If ghosts are consistent, he would have said, "These people are all wasting their time, just as Gilbert and Kepler and Galileo and my worthy physician Harvey did in my day. Where are the fruits of the restoration of science which I promised? This accumulation of bare knowledge is all very well, but *cui bono?* Not one of these people is doing what I told him specially to do, and seeking that secret of the cause of forms which will enable men to deal, at will, with matter, and superinduce new natures upon the old foundations."

But, a little later, that growth of knowledge beyond imaginable utilitarian ends, which is the condition precedent of its practical utility, began to produce some effect upon practical life; and the operation of that part of nature we call human upon the rest began to create, not "new natures," in Bacon's sense, but a new Nature, the existence of which is dependent upon men's efforts, which is subservient to their wants, and which would disappear if man's shaping and guiding hand were withdrawn. Every mechanical artifice, every chemically pure substance employed in manufacture, every abnormally fertile race of plants, or rapidly growing and fattening breed of animals, is a part of the new Nature created by science. Without it, the most densely populated regions of modern Europe and America must retain their primitive, sparsely inhabited, agricultural or pastoral condition; it is the foundation of our wealth and the condition of our safety from submergence by another flood of barbarous hordes; it is the bond which unites into a solid political whole, regions larger than any empire of antiquity; it secures us from the recurrence of the pestilences and famines of former times; it is the source of endless comforts and conveniences, which are not mere luxuries, but conduce to physical and moral well-being. During the last fifty years, this new birth of time, this new Nature begotten by science upon fact, has pressed itself daily and hourly upon our attention, and has worked miracles which have modified the whole fashion of our lives.

What wonder, then, if these astonishing fruits of the tree of knowledge are too often regarded by both friends and enemies as the be-all and end-all of science ? What wonder if some eulogise, and others revile, the new philosophy for its utilitarian ends and its merely material triumphs ?

In truth, the new philosophy deserves neither the praise of its eulogists, nor the blame of its slanderers. As I have pointed out, its disciples were guided by no search after practical fruits, during the great period of its growth, and it reached adolescence without being stimulated by any rewards of that nature. The bare enumeration of the names of the men who were the great lights of science in the latter part of the eighteenth and the first decade of the nineteenth century, of Herschel, of Laplace, of Young, of Fresnel, of Oersted, of Cavendish, of Lavoisier, of Davy, of Lamarck, of Cuvier, of Jussieu, of Decandolle, of Werner and of Hutton, suffices to indicate the strength of physical science in the age immediately preceding that of which I have to treat. But of which of these great men can it be said that their labours were directed to practical ends ? I do not call to mind even an invention of practical utility which we owe to any of them, except the safety-lamp of Davy. Werner certainly paid attention to mining, and I have not forgotten

James Watt. But, though some of the most important of the improvements by which Watt converted the steam-engine, invented long before his time, into the obedient slave of man, were suggested and guided by his acquaintance with scientific principles, his skill as a practical mechanician and the efficiency of Bolton's workmen had quite as much to do with the realisation of his projects.

In fact, the history of physical science teaches (and we cannot too carefully take the lesson to heart) that the practical advantages, attainable through its agency, never have been, and never will be, sufficiently attractive to men inspired by the inborn genius of the interpreter of Nature, to give them courage to undergo the toils and make the sacrifices which that calling requires from its votaries. That which stirs their pulses is the love of knowledge and the joy of the discovery of the causes of things sung by the old poet—the supreme delight of extending the realm of law and order ever farther towards the unattainable goals of the infinitely great and the infinitely small, between which our little race of life is run. In the course of this work, the physical philosopher, sometimes intentionally, much more often unintentionally, lights upon something which proves to be of practical value. Great is the rejoicing of those who are benefited thereby; and, for the moment, science is the Diana of all the

craftsmen.   But, even while the cries of jubilation
resound and this flotsam and jetsam of the tide of
investigation is being turned into the wages of
workmen and the wealth of capitalists, the crest
of the wave of scientific investigation is far away
on its course over the illimitable ocean of the unknown.

Far be it from me to depreciate the value of the
gifts of science to practical life, or to cast a doubt
upon the propriety of the course of action of those
who follow science in the hope of finding wealth
alongside truth, or even wealth alone.   Such a
profession is as respectable as any other.   And
quite as little do I desire to ignore the fact that,
if industry owes a heavy debt to science, it has
largely repaid the loan by the important aid
which it has, in its turn, rendered to the advancement of science.   In considering the causes which
hindered the progress of physical knowledge in
the schools of Athens and of Alexandria, it has
often struck me [1] that where the Greeks did
wonders was in just those branches of science,
such as geometry, astronomy, and anatomy, which
are susceptible of very considerable development
without any, or any but the simplest, appliances.
It is a curious speculation to think what would
have become of modern physical science if glass

[1] There are excellent remarks to the same effect in Zeller's
Philosophie der Griechen, Theil II. Abth. ii. p. 407, and in
Eucken's *Die Methode der Aristotelischen Forschung*, pp. 138
et seq.

and alcohol had not been easily obtainable ; and
if the gradual perfection of mechanical skill for
industrial ends had not enabled investigators to
obtain, at comparatively little cost, microscopes,
telescopes, and all the exquisitely delicate apparatus for determining weight and measure and for
estimating the lapse of time with exactness, which
they now command.   If science has rendered the
colossal development of modern industry possible,
beyond a doubt industry has done no less for
modern physics and chemistry, and for a great
deal of modern biology.   And as the captains of
industry have, at last, begun to be aware that the
condition of success in that warfare, under the
forms of peace, which is known as industrial
competition, lies in the discipline of the troops and
the use of arms of precision, just as much as it
does in the warfare which is called war, their
demand for that discipline, which is technical
education, is reacting upon science in a manner
which will, assuredly, stimulate its future growth
to an incalculable extent.   It has become obvious
that the interests of science and of industry are
identical ; that science cannot make a step forward
without, sooner or later, opening up new channels
for industry ; and, on the other hand, that every
advance of industry facilitates those experimental
investigations, upon which the growth of science
depends.   We may hope that, at last, the weary
misunderstanding between the practical men who

professed to despise science, and the high and dry philosophers who professed to despise practical results, is at an end.

Nevertheless, that which is true of the infancy of physical science in the Greek world, that which is true of its adolescence in the seventeenth and eighteenth centuries, remains true of its riper age in these latter days of the nineteenth century The great steps in its progress have been made, are made, and will be made, by men who seek knowledge simply because they crave for it. They have their weaknesses, their follies, their vanities, and their rivalries, like the rest of the world ; but, whatever by-ends may mar their dignity and impede their usefulness, this chief end redeems them.[1] Nothing great in science has ever been done by men, whatever their powers, in whom the divine afflatus of the truth-seeker was wanting. Men of moderate capacity have

---

[1] Fresnel, after a brilliant career of discovery in some of the most difficult regions of physico-mathematical science, died at thirty-nine years of age. The following passage of a letter from him to Young (written in November, 1824), quoted by Whewell, so aptly illustrates the spirit which animates the scientific inquirer that I may cite it :

"For a long time that sensibility, or that vanity, which people call love of glory is much blunted in me. I labour much less to catch the suffrages of the public than to obtain an inward approval which has always been the mental reward of my efforts. Without doubt I have often wanted the spur of vanity to excite me to pursue my researches in moments of disgust and discouragement. But all the compliments which I have received from MM. Arago, De Laplace, or Biot, never gave me so much pleasure as the discovery of a theoretical truth or the confirmation of a calculation by experiment."

done great things because it animated them ; and men of great natural gifts have failed, absolutely or relatively, because they lacked this one thing needful.

To any one who knows the business of investigation practically, Bacon's notion of establishing a company of investigators to work for " fruits," as if the pursuit of knowledge were a kind of mining operation and only required well-directed picks and shovels, seems very strange.[1] In science, as in art, and, as I believe, in every other sphere of human activity, there may be wisdom in a multitude of counsellors, but it is only in one or two of them.   And, in scientific inquiry, at any rate, it is to that one or two that we must look for light and guidance. Newton said that he made his discoveries by " intending " his mind on the subject ; no doubt, truly. But to equal his success one must have the mind which he " intended." Forty lesser men might have intended their minds till they cracked, without any like result. It would be idle either to affirm or to deny that the last half-century has produced men of science of the calibre of Newton. It is sufficient that it can show a few capacities of the first rank, competent not only to deal profitably with the inheritance

[1] "Mémorable exemple de l'impuissance des recherches collectives appliquées à la découverte des vérités nouvelles !" says one of the most distinguished of living French *savants*, of the corporate chemical work of the old Académie des Sciences. (See Berthelot, *Science et Philosophie*, p. 201.)

bequeathed by their scientific forefathers, but to pass on to their successors physical truths of a higher order than any yet reached by the human race. And if they have succeeded as Newton succeeded, it is because they have sought truth as he sought it, with no other object than the finding it.

I am conscious that in undertaking to give even the briefest sketch of the progress of physical science, in all its branches, during the last half-century, I may be thought to have exhibited more courage than discretion, and perhaps more presumption than either. So far as physical science is concerned, the days of Admirable Crichtons have long been over, and the most indefatigable of hard workers may think he has done well if he has mastered one of its minor subdivisions. Nevertheless, it is possible for any one, who has familiarised himself with the operations of science in one department, to comprehend the significance, and even to form a general estimate of the value, of the achievements of specialists in other departments.

Nor is there any lack either of guidance, or of aids to ignorance. By a happy chance, the first edition of Whewell's " History of the Inductive Sciences " was published in 1837, and it affords a very useful view of the state of things at the commencement of the Victorian epoch. As to subsequent events, there are numerous excellent summaries of the progress of various branches of science, especially up to 1881, which was the jubilee year of the British Association.[1] And, with respect to the biological sciences, with some parts of which my studies have familiarised me, my personal experience nearly coincides with the preceding half-century. I may hope, therefore, that my chance of escaping serious errors is as good as that of any one else, who might have been persuaded to undertake the somewhat perilous enterprise in which I find myself engaged.

There is yet another prefatory remark which it seems desirable I should make. It is that I think it proper to confine myself to the work done, without saying anything about the doers of it. Meddling with questions of merit and priority is a thorny business at the best of times, and, unless in case of necessity, altogether undesirable when one is dealing with contemporaries. No such necessity lies upon me; and I shall, therefore, mention no names of living men, lest, perchance, I should incur the reproof which the Israelites, who struggled with one another in the field, addressed to Moses—"Who made thee a prince and a judge over us?"

---

[1] I am particularly indebted to my friend and colleague, Professor Rücker, F.R.S., for the many acute criticisms and suggestions on my remarks respecting the ultimate problems of physics, with which he has favoured me, and by which I have greatly profited.

Physical science is one and indivisible. Although, for practical purposes, it is convenient to mark it out into the primary regions of Physics, Chemistry, and Biology, and to subdivide these into subordinate provinces, yet the method of investigation and the ultimate object of the physical inquirer are everywhere the same.

The object is the discovery of the rational order which pervades the universe ; the method consists of observation and experiment (which is observation under artificial conditions) for the determination of the facts of Nature; of inductive and deductive reasoning for the discovery of their mutual relations and connection. The various branches of physical science differ in the extent to which, at any given moment of their history, observation on the one hand, or ratiocination on the other, is their more obvious feature, but in no other way ; and nothing can be more incorrect than the assumption one sometimes meets with, that physics has one method, chemistry another, and biology a third.

All physical science starts from certain postulates. One of them is the objective existence of a material world. It is assumed that the phenomena which are comprehended under this name have a " substratum " of extended, impenetrable, mobile substance, which exhibits the quality known as inertia, and is termed matter.[1]   Another

[1] I am aware that this proposition may be challenged.   It

postulate is the universality of the law of causation; that nothing happens without a cause (that is, a necessary precedent condition), and that the state of the physical universe, at any given moment, is the consequence of its state at any preceding moment. Another is that any of the rules, or so-called " laws of Nature," by which the relation of phenomena is truly defined, is true for all time. The validity of these postulates is a problem of metaphysics; they are neither self-evident nor are they, strictly speaking, demonstrable. The justification of their employment, as axioms of physical philosophy, lies in the circumstance that expectations logically based upon them are verified, or, at any rate, not contradicted, whenever they can be tested by experience.

Physical science therefore rests on verified or uncontradicted hypotheses ; and, such being the case, it is not surprising that a great condition of

may be said, for example, that, on the hypothesis of Boscovich, matter has no extension, being reduced to mathematical points serving as centres of "forces." But as the "forces" of the various centres are conceived to limit one another's action in such a manner that an area around each centre has an individuality of its own, extension comes back in the form of that area. Again, a very eminent mathematician and physicist—the late Clerk Maxwell—has declared that impenetrability is not essential to our notions of matter, and that two atoms may conceivably occupy the same space. I am loth to dispute any dictum of a philosopher as remarkable for the subtlety of his intellect as for his vast knowledge ; but the assertion that one and the same point or area of space can have different (conceivably opposite) attributes appears to me to violate the principle of contradic-tion, which is the foundation not only of physical science, but of logic in general. It means that A can be not-A.

its progress has been the invention of verifiable hypotheses. It is a favourite popular delusion that the scientific inquirer is under a sort of moral obligation to abstain from going beyond that generalisation of observed facts which is absurdly called " Baconian " induction. But any one who is practically acquainted with scientific work is aware that those who refuse to go beyond fact, rarely get as far as fact ; and any one who has studied the history of science knows that almost every great step therein has been made by the " anticipation of Nature," that is, by the invention of hypotheses, which, though verifiable, often had very little foundation to start with ; and, not unfrequently, in spite of a long career of usefulness, turned out to be wholly erroneous in the long run.

The geocentric system of astronomy, with its eccentrics and its epicycles, was an hypothesis utterly at variance with fact, which nevertheless did great things for the advancement of astronomical knowledge. Kepler was the wildest of guessers. Newton's corpuscular theory of light was of much temporary use in optics, though nobody now believes in it ; and the undulatory theory, which has superseded the corpuscular theory and has proved one of the most fertile of instruments of research, is based on the hypothesis of the existence of an "ether," the properties of which are defined in propositions, some of which, to ordinary apprehension, seem physical antinomies.

It sounds paradoxical to say that the attainment of scientific truth has been effected, to a great extent, by the help of scientific errors. But the subject-matter of physical science is furnished by observation, which cannot extend beyond the limits of our faculties; while, even within those limits, we cannot be certain that any observation is absolutely exact and exhaustive. Hence it follows that any given generalisation from observation may be true, within the limits of our powers of observation at a given time, and yet turn out to be untrue, when those powers of observation are directly or indirectly enlarged. Or, to put the matter in another way, a doctrine which is untrue absolutely, may, to a very great extent, be susceptible of an interpretation in accordance with the truth. At a certain period in the history of astronomical science, the assumption that the planets move in circles was true enough to serve the purpose of correlating such observations as were then possible; after Kepler, the assumption that they move in ellipses became true enough in regard to the state of observational astronomy at that time. We say still that the orbits of the planets are ellipses, because, for all ordinary purposes, that is a sufficiently near approximation to the truth; but, as a matter of fact, the centre of gravity of a planet describes neither an ellipse nor any other simple curve, but an immensely complicated undulating line. It may fairly be doubted whether any generalisation, or hypothesis, based upon physical data is absolutely true, in the sense that a mathematical proposition is so; but, if its errors can become apparent only outside the limits of practicable observation, it may be just as usefully adopted for one of the symbols of that algebra by which we interpret Nature, as if it were absolutely true.

The development of every branch of physical knowledge presents three stages, which, in their logical relation, are successive. The first is the determination of the sensible character and order of the phenomena. This is *Natural History*, in the original sense of the term, and here nothing but observation and experiment avail us. The second is the determination of the constant relations of the phenomena thus defined, and their expression in rules or laws. The third is the explication of these particular laws by deduction from the most general laws of matter and motion. The last two stages constitute *Natural Philosophy* in its original sense. In this region, the invention of verifiable hypotheses is not only permissible, but is one of the conditions of progress.

Historically, no branch of science has followed this order of growth; but, from the dawn of exact knowledge to the present day, observation, experiment, and speculation have gone hand in hand ; and, whenever science has halted or strayed from the right path, it has been, either because its votaries have been content with mere unverified or unverifiable speculation (and this is the commonest case, because observation and experiment are hard work, while speculation is amusing) ; or it has been, because the accumulation of details of observation has for a time excluded speculation.

The progress of physical science, since the revival of learning, is largely due to the fact that men have gradually learned to lay aside the consideration of unverifiable hypotheses ; to guide observation and experiment by verifiable hypotheses ; and to consider the latter, not as ideal truths, the real entities of an intelligible world behind phenomena, but as a symbolical language, by the aid of which Nature can be interpreted in terms apprehensible by our intellects. And if physical science, during the last fifty years, has attained dimensions beyond all former precedent, and can exhibit achievements of greater importance than any former such period can show, it is because able men, animated by the true scientific spirit, carefully trained in the method of science, and having at their disposal immensely improved appliances, have devoted themselves to the enlargement of the boundaries of natural knowledge in greater number than during any previous half-century of the world's history.

I have said that our epoch can produce achievements in physical science of greater moment than any other has to show, advisedly; and I think that there are three great products of our time which justify the assertion. One of these is that doctrine concerning the constitution of matter which, for want of a better name, I will call "molecular;" the second is the doctrine of the conservation of energy; the third is the doctrine of evolution. Each of these was foreshadowed, more or less distinctly, in former periods of the history of science; and, so far is either from being the outcome of purely inductive reasoning, that it would be hard to overrate the influence of metaphysical, and even of theological, considerations upon the development of all three. The peculiar merit of our epoch is that it has shown how these hypotheses connect a vast number of seemingly independent partial generalisations; that it has given them that precision of expression which is necessary for their exact verification; and that it has practically proved their value as guides to the discovery of new truth. All three doctrines are intimately connected, and each is applicable to the whole physical cosmos. But, as might have been expected from the nature of the case, the first two grew, mainly, out of the consideration of physico-chemical phenomena; while the third, in great measure, owes its rehabilitation, if not its origin, to the study of biological phenomena.

In the early decades of this century, a number of important truths applicable, in part, to matter in general, and, in part, to particular forms of matter, had been ascertained by the physicists and chemists.

The laws of motion of visible and tangible, or *molar*, matter had been worked out to a great degree of refinement and embodied in the branches of science known as Mechanics, Hydrostatics, and Pneumatics. These laws had been shown to hold good, so far as they could be checked by observation and experiment, throughout the universe, on the assumption that all such masses of matter possessed inertia and were susceptible of acquiring motion, in two ways, firstly by impact, or impulse from without ; and, secondly, by the operation of certain hypothetical causes of motion termed "forces," which were usually supposed to be resident in the particles of the masses themselves, and to operate at a distance, in such a way as to tend to draw any two such masses together, or to separate them more widely.

With respect to the ultimate constitution of these masses, the same two antagonistic opinions which had existed since the time of Democritus and of Aristotle were still face to face. According to the one, matter was discontinuous and consisted of minute indivisible particles or atoms, separated by a universal vacuum ; according to the other, it was continuous, and the finest distinguishable, or imaginable, particles were scattered through the attenuated general substance of the plenum. A rough analogy to the latter case would be afforded by granules of ice diffused through water; to the former, such granules diffused through absolutely empty space.

In the latter part of the eighteenth century, the chemists had arrived at several very important generalisations respecting those properties of matter with which they were especially concerned. However plainly ponderable matter seemed to be originated and destroyed in their operations, they proved that, as mass or body, it remained indestructible and ingenerable; and that, so far, it varied only in its perceptibility by our senses. The course of investigation further proved that a certain number of the chemically separable kinds of matter were unalterable by any known means (except in so far as they might be made to change their state from solid to fluid, or *vice versâ*), unless they were brought into contact with other kinds of matter, and that the properties of these several kinds of matter were always the same, whatever their origin. All other bodies were found to consist of two or more of these, which thus took the place of the four "elements" of the ancient philosophers. Further, it was proved that, in forming chemical compounds, bodies always unite in a definite proportion by weight, or in simple multiples of that proportion, and that, if any one body were taken as a standard, every other could have a number assigned to it as its proportional combining weight. It was on this foundation of fact that Dalton based his re-establishment of the old atomic hypothesis on a new empirical foundation. It is obvious, that if elementary matter consists of indestructible and indivisible particles, each of which constantly preserves the same weight relatively to all the others, compounds formed by the aggregation of two, three, four, or more such particles must exemplify the rule of combination in definite proportions deduced from observation.

In the meanwhile, the gradual reception of the undulatory theory of light necessitated the assumption of the existence of an " ether " filling all space. But whether this ether was to be regarded as a strictly material and continuous substance, was an undecided point, and hence the revived atomism escaped strangling in its birth. For it is clear, that if the ether is admitted to be a continuous material substance, Democritic atomism is at an end and Cartesian continuity takes its place.

The real value of the new atomic hypothesis, however, did not lie in the two points which Democritus and his followers would have considered essential—namely, the indivisibility of the " atoms " and the presence of an interatomic vacuum—but in the assumption that, to the extent to which our means of analysis take us, material bodies consist of definite minute masses, each of which, so far as physical and chemical processes of division go, may be regarded as a unit —having a practically permanent individuality. Just as a man is the unit of sociology, without reference to the actual fact of his divisibility, so such a minute mass is the unit of physico-chemical science—that smallest material particle which under any given circumstances acts as a whole.[1]

The doctrine of specific heat originated in the eighteenth century. It means that the same mass of a body, under the same circumstances, always requires the same quantity of heat to raise it to a given temperature, but that equal masses of different bodies require different quantities. Ultimately, it was found that the quantities of heat required to raise equal masses of the more perfect gases, through equal ranges of temperature, were inversely proportional to their combining weights. Thus a definite relation was established between the hypothetical units and heat. The phenomena of electrolytic decomposition showed that there was a like close relation between these units and electricity. The quantity of electricity generated by the combination of any two units is sufficient to separate any other two which are susceptible of

[1] "Molecule" would be the more appropriate name for such a particle. Unfortunately, chemists employ this term in a special sense, as a name for an aggregation of their smallest particles, for which they retain the designation of "atoms."

such decomposition. The phenomena of iso-
morphism showed a relation between the units
and crystalline forms ; certain units are thus able
to replace others in a crystalline body without
altering its form, and others are not.

Again, the laws of the effect of pressure and
heat on gaseous bodies, the fact that they combine
in definite proportions by volume, and that such
proportion bears a simple relation to their combining weights, all harmonised with the Daltonian
hypothesis, and led to the bold speculation known
as the law of Avogadro—that all gaseous bodies,
under the same physical conditions, contain the
same number of units. In the form in which it
was first enunciated, this hypothesis was incorrect
—perhaps it is not exactly true in any form ; but
it is hardly too much to say that chemistry and
molecular physics would never have advanced to
their present condition unless it had been assumed
to be true. Another immense service rendered by
Dalton, as a corollary of the new atomic doctrine,
was the creation of a system of symbolic notation,
which not only made the nature of chemical
compounds and processes easily intelligible and
easy of recollection, but, by its very form, suggested
new lines of inquiry. The atomic notation was as
serviceable to chemistry as the binomial nomen-
clature and the classificatory schematism of
Linnæus were to zoology and botany.

Side by side with these advances arose another,

which also has a close parallel in the history of
biological science. If the unit of a compound is
made up by the aggregation of elementary units,
the notion that these must have some sort of
definite arrangement inevitably suggests itself ;
and such phenomena as double decomposition
pointed, not only to the existence of a molecular
architecture, but to the possibility of modifying a
molecular fabric without destroying it, by taking
out some of the component units and replacing
them by others. The class of neutral salts, for
example, includes a great number of bodies in
many ways similar, in which the basic molecules,
or the acid molecules, may be replaced by other
basic and other acid molecules, without altering the
neutrality of the salt ; just as a cube of bricks remains a cube, so long as any brick that is taken
out is replaced by another of the same shape and
dimensions whatever its weight or other properties
may be. Facts of this kind gave rise to the conception of " types" of molecular structure, just as
the recognition of the unity in diversity of the
structure of the species of plants and animals gave
rise to the notion of biological " types." The
notation of chemistry enabled these ideas to be
represented with precision ; and they acquired an
immense importance, when the improvement of
methods of analysis, which took place about the
beginning of our period, enabled the composition
of the so-called " organic " bodies to be determined

with rapidity and precision.[1]   A large proportion of these compounds contain not more than three or four elements, of which carbon is the chief; but their number is very great, and the diversity of their physical and chemical properties is astonishing.   The ascertainment of the proportion of each element in these compounds affords little or no help towards accounting for their diversities; widely different bodies being often very similar, or even identical, in that respect.   And, in the last case, that of *isomeric* compounds, the appeal to diversity of arrangement of the identical component units was the only obvious way out of the difficulty.   Here, again, hypothesis proved to be of great value; not only was the search for evidence of diversity of molecular structure successful, but the study of the process of taking to pieces led to the discovery of the way to put together; and vast numbers of compounds, some of them previously known only as products of the living economy, have thus been artificially constructed.   Chemical work, at the present day, is, to a large extent, synthetic or creative—that is to say, the chemist determines, theoretically, that certain non-existent compounds ought to be producible, and he proceeds to produce them.

It is largely because the chemical theory and

---

[1] " At present, more organic analyses are made in a single day than were accomplished before Liebig's time in a whole year."—Hofmann, *Faraday Lecture*, .p. 46.

practice of our epoch have passed into this deductive and synthetic stage, that they are entitled
to the name of the " New Chemistry " which they
commonly receive. But this new chemistry has
grown up by the help of hypotheses, such as those
of Dalton and of Avogadro, and that singular
conception of " bonds " invented to colligate the
facts of " valency " or " atomicity," the first of which
took some time to make its way ; while the second
fell into oblivion, for many years after it was propounded, for lack of empirical justification. As
for the third, it may be doubted if any one regards
it as more than a temporary contrivance.

But some of these hypotheses have done yet
further service. Combining them with the mechanical theory of heat and the doctrine of the conservation of energy, which are also products of our time,
physicists have arrived at an entirely new conception of the nature of gaseous bodies and of the
relation of the physico-chemical units of matter to
the different forms of energy. The conduct of
gases under varying pressure and temperature,
their diffusibility, their relation to radiant heat
and to light, the evolution of heat when bodies
combine, the absorption of heat when they are
dissociated, and a host of other molecular phenomena, have been shown to be deducible from the
dynamical and statical principles which apply to
molar motion and rest ; and the tendency of
physico-chemical science is clearly towards the

reduction of the problems of the world of the infinitely little, as it already has reduced those of
the infinitely great world, to questions of mechanics.[1]

In the meanwhile, the primitive atomic theory,
which has served as the scaffolding for the edifice
of modern physics and chemistry, has been quietly
dismissed. I cannot discover that any contemporary physicist or chemist believes in the real indivisibility of atoms, or in an interatomic matterless
vacuum. The term "atoms" appears to be used
as a mere name for physico-chemical units which
have not yet been subdivided, and "molecules"
for physico-chemical units which are aggregates of
the former. And these individualised particles are
supposed to move in an endless ocean of a vastly
more subtle matter—the ether. If this ether is
a continuous substance, therefore, we have got
back from the hypothesis of Dalton to that of
Descartes. But there is much reason to believe
that science is going to make a still further
journey, and, in form, if not altogether in substance,
to return to the point of view of Aristotle.

The greater number of the so-called "elementary" bodies, now known, had been discovered
before the commencement of our epoch; and it
had become apparent that they were by no means

[1] In the preface to his *Mécanique Chimique*, M. Berthelot
declares his object to be "ramener la chimie tout entière . . . aux
mêmes principes mécaniques qui régissent déjà les diverses
branches de la physique."

equally similar or dissimilar, but that some of them, at any rate, constituted groups, the several members of which were as much like one another as they were unlike the rest. Chlorine, iodine, bromine, and fluorine thus formed a very distinct group; sulphur and selenium another; boron and silicon another; potassium, sodium, and lithium another; and so on. In some cases, the atomic weights of such allied bodies were nearly the same, or could be arranged in series, with like differences between the several terms. In fact, the elements afforded indications that they were susceptible of a classification in natural groups, such as those into which animals and plants fall.

Recently this subject has been taken up afresh, with a result which may be stated roughly in the following terms. If the sixty-five or sixty-eight recognised "elements" are arranged in the order of their atomic weights—from hydrogen, the lightest, as unity, to uranium, the heaviest, as 240—the series does not exhibit one continuous progressive modification in the physical and chemical characters of its several terms, but breaks up into a number of sections, in each of which the several terms present analogies with the corresponding terms of the other series.

Thus, the whole series does not run

$$a, b, c, d, e, f, g, h, i, k, \text{&c.,}$$

but

$$a, b, c, d, \text{A, B, C, D}, \alpha, \beta, \gamma, \delta, \text{&c.;}$$

so that it is said to express a *periodic law* of re-
current similarities.   Or the relation may be
expressed in another way.   In each section of the
series, the atomic weight is greater than in the
preceding section, so that if w is the atomic weight
of any element in the first segment, $w+x$ will represent the atomic weight of any element in the next,
and $w+x+y$ the atomic weight of any element in
the next, and so on.   Therefore the sections may
be represented as parallel series, the corresponding terms of which have analogous properties ; each
successive series starting with a body the atomic
weight of which is greater than that of any in the
preceding series, in the following fashion :

d	D	δ
c	C	γ
b	B	β
a	A	a
w	$w+x$	$w+x+y$

This is a conception with which biologists are
very familiar, animal and plant groups constantly
appearing as series of parallel modifications of
similar and yet different primary forms.   In the
living world, facts of this kind are now understood
to mean evolution from a common prototype.   It
is difficult to imagine that in the not-living world
they are devoid of significance.   Is it not possible,
nay, probable, that they may mean the evolution of our " elements " from a primary undifferen-

tiated form of matter? Fifty years ago, such a
suggestion would have been scouted as a revival
of the dreams of the alchemists. At present, it
may be said to be the burning question of physico-
chemical science.

In fact, the so-called "vortex-ring" hypothesis
is a very serious and remarkable attempt to deal
with material units from a point of view which is
consistent with the doctrine of evolution. It
supposes the ether to be a uniform substance, and
that the "elementary" units are, broadly speaking, permanent whirlpools, or vortices, of this
ether, the properties of which depend on their
actual and potential modes of motion. It is
curious and highly interesting to remark that this
hypothesis reminds us not only of the speculations
of Descartes, but of those of Aristotle. The resemblance of the "vortex-rings" to the "tour-
billons" of Descartes is little more than nominal;
but the correspondence between the modern and
the ancient notion of a distinction between
primary and derivative matter is, to a certain
extent, real. For this ethereal "Urstoff" of the
modern corresponds very closely with the πρώτη
ὕλη of Aristotle, the *materia prima* of his mediæval followers; while matter, differentiated into
our elements, is the equivalent of the first stage
of progress towards the ἐσχάτη ὕλη, or finished
matter, of the ancient philosophy.

If the material units of the existing order of

Nature are specialised portions of a relatively
homogeneous *materia prima*—which were originated under conditions that have long ceased to
exist and which remain unchanged and unchangeable under all conditions, whether natural or
artificial, hitherto known to us—it follows that
the speculation that they may be indefinitely
altered, or that new units may be generated under
conditions yet to be discovered, is perfectly legitimate. Theoretically, at any rate, the transmut-
ability of the elements is a verifiable scientific
hypothesis; and such inquiries as those which
have been set afoot, into the possible dissociative
action of the great heat of the sun upon our
elements, are not only legitimate, but are likely
to yield results which, whether affirmative or
negative, will be of great importance. The idea
that atoms are absolutely ingenerable and im-
mutable "manufactured articles" stands on the
same sort of foundation as the idea that biological
species are "manufactured articles" stood thirty
years ago; and the supposed constancy of the
elementary atoms, during the enormous lapse of
time measured by the existence of our universe,
is of no more weight against the possibility of
change in them, in the infinity of antecedent
time, than the constancy of species in Egypt,
since the days of Rameses or of Cheops, is
evidence of their immutability during all past
epochs of the earth's history. It seems safe to

prophesy that the hypothesis of the evolution of the elements from a primitive matter will, in future, play no less a part in the history of science than the atomic hypothesis, which, to begin with, had no greater, if so great, an empirical foundation.

It may perhaps occur to the reader that the boasted progress of physical science does not come to much, if our present conceptions of the fundamental nature of matter are expressible in terms employed, more than two thousand years ago, by the old "master of those that know." Such a criticism, however, would involve forgetfulness of the fact, that the connotation of these terms, in the mind of the modern, is almost infinitely different from that which they possessed in the mind of the ancient philosopher. In antiquity, they meant little more than vague speculation; at the present day, they indicate definite physical conceptions, susceptible of mathematical treatment, and giving rise to innumerable deductions, the value of which can be experimentally tested. The old notions produced little more than floods of dialectics; the new are powerful aids towards the increase of solid knowledge.

Everyday observation shows that, of the bodies which compose the material world, some are in motion and some are, or appear to be, at rest. Of the bodies in motion, some, like the sun and stars,

exhibit a constant movement, regular in amount
and direction, for which no external cause appears.
Others, as stones and smoke, seem also to move of
themselves when external impediments are taken
away. But these appear to tend to move in opposite directions : the bodies we call heavy, such as
stones, downwards, and the bodies we call light, at
least such as smoke and steam, upwards. And,
as we further notice that the earth, below our feet,
is made up of heavy matter, while the air, above
our heads, is extremely light matter, it is easy to
regard this fact as evidence that the lower region
is the place to which heavy things tend—their
proper place, in short—while the upper region is
the proper place of light things ; and to generalise
the facts observed by saying that bodies, which are
free to move, tend towards their proper places. All
these seem to be natural motions, dependent on
the inherent faculties, or tendencies, of bodies
themselves. But there are other motions, which
are artificial or violent, as when a stone is thrown
from the hand, or is knocked by another stone in
motion. In such cases as these, for example,
when a stone is cast from the hand, the distance
travelled by the stone appears to depend partly on
its weight, and partly upon the exertion of the
thrower. So that, the weight of the stone remain-
ing the same, it looks as if the motive power
communicated to it were measured by the distance
to which the stone travels—as if, in other words,

the power needed to send it a hundred yards was twice as great as that needed to send it fifty yards. These, apparently obvious, conclusions from the everyday appearances of rest and motion fairly represent the state of opinion upon the subject which prevailed among the ancient Greeks, and remained dominant until the age of Galileo. The publication of the " Principia " of Newton, in 1686-7, marks the epoch at which the progress of mechanical physics had effected a complete revolution of thought on these subjects. By this time, it had been made clear that the old generalisations were either incomplete or totally erroneous ; that a body, once set in motion, will continue to move in a straight line for any conceivable time or distance, unless it is interfered with ; that any change of motion is proportional to the " force " which causes it, and takes place in the direction in which that " force " is exerted ; and that, when a body in motion acts as a cause of motion on another, the latter gains as much as the former loses, and *vice versâ*. It is to be noted, however, that while, in contradistinction to the ancient idea of the inherent tendency to motion of bodies, the absence of any such spontaneous power of motion was accepted as a physical axiom by the moderns, the old conception virtually maintained itself in a new shape. For, in spite of Newton's well-known warning against the " absurdity " of supposing that one body can act on another at a distance through a vacuum, the ultimate particles of matter were generally assumed to be the seats of perennial causes of motion termed "attractive and repulsive forces," in virtue of which, any two such particles, without any external impression of motion, or intermediate material agent, were supposed to tend to approach or remove from one another : and this view of the duality of the causes of motion is very widely held at the present day.

Another important result of investigation, attained in the seventeenth century, was the proof and quantitative estimation of physical inertia. In the old philosophy, a curious conjunction of ethical and physical prejudices had led to the notion that there was something ethically bad and physically obstructive about matter. Aristotle attributes all irregularities and apparent dysteleologies in nature to the disobedience, or sluggish yielding, of matter to the shaping and guiding influence of those reasons and causes which were hypostatised in his ideal "Forms." In modern science, the conception of the inertia, or resistance to change, of matter is complex. In part, it contains a corollary from the law of causation : A body cannot change its state in respect of rest or motion without a sufficient cause. But, in part, it contains generalisations from experience. One of these is that there is no such sufficient cause resident in any body, and that therefore it will rest, or continue in motion, so long as no external cause of change acts upon it. The other is that the effect which the impact of a body in motion produces upon the body on which it impinges depends, other things being alike, on the relation of a certain quality of each which is called "mass." Given a cause of motion of a certain value, the amount of motion, measured by distance travelled in a certain time, which it will produce in a given quantity of matter, say a cubic inch, is not always the same, but depends on what that matter is—a cubic inch of iron will go faster than a cubic inch of gold. Hence, it appears, that since equal amounts of motion have, *ex hypothesi*, been produced, the amount of motion in a body does not depend on its speed alone, but on some property of the body. To this the name of "mass" has been given. And, since it seems reasonable to suppose that a large quantity of matter, moving slowly, possesses as much motion as a small quantity moving faster, "mass" has been held to express "quantity of matter." It is further demonstrable that, at any given time and place, the relative mass of any two bodies is expressed by the ratio of their weights.

When all these great truths respecting molar motion, or the movements of visible and tangible masses, had been shown to hold good not only of terrestrial bodies, but of all those which constitute the visible universe ; and the movements of the macrocosm had thus been expressed by a general

mechanical theory, there remained a vast number
of phenomena, such as those of light, heat, electricity, magnetism, and those of the physical and
chemical changes which do not involve molar
motion. Newton's corpuscular theory of light
was an attempt to deal with one great series of
these phenomena on mechanical principles, and it
maintained its ground until, at the beginning of
the nineteenth century, the undulatory theory
proved itself to be a much better working hypothesis. Heat, up to that time, and indeed much
later, was regarded as an imponderable substance,
caloric ; as a thing which was absorbed by bodies
when they were warmed, and was given out as
they cooled ; and which, moreover, was capable
of entering into a sort of chemical combination
with them, and so becoming latent. Rumford
and Davy had given a great blow to this view of
heat by proving that the quantity of heat which
two portions of the same body could be made to
give out, by rubbing them together, was practically
illimitable. This result brought philosophers face
to face with the contradiction of supposing that a
finite body could contain an infinite quantity of
another body ; but it was not until 1843, that
clear and unquestionable experimental proof was
given of the fact that there is a definite relation
between mechanical work and heat ; that so much
work always gives rise, under the same conditions,
to so much heat, and so much heat to so much

mechanical work. Thus originated the mechanical theory of heat, which became the starting point of the modern doctrine of the conservation of energy. Molar motion had appeared to be destroyed by friction. It was proved that no destruction took place, but that an exact equivalent of the energy of the lost molar motion appears as that of the *molecular* motion, or motion of the smallest particles of a body, which constitutes heat. The loss of the masses is the gain of their particles.

Before 1843, however, the doctrine of the conservation of energy had been approached. Bacon's chief contribution to positive science is the happy guess (for the context shows that it was little more) that heat may be a mode of motion; Descartes affirmed the quantity of motion in the world to be constant ; Newton nearly gave expression to the complete theorem ; while Rumford's and Davy's experiments suggested, though they did not prove, the equivalency of mechanical and thermal energy. Again, the discovery of voltaic electricity, and the marvellous development of knowledge, in that field, effected by such men as Davy, Faraday, Oersted, Ampère, and Melloni, had brought to light a number of facts which tended to show that the so-called " forces " at work in light, heat, electricity, and magnetism, in chemical and in mechanical operations, were intimately, and, in various cases, quantitatively, related. It was demonstrated that any one could be obtained at the expense of any other; and apparatus was devised which exhibited the evolution of all these kinds of action from one source of energy. Hence the idea of the "correlation of forces" which was the immediate forerunner of the doctrine of the conservation of energy.

It is a remarkable evidence of the greatness of the progress in this direction which has been effected in our time, that even the second edition of the "History of the Inductive Sciences," which was published in 1846, contains no allusion either to the general view of the "Correlation of Forces" published in England in 1842, or to the publication in 1843 of the first of the series of experiments by which the mechanical equivalent of heat was correctly ascertained.[1] Such a failure on the part of a contemporary, of great acquirements and remarkable intellectual powers, to read the signs of the times, is a lesson and a warning worthy of being deeply pondered by any one who

[1] This is the more curious, as Ampère's hypothesis that vibrations of molecules, causing and caused by vibrations of the ether, constitute heat, is discussed. · See vol. ii. p. 587, 2nd ed. In the *Philosophy of the Inductive Sciences*, 2nd ed. 1847, p. 239, Whewell remarks, *à propos* of Bacon's definition of heat, "that it is an expansive, restrained motion, modified in certain ways, and exerted in the smaller particles of the body;" that "although the exact nature of heat is still an obscure and controverted matter, the science of heat now consists of many important truths; and that to none of these truths is there any approximation in Bacon's essay." In point of fact, Bacon's statement, however much open to criticism, does contain a distinct approximation to the most important of all the truths respecting heat which had been discovered when Whewell wrote.

attempts to prognosticate the course of scientific progress.

I have pointed out that the growth of clear and definite views respecting the constitution of matter has led to the conclusion that, so far as natural agencies are concerned, it is ingenerable and indestructible. In so far as matter may be conceived to exist in a purely passive state, it is, imaginably, older than motion. But, as it must be assumed to be susceptible of motion, a particle of bare matter at rest must be endowed with the potentiality of motion. Such a particle, however, by the supposition, can have no energy, for there is no cause why it should move. Suppose now that it receives an impulse, it will begin to move with a velocity inversely proportional to its mass, on the one hand, and directly proportional to the strength of the impulse, on the other, and will possess *kinetic energy,* in virtue of which it will not only continue to move for ever if unimpeded, but if it impinges on another such particle, it will impart more or less of its motion to the latter. Let it be conceived that the particle acquires a tendency to move, and that nevertheless it does not move. It is then in a condition totally different from that in which it was at first. A cause competent to produce motion is operating upon it, but, for some reason or other, is unable to give rise to motion. If the obstacle is removed, the energy which was there, but could not manifest itself, at once gives rise to motion. While the restraint lasts, the energy of the particle is merely potential; and the case supposed illustrates what is meant by *potential energy*. In this contrast of the potential with the actual, modern physics is turning to account the most familiar of Aristotelian distinctions—that between δύναμις and ἐνέργεια.

That kinetic energy appears to be imparted by impact is a fact of daily and hourly experience : we see bodies set in motion by bodies, already in motion, which seem to come in contact with them. It is a truth which could have been learned by nothing but experience, and which cannot be explained, but must be taken as an ultimate fact about which, explicable or inexplicable, there can be no doubt. Strictly speaking, we have no direct apprehension of any other cause of motion. But experience furnishes innumerable examples of the production of kinetic energy in a body previously at rest, when no impact is discernible as the cause of that energy. In all such cases, the presence of a second body is a necessary condition ; and the amount of kinetic energy, which its presence enables the first to gain, is strictly dependent on the relative positions of the two. Hence the phrase *energy of position*, which is frequently used as equivalent to potential energy. If a stone is picked up and held, say, six feet above the ground, it has *potential energy*, because, if let go, it will immediately begin to move towards the earth ;

7

and this energy may be said to be *energy of position,*
because it depends upon the relative position of
the earth and the stone.   The stone is solicited to
move but cannot, so long as the muscular strength
of the holder prevents the solicitation from taking
effect.   The stone, therefore, has potential energy,
which becomes kinetic if it is let go, and the
amount of that kinetic energy which will be
developed before it strikes the earth depends on
its position—on the fact that it is, say, six feet off
the earth, neither more nor less.   Moreover. it can
be proved that the raiser of the stone had to exert
as much energy in order to place it in its position,
as it will develop in falling.   Hence the energy
which was exerted, and apparently exhausted, in
raising the stone, is potentially in the stone, in its
raised position, and will manifest itself when the
stone is set free.   Thus the energy, withdrawn
from the general stock to raise the stone, is returned when it falls, and there is no change in the
total amount.   Energy, as a whole, is conserved.

Taking this as a very broad and general statement of the essential facts of the case, the raising
of the stone is intelligible enough, as a case of
the communication of motion from one body to
another.   But the potential energy of the raised
stone is not so easily intelligible.   To all appearance, there is nothing either pushing or pulling it
towards the earth, or the earth towards it ; and
yet it is quite certain that the stone tends to move

towards the earth and the earth towards the stone, in the way defined by the law of gravitation.

In the currently accepted language of science, the cause of motion, in all such cases as this, when bodies tend to move towards or away from one another, without any discernible impact of other bodies, is termed a " force," which is called " attractive " in the one case, and " repulsive " in the other. And such attractive or repulsive forces are often spoken of as if they were real things, capable of exerting a pull, or a push, upon the particles of matter concerned. Thus the potential energy of the stone is commonly said to be due to the " force " of gravity which is continually operating upon it.

Another illustration may make the case plainer. The bob of a pendulum swings first to one side and then to the other of the centre of the arc which it describes. Suppose it to have just reached the summit of its right-hand half-swing. It is said that the " attractive forces " of the bob for the earth, and of the earth for the bob, set the former in motion ; and as these " forces " are continually in operation, they confer an accelerated velocity on the bob ; until, when it reaches the centre of its swing, it is, so to speak, fully charged with kinetic energy. If, at this moment, the whole material universe, except the bob, were abolished, it would move for ever in the direction of a tangent to the middle of the arc described.

As a matter of fact, it is compelled to travel through its left-hand half-swing, and thus virtually to go up hill. Consequently, the "attractive forces" of the bob and the earth are now acting against it, and constitute a resistance which the charge of kinetic energy has to overcome. But, as this charge represents the operation of the attractive forces during the passage of the bob through the right-hand half-swing down to the centre of the arc, so it must needs be used up by the passage of the bob upwards from the centre of the arc to the summit of the left-hand half-swing. Hence, at this point, the bob comes to a momentary rest. The last fraction of kinetic energy is just neutralised by the action of the attractive forces, and the bob has only potential energy equal to that with which it started. So that the sum of the phenomena may be stated thus : At the summit of either half-arc of its swing, the bob has a certain amount of potential energy ; as it descends it gradually exchanges this for kinetic energy, until at the centre it possesses an equivalent amount of kinetic energy ; from this point onwards, it gradually loses kinetic energy as it ascends until, at the summit of the other half-arc, it has acquired an exactly similar amount of potential energy. Thus, on the whole transaction, nothing is either lost or gained ; the quantity of energy is always the same, but it passes from one form into the other.

To all appearance, the phenomena exhibited by
the pendulum are not to be accounted for by
impact: in fact, it is usually assumed that corresponding phenomena would take place if the earth
and the pendulum were situated in an absolute
vacuum, and at any conceivable distance from
one another. If this be so, it follows that there
must be two totally different kinds of causes of
motion: the one impact—*a vera causa*, of which,
to all appearance, we have constant experience;
the other, attractive or repulsive "force"—a
metaphysical entity which is physically inconceivable. Newton expressly repudiated the notion
of the existence of attractive forces, in the sense
in which that term is ordinarily understood; and
he refused to put forward any hypothesis as to
the physical cause of the so-called "attraction
of gravitation." As a general rule, his successors
have been content to accept the doctrine of
attractive and repulsive forces, without troubling
themselves about the philosophical difficulties
which it involves. But this has not always been
the case; and the attempt of Le Sage, in the last
century, to show that the phenomena of attraction and repulsion are susceptible of explanation
by his hypothesis of bombardment by ultra-
mundane particles, whether tenable or not, has
the great merit of being an attempt to get rid of
the dual conception of the causes of motion which
has hitherto prevailed. On this hypothesis, the

hammering of the ultra-mundane corpuscles on the bob confers its kinetic energy, on the one hand, and takes it away on the other; and the state of potential energy means the condition of the bob during the instant at which the energy, conferred by the hammering during the one half-arc, has just been exhausted by the hammering during the other half-arc. It seems safe to look forward to the time when the conception of attractive and repulsive forces, having served its purpose as a useful piece of scientific scaffolding, will be replaced by the deduction of the phenomena known as attraction and repulsion, from the general laws of motion.

The doctrine of the conservation of energy which I have endeavoured to illustrate is thus defined by the late Clerk Maxwell:

"The total energy of any body or system of bodies is a quantity which can neither be increased nor diminished by any mutual action of such bodies, though it may be transformed into any one of the forms of which energy is susceptible." It follows that energy, like matter, is indestructible and ingenerable in nature. The phenomenal world, so far as it is material, expresses the evolution and involution of energy, its passage from the kinetic to the potential condition and back again. Wherever motion of matter takes place, that motion is effected at the expense of part of the total store of energy.

Hence, as the phenomena exhibited by living beings, in so far as they are material, are all molar or molecular motions, these are included under the general law. A living body is a machine by which energy is transformed in the same sense as a steam-engine is so, and all its movements, molar and molecular, are to be accounted for by the energy which is supplied to it. The phenomena of consciousness which arise, along with certain transformations of energy, cannot be interpolated in the series of these transformations, inasmuch as they are not motions to which the doctrine of the conservation of energy applies. And, for the same reason, they do not necessitate the using up of energy; a sensation has no mass and cannot be conceived to be susceptible of movement. That a particular molecular motion does give rise to a state of consciousness is experimentally certain; but the how and why of the process are just as inexplicable as in the case of the communication of kinetic energy by impact.

When dealing with the doctrine of the ultimate constitution of matter, we found a certain resemblance between the oldest speculations and the newest doctrines of physical philosophers. But there is no such resemblance between the ancient and modern views of motion and its causes, except in so far as the conception of attractive and repulsive forces may be regarded as the modified descendant of the Aristotelian conception of forms.

In fact, it is hardly too much to say that the essential and fundamental difference between ancient and modern physical science lies in the ascertainment of the true laws of statics and dynamics in the course of the last three centuries; and in the invention of mathematical methods of dealing with all the consequences of these laws. The ultimate aim of modern physical science is the deduction of the phenomena exhibited by material bodies from physico-mathematical first principles. Whether the human intellect is strong enough to attain the goal set before it may be a question, but thither will it surely strive.

The third great scientific event of our time, the rehabilitation of the doctrine of evolution, is part of the same tendency of increasing knowledge to unify itself, which has led to the doctrine of the conservation of energy. And this tendency, again is mainly a product of the increasing strength conferred by physical investigation on the belief in the universal validity of that orderly relation of facts, which we express by the so-called " Laws of Nature."

The growth of a plant from its seed, of an animal from its egg, the apparent origin of in-numerable living things from mud, or from the putrefying remains of former organisms, had furnished the earlier scientific thinkers with abundant analogies suggestive of the conception of a corresponding method of cosmic evolution from a formless "chaos" to an ordered world which might either continue for ever or undergo dissolution into its elements before starting on a new course of evolution. It is therefore no wonder that, from the days of the Ionian school onwards, the view that the universe was the result of such a process should have maintained itself as a leading dogma of philosophy. The emanistic theories which played so great a part in Neoplatonic philosophy and in Gnostic theology are forms of evolution. In the seventeenth century, Descartes propounded a scheme of evolution, as an hypothesis of what might have been the mode of origin of the world, while professing to accept the ecclesiastical scheme of creation, as an account of that which actually was its manner of coming into existence. In the eighteenth century, Kant put forth a remarkable speculation as to the origin of the solar system, closely similar to that subsequently adopted by Laplace and destined to become famous under the title of the "nebular hypothesis."

The careful observations and the acute reasonings of the Italian geologists of the seventeenth and eighteenth centuries; the speculations of Leibnitz in the " Protogæa " and of Buffon in his " Théorie de la Terre ; " the sober and profound reasonings of Hutton, in the latter part of the eighteenth century; all these tended to show that the fabric of the earth itself implied the continuation of processes of natural causation for a period of time as great, in relation to human history, as the distances of the heavenly bodies from us are, in relation to terrestrial standards of measurement. The abyss of time began to loom as large as the abyss of space. And this revelation to sight and touch, of a link here and a link there of a practically infinite chain of natural causes and effects, prepared the way, as perhaps nothing else has done, for the modern form of the ancient theory of evolution.

In the beginning of the eighteenth century, De Maillet made the first serious attempt to apply the doctrine to the living world. In the latter part of it, Erasmus Darwin, Goethe, Treviranus, and Lamarck took up the work more vigorously and with better qualifications. The question of special creation, or evolution, lay at the bottom of the fierce disputes which broke out in the French Academy between Cuvier and St.-Hilaire; and, for a time, the supporters of biological evolution were silenced, if not answered, by the alliance of the greatest naturalist of the age with their ecclesiastical opponents. Catastrophism, a short-sighted teleology, and a still more short-sighted othodoxy, joined forces to crush evolution.

Lyell and Poulett Scrope, in this country, resumed the work of the Italians and of Hutton; and the

former, aided by a marvellous power of clear exposition, placed upon an irrefragable basis the truth
that natural causes are competent to account for
all events, which can be proved to have occurred,
in the course of the secular changes which have
taken place during the deposition of the stratified
rocks.   The publication of " The Principles of Geology," in 1830, constituted an epoch in geological
science.   But it also constituted an epoch in the
modern history of the doctrine of evolution, by
raising in the mind of every intelligent reader this
question : If natural causation is competent to account for the not-living part of our globe, why
should it not account for the living part ?

By keeping this question before the public for
some thirty years, Lyell, though the keenest and
most formidable of the opponents of the transmutation theory, as it was formulated by Lamarck,
was of the greatest possible service in facilitating
the reception of the sounder doctrines of a later
day.   And, in like fashion, another vehement op-
ponent of the transmutation of species, the elder
Agassiz, was doomed to help the cause he hated.
Agassiz not only maintained the fact of the progressive advance in organisation of the inhabitants
of the earth at each successive geological epoch,
but he insisted upon the analogy of the steps of
this progression with those by which the embryo
advances to the adult condition, among the highest
forms of each group.   In fact, in endeavouring to

support these views he went a good way beyond the limits of any cautious interpretation of the facts then known.

Although little acquainted with biological science, Whewell seems to have taken particular pains with that part of his work which deals with the history of geological and biological speculation ; and several chapters of his seventeenth and eighteenth books, which comprise the history of physiology, of comparative anatomy and of the palætiological sciences, vividly reproduce the controversies of the early days of the Victorian epoch. But here, as in the case of the doctrine of the conservation of energy, the historian of the inductive sciences has no prophetic insight ; not even a suspicion of that which the near future was to bring forth. And those who still repeat the once favourite objection that Darwin's "Origin of Species" is nothing but a new version of the " Philosophie zoologique " will find that, so late as 1844, Whewell had not the slightest suspicion of Darwin's main theorem, even as a logical possibility. In fact, the publication of that theorem by Darwin and Wallace, in 1859, took all the biological world by surprise. Neither those who were inclined towards the " progressive transmutation " or " development " doctrine, as it was then called, nor those who were opposed to it, had the slightest suspicion that the tendency to variation in living beings, which all admitted as a matter of fact ; the selective influence of conditions, which no one could deny to be a matter of fact, when his attention was drawn to the evidence; and the occurrence of great geological changes, which also was matter of fact; could be used as the only necessary postulates of a theory of the evolution of plants and animals which, even if not, at once, competent to explain all the known facts of biological science, could not be shown to be inconsistent with any. So far as biology is concerned, the publication of the "Origin of Species," for the first time, put the doctrine of evolution, in its application to living things, upon a sound scientific foundation. It became an instrument of investigation, and in no hands did it prove more brilliantly profitable than in those of Darwin himself. His publications on the effects of domestication in plants and animals, on the influence of cross-fertilisation, on flowers as organs for effecting such fertilisation, on insectivorous plants, on the motions of plants, pointed out the routes of exploration which have since been followed by hosts of inquirers, to the great profit of science.

Darwin found the biological world a more than sufficient field for even his great powers, and left the cosmical part of the doctrine to others. Not much has been added to the nebular hypothesis, since the time of Laplace, except that the attempt to show (against that hypothesis) that all nebulæ are star clusters, has been met by the spectroscopic

proof of the gaseous condition of some of them.
Moreover, physicists of the present generation
appear now to accept the secular cooling of the
earth, which is one of the corollaries of that hypothesis.   In fact, attempts have been made, by
the help of deductions from the data of physics, to
lay down an approximate limit to the number of
millions of years which have elapsed since the
earth was habitable by living beings.   If the conclusions thus reached should stand the test of further investigation, they will undoubtedly be very
valuable.   But, whether true or false, they can
have no influence upon the doctrine of evolution in
its application to living organisms. The occurrence
of successive forms of life upon our globe is an
historical fact, which cannot be disputed ; and the
relation of these successive forms, as stages of evolution of the same type, is established in various
cases.   The biologist has no means of determining
the time over which the process of evolution has
extended, but accepts the computation of the
physical geologist and the physicist, whatever
that may be.

Evolution, as a philosophical doctrine applicable
to all phenomena, whether physical or mental,
whether manifested by material atoms or by men
in society, has been dealt with systematically in
the "Synthetic Philosophy" of Mr. Herbert
Spencer. Comment on that great undertaking
would not be in place here.   I mention it because,

so far as I know, it is the first attempt to deal, on
scientific principles, with modern scientific facts
and speculations.   For the " Philosophie positive "
of M. Comte, with which Mr. Spencer's system of
philosophy is sometimes compared, though it
professes a similar object, is unfortunately permeated by a thoroughly unscientific spirit, and its
author had no adequate acquaintance with the
physical sciences even of his own time.

The doctrine of evolution, so far as the present
physical cosmos is concerned, postulates the fixity
of the rules of operation of the causes of motion
in the material universe.   If all kinds of matter
are modifications of one kind, and if all modes of
motion are derived from the same energy, the
orderly evolution of physical nature out of one
substratum and one energy implies that the rules
of action of that energy should be fixed and
definite.   In the past history of the universe,
back to that point, there can be no room for
chance or disorder.   But it is possible to raise
the question whether this universe of simplest
matter and definitely operating energy, which
forms our hypothetical starting point, may not
itself be a product of evolution from a universe of
such matter, in which the manifestations of
energy were not definite—in which, for example,
our laws of motion held good for some units and
not for others, or for the same units at one time

and not at another—and which would therefore
be a real epicurean chance-world ?

For myself, I must confess that I find the air of
this region of speculation too rarefied for my constitution, and I am disposed to take refuge in
" ignoramus et ignorabimus."

The execution of my further task, the indication of the most important achievements in the
several branches of physical science during the
last fifty years, is embarrassed by the abundance
of the objects of choice ; and by the difficulty
which every one, but a specialist in each department, must find in drawing a due distinction between discoveries which strike the imagination by
their novelty, or by their practical influence, and
those unobtrusive but pregnant observations and
experiments in which the germs of the great
things of the future really lie. Moreover, my
limits restrict me to little more than a bare
chronicle of the events which I have to notice.

In physics and chemistry, the old boundaries of
which sciences are rapidly becoming effaced, one
can hardly go wrong in ascribing a primary value
to the investigations into the relation between the
solid, liquid, and gaseous states of matter on the
one hand, and degrees of pressure and of heat on
the other. Almost all, even the most refractory,
solids have been vapourised by the intense heat
of the electric arc ; and the most refractory gases

have been forced to assume the liquid, and even
the solid, forms by the combination of high
pressure with intense cold. It has further been
shown that there is no discontinuity between
these states—that a gas passes into the liquid
state through a condition which is neither one
nor the other, and that a liquid body becomes
solid, or a solid liquid, by the intermediation of a
condition in which it is neither truly solid nor
truly liquid.

Theoretical and experimental investigations
have concurred in the establishment of the view
that a gas is a body, the particles of which are in
incessant rectilinear motion at high velocities, col-
liding with one another and bounding back when
they strike the walls of the containing vessel; and,
on this theory, the already ascertained relations of
gaseous bodies to heat and pressure have been
shown to be deducible from mechanical principles.
Immense improvements have been effected in the
means of exhausting a given space of its gaseous
contents; and experimentation on the phenomena
which attend the electric discharge and the action
of radiant heat, within the extremely rarefied media
thus produced, has yielded a great number of remarkable results, some of which have been made
familiar to the public by the Gieseler tubes and
the radiometer. Already, these investigations have
afforded an unexpected insight into the constitution of matter and its relations with thermal and

8

electric energy, and they open up a vast field for future inquiry into some of the deepest problems of physics. Other important steps, in the same direction, have been effected by investigations into the absorption of radiant heat proceeding from different sources by solid, fluid, and gaseous bodies. And it is a curious example of the interconnection of the various branches of physical science, that some of the results thus obtained have proved of great importance in meteorology.

The existence of numerous dark lines, constant in their number and position in the various regions of the solar spectrum, was made out by Fraunhofer in the early part of the present century, but more than forty years elapsed before their causes were ascertained and their importance recognised. Spectroscopy, which then took its rise, is probably that employment of physical knowledge, already won, as a means of further acquisition, which most impresses the imagination. For it has suddenly and immensely enlarged our power of overcoming the obstacles which almost infinite minuteness on the one hand, and almost infinite distance on the other, have hitherto opposed to the recognition of the presence and the condition of matter. One eighteen-millionth of a grain of sodium in the flame of a spirit-lamp may be detected by this instrument; and, at the same time, it gives trustworthy indications of the material constitution not only of the sun, but of the farthest of those fixed stars and nebulæ which afford sufficient light to affect the eye, or the photographic plate, of the inquirer.

The mathematical and experimental elucidation of the phenomena of electricity, and the study of the relations of this form of energy with chemical and thermal action, had made extensive progress before 1837. But the determination of the influence of magnetism on light, the discovery of diamagnetism, of the influence of crystalline structure on magnetism, and the completion of the mathematical theory of electricity, all belong to the present epoch. To it also appertain the practical execution and the working out of the results of the great international system of observations on terrestrial magnetism, suggested by Humboldt in 1836 ; and the invention of instruments of infinite delicacy and precision for the quantitative determination of electrical phenomena. The voltaic battery has received vast improvements ; while the invention of magneto-electric engines and of improved means of producing ordinary electricity has provided sources of electrical energy vastly superior to any before extant in power, and far more convenient for use.

It is perhaps this branch of physical science which may claim the palm for its practical fruits, no less than for the aid which it has furnished to the investigation of other parts of the field of physical science. The idea of the practicability of establishing a communication between distant points, by means of electricity, could hardly fail to have simmered in the minds of ingenious men since, well-nigh a century ago, experimental proof was given that electric disturbances could be propagated through a wire twelve thousand feet long. Various methods of carrying the suggestion into practice had been carried out with some degree of success; but the system of electric telegraphy, which, at the present time, brings all parts of the civilised world within a few minutes of one another, originated only about the commencement of the epoch under consideration. In its influence on the course of human affairs, this invention takes its place beside that of gunpowder, which tended to abolish the physical inequalities of fighting men; of printing, which tended to destroy the effect of inequalities in wealth among learning men; of steam transport, which has done the like for travelling men. All these gifts of science are aids in the process of levelling up; of removing the ignorant and baneful prejudices of nation against nation, province against province, and class against class; of assuring that social order which is the foundation of progress, which has redeemed Europe from barbarism, and against which one is glad to think that those who, in our time, are employing themselves in fanning the embers of ancient wrong, in setting class against class, and in trying to tear asunder the existing bonds of unity, are undertaking a futile struggle. The telephone is only

second in practical importance to the electric telegraph. Invented, as it were, only the other day,
it has already taken its place as an appliance of
daily life. Sixty years ago, the extraction of
metals from their solutions, by the electric current,
was simply a highly interesting scientific fact. At
the present day, the galvano-plastic art is a great
industry ; and, in combination with photography,
promises to be of endless service in the arts.
Electric lighting is another great gift of science to
civilisation, the practical effects of which have not
yet been fully developed, largely on account of its
cost. But those whose memories go back to the
tinder-box period, and recollect the cost of the
first lucifer matches, will not despair of the results
of the application of science and ingenuity to the
cheap production of anything for which there is a
large demand.

The influence of the progress of electrical knowledge and invention upon that of investigation in
other fields of science is highly remarkable. The
combination of electrical with mechanical contrivances has produced instruments by which, not
only may extremely small intervals of time be exactly measured, but the varying rapidity of movements, which take place in such intervals and
appear to the ordinary sense instantaneous, is
recorded. The duration of the winking of an eye
is a proverbial expression for an instantaneous
action ; but, by the help of the revolving cylinder

and the electrical marking-apparatus, it is possible to obtain a graphic record of such an action, in which, if it endures a second, that second shall be subdivided into a hundred, or a thousand, equal parts, and the state of the action at each hundredth, or thousandth, of a second exhibited. In fact, these instruments may be said to be time-microscopes. Such appliances have not only effected a revolution in physiology, by the power of analysing the phenomena of muscular and nervous activity which they have conferred, but they have furnished new methods of measuring the rate of movement of projectiles to the artillerist. Again, the microphone, which renders the minutest movements audible, and which enables a listener to hear the footfall of a fly, has equipped the sense of hearing with the means of entering almost as deeply into the penetralia of Nature, as does the sense of sight.

That light exerts a remarkable influence in bringing about certain chemical combinations and decompositions was well known fifty years ago, and various more or less successful attempts to produce permanent pictures, by the help of that knowledge, had already been made. It was not till 1839, however, that practical success was obtained; but the "daguerreotypes" were both cumbrous and costly, and photography would never have attained its present important development had not the progress of invention substituted paper and glass for the silvered plates then in use. It is not my affair to dwell upon the practical application of the photography of the present day, but it is germane to my purpose to remark that it has furnished a most valuable accessory to the methods of recording motions and lapse of time already in existence. In the hands of the astronomer and the meteorologist, it has yielded means of registering terrestrial, solar, planetary, and stellar phenomena, independent of the sources of error attendant on ordinary observation; in the hands of the physicist, not only does it record spectroscopic phenomena with unsurpassable ease and precision, but it has revealed the existence of rays having powerful chemical energy, or beyond the visible limits of either end of the spectrum; while, to the naturalist, it furnishes the means by which the forms of many highly complicated objects may be represented, without that possibility of error which is inherent in the work of the draughtsman. In fact, in many cases, the stern impartiality of photography is an objection to its employment: it makes no distinction between the important and the unimportant; and hence photographs of dissections, for example, are rarely so useful as the work of a draughtsman who is at once accurate and intelligent.

The determination of the existence of a new planet, Neptune, far beyond the previously known bounds of the solar system, by mathematical deduction from the facts of perturbation ; and the immediate confirmation of that determination, in the year 1846, by observers who turned their telescopes into the part of the heavens indicated as its place, constitute a remarkable testimony of nature to the validity of the principles of the astronomy of our time.   In addition, so many new asteroids have been added to those which were already known to circulate in the place which theoretically should be occupied by a planet, between Mars and Jupiter, that their number now amounts to between two and three hundred.   I have already alluded to the extension of our knowledge of the nature of the heavenly bodies by the employment of spectroscopy.   It has not only thrown wonderful light upon the physical and chemical constitution of the sun, fixed stars, and nebulæ, and comets, but it holds out a prospect of obtaining definite evidence as to the nature of our so-called elementary bodies.

The application of the generalisations of thermotics to the problem of the duration of the earth, and of deductions from tidal phenomena to the determination of the length of the day and of the time of revolution of the moon, in past epochs of the history of the universe ; and the demonstration of the competency of the great secular changes, known under the general name of the precession of the equinoxes, to cause corresponding modifications in the climate of the two hemispheres of our globe, have brought astronomy into intimate relation with geology. Geology, in fact, proves that, in the course of the past history of the earth, the climatic conditions of the same region have been widely different, and seeks the explanation of this important truth from the sister sciences. The facts that, in the middle of the Tertiary epoch, evergreen trees abounded within the arctic circle; and that, in the long subsequent Quaternary epoch, an arctic climate, with its accompaniment of gigantic glaciers, obtained in the northern hemisphere, as far south as Switzerland and Central France, are as well established as any truths of science. But, whether the explanation of these extreme variations in the mean temperature of a great part of the northern hemisphere is to be sought in the concomitant changes in the distribution of land and water surfaces of which geology affords evidence, or in astronomical conditions, such as those to which I have referred, is a question which must await its answer from the science of the future.

Turning now to the great steps in that vast progress which the biological sciences have made since 1837, we are met, on the threshold of our epoch, with perhaps the greatest of all—namely, the promulgation by Schwann, in 1839, of the generalisation known as the "cell theory," the application and extension of which by a host of subsequent investigators has revolutionised morphology, development, and physiology. Thanks to the immense series of labours thus inaugurated, the following fundamental truths have been established.

All living bodies contain substances of closely similar physical and chemical composition, which constitute the physical basis of life, known as protoplasm. So far as our present knowledge goes, this takes its origin only from pre-existing protoplasm.

All complex living bodies consist, at one period of their existence, of an aggregate of minute portions of such substance, of similar structure, called cells, each cell having its own life independent of the others, though influenced by them.

All the morphological characters of animals and plants are the results of the mode of multiplication, growth, and structural metamorphosis of these cells, considered as morphological units.

All the physiological activities of animals and plants—assimilation, secretion, excretion, motion, generation—are the expression of the activities of the cells considered as physiological units. Each individual, among the higher animals and plants, is a synthesis of millions of subordinate individualities. Its individuality, therefore, is that of a "civitas" in the ancient sense, or that of the Leviathan of Hobbes.

There is no absolute line of demarcation between

animals and plants. The intimate structure, and
the modes of change, in the cells of the two are
fundamentally the same. Moreover, the higher
forms are evolved from lower, in the course of their
development, by analogous processes of differen-
tiation, coalescence, and reduction in both the
vegetable and the animal worlds.

At the present time, the cell theory, in
consequence of recent investigations into the
structure and metamorphosis of the "nucleus," is
undergoing a new development of great significance, which among other things, foreshadows
the possibility of the establishment of a physical theory of heredity, on a safer foundation
than those which Buffon and Darwin have
devised.

The popular belief in abiogenesis, or the so-
called "spontaneous" generation of the lower forms
of life, which was accepted by all the philosophers
of antiquity, held its ground down to the middle
of the seventeenth century. Notwithstanding the
frequent citation of the phrase, wrongfully
attributed to Harvey, "Omne vivum ex ovo," that
great physiologist believed in spontaneous
generation as firmly as Aristotle did. And it was
only in the latter part of the seventeenth century,
that Redi, by simple and well-devised experiments,
demonstrated that, in a great number of cases of
supposed spontaneous generation, the animals
which made their appearance owed their origin to

the ordinary process of reproduction, and thus shook the ancient doctrine to its foundations. In the middle of the eighteenth century, it was revived, in a new form, by Needham and Buffon; but the experiments of Spallanzani enforced the conclusions of Redi, and compelled the advocates of the occurrence of spontaneous generation to seek evidence for their hypothesis only among the parasites and the lowest and minutest organisms. It is just fifty years since Schwann and others proved that, even with respect to them, the supposed evidence of abiogenesis was untrustworthy.

During the present epoch, the question, whether living matter can be produced in any other way than by the physiological activity of other living matter, has been discussed afresh with great vigour; and the problem has been investigated by experimental methods of a precision and refinement unknown to previous investigators. The result is that the evidence in favour of abiogenesis has utterly broken down, in every case which has been properly tested. So far as the lowest and minutest organisms are concerned, it has been proved that they never make their appearance, if those precautions by which their germs are certainly excluded are taken. And, in regard to parasites, every case which seemed to make for their generation from the substance of the animal, or plant, which they infest has been proved to have a totally different significance. Whether not-living matter may pass, or ever has, under any conditions, passed into living matter, without the agency of pre-existing living matter, necessarily remains an open question; all that can be said is that it does not undergo this metamorphosis under any known conditions. Those who take a monistic view of the physical world may fairly hold abiogenesis as a pious opinion, supported by analogy and defended by our ignorance. But, as matters stand, it is equally justifiable to regard the physical world as a sort of dual monarchy. The kingdoms of living matter and of not-living matter are under one system of laws, and there is a perfect freedom of exchange and transit from one to the other. But no claim to biological nationality is valid except birth.

In the department of anatomy and development, a host of accurate and patient inquirers, aided by novel methods of preparation, which enable the anatomist to exhaust the details of visible structure and to reproduce them with geometrical precision, have investigated every important group of living animals and plants, no less than the fossil relics of former faunæ and floræ. An enormous addition has thus been made to our knowledge, especially of the lower forms of life, and it may be said that morphology, however inexhaustible in detail, is complete in its broad features. Classification, which is merely a convenient summary expression of morphological facts, has undergone a corresponding improvement. The breaks which formerly separated our groups from one another, as animals from plants, vertebrates from invertebrates, cryptogams from phanerogams, have either been filled up, or shown to have no theoretical significance. The question of the position of man, as an animal, has given rise to much disputation, with the result of proving that there is no anatomical or developmental character by which he is more widely distinguished from the group of animals most nearly allied to him, than they are from one another. In fact, in this particular, the classification of Linnæus has been proved to be more in accordance with the facts than those of most of his successors.

The study of man, as a genus and species of the animal world, conducted with reference to no other considerations than those which would be admitted by the investigator of any other form of animal life, has given rise to a special branch of biology, known as Anthropology, which has grown with great rapidity. Numerous societies devoted to this portion of science have sprung up, and the energy of its devotees has produced a copious literature. The physical characters of the various races of men have been studied with a minuteness and accuracy heretofore unknown; and demonstrative evidence of the existence of human contemporaries of the extinct animals of the latest

geological epoch has been obtained. Physical
science has thus been brought into the closest
relation with history and with archæology; and
the striking investigations which, during our
time, have put beyond doubt the vast antiquity
of Babylonian and Egyptian civilisation, are in
perfect harmony with the conclusions of anthropology as to the antiquity of the human species.

Classification is a logical process which consists
in putting together those things which are like
and keeping asunder those which are unlike; and
a morphological classification, of course, takes note
only of morphological likeness and unlikeness.
So long, therefore, as our morphological knowledge
was almost wholly confined to anatomy, the characters of groups were solely anatomical; but as
the phenomena of embryology were explored, the
likeness and unlikeness of individual development
had to be taken into account; and, at present, the
study of ancestral evolution introduces a new element of likeness and unlikeness which is not only
eminently deserving of recognition, but must
ultimately predominate over all others. A classification which shall represent the process of
ancestral evolution is, in fact, the end which the
labours of the philosophical taxonomist must keep
in view. But it is an end which cannot be attained until the progress of palæontology has
given us far more insight, than we yet possess, into the historical facts of the case. Much of the

speculative "phylogeny," which abounds among my present contemporaries, reminds me very forcibly of the speculative morphology, unchecked by a knowledge of development, which was rife in my youth. As hypothesis, suggesting inquiry in this or that direction, it is often extremely useful; but, when the product of such speculation is placed on a level with those generalisations of morphological truths which are represented by the definitions of natural groups, it tends to confound fancy with fact and to create mere confusion. We are in danger of drifting into a new "Natur-Philosophie" worse than the old, because there is less excuse for it. Boyle did great service to science by his "Sceptical Chemist," and I am inclined to think that, at the present day, a "Sceptical Biologist" might exert an equally beneficent influence.

Whoso wishes to gain a clear conception of the progress of physiology, since 1837, will do well to compare Müller's "Physiology," which appeared in 1835, and Drapiez's edition of Richard's "Nouveaux Eléments de Botanique," published in 1837, with any of the present handbooks of animal and vegetable physiology. Müller's work was a masterpiece, unsurpassed since the time of Haller, and Richard's book enjoyed a great reputation at the time; but their successors transport one into a new world. That which characterises the new physiology is that it is permeated by, and indeed based upon, conceptions which, though not wholly absent, are but dawning on the minds of the older writers.

Modern physiology sets forth as its chief ends: Firstly, the ascertainment of the facts and conditions of cell-life in general. Secondly, in composite organisms, the analysis of the functions of organs into those of the cells of which they are composed. Thirdly, the explication of the processes by which this local cell-life is directly, or indirectly, controlled and brought into relation with the life of the rest of the cells which compose the organism. Fourthly, the investigation of the phenomena of life in general, on the assumption that the physical and chemical processes which take place in the living body are of the same order as those which take place out of it; and that whatever energy is exerted in producing such phenomena is derived from the common stock of energy in the universe. In the fifth place, modern physiology investigates the relation between physical and psychical phenomena, on the assumption that molecular changes in definite portions of nervous matter stand in the relation of necessary antecedents to definite mental states and operations. The work which has been done in each of the directions here indicated is vast, and the accumulation of solid knowledge, which has been effected, is correspondingly great. For the first time in the history of science, physiologists are now in a position to say that they have arrived at clear and distinct, though by no means complete, conceptions of the manner in which the great functions of assimilation, respiration, secretion, distribution of nutriment, removal of waste products, motion, sensation, and reproduction are performed; while the operation of the nervous system, as a regulative apparatus, which influences the origination and the transmission of manifestations of activity, either within itself or in other organs, has been largely elucidated.

I have pointed out, in an earlier part of this essay, that the history of all branches of science proves that they must attain a considerable stage of development before they yield practical "fruits;" and this is eminently true of physiology. It is only within the present epoch, that physiology and chemistry have reached the point at which they could offer a scientific foundation to agriculture; and it is only within the present epoch, that zoology and physiology have yielded any very great aid to pathology and hygiene. But, within that time, they have already rendered highly important services by the exploration of the phenomena of parasitism. Not only have the history of the animal parasites, such as the tapeworms and the trichina, which infest men and animals, with deadly results, been cleared up by means of experimental investigations, and efficient modes of prevention deduced from the data so obtained; but the terrible agency of the parasitic fungi and of the infinitesimally minute microbes, which work far greater havoc among plants and animals, has been brought to light. The "particulate" or "germ" theory of disease, as it is called, long since suggested, has obtained a firm foundation, in so far as it has been proved to be true in respect of sundry epidemic disorders. Moreover, it has theoretically justified prophylactic measures, such as vaccination, which formerly rested on a merely empirical basis; and it has been extended to other diseases with excellent results. Further, just as the discovery of the cause of scabies proved the absurdity of many of the old prescriptions for the prevention and treatment of that disease; so the discovery of the cause of splenic fever, and other such maladies, has given a new direction to prophylactic and curative measures against the worst scourges of humanity. Unless the fanaticism of philozoic sentiment overpowers the voice of philanthropy, and the love of dogs and cats supersedes that of one's neighbour, the progress of experimental physiology and pathology will, indubitably, in course of time, place medicine and hygiene upon a rational basis. Two centuries ago England was devastated by the plague; cleanliness and common sense were enough to free us from its ravages. One century since, small-pox was almost as great a scourge; science, though working empirically, and almost in the dark, has reduced that evil to relative insignificance. At the present time, science, working in the light of clear knowledge, has attacked splenic fever and has beaten it; it is attacking hydrophobia with no mean promise of success; sooner or later it will deal, in the same way, with diphtheria, typhoid and scarlet fever. To one who has seen half a street swept clear of its children, or has lost his own by these horrible pestilences, passing one's offspring through the fire to Moloch seems humanity, compared with the proposal to deprive them of half their chances of health and life because of the discomfort to dogs and cats, rabbits and frogs, which may be involved in the search for means of guarding them.

An immense extension has been effected in our knowledge of the distribution of plants and animals ; and the elucidation of the causes which have brought about that distribution has been greatly advanced. The establishment of meteorological observations by all civilised nations, has furnished a solid foundation to climatology ; while a growing sense of the importance of the influence of the " struggle for existence " affords a wholesome check to the tendency to overrate the influence of climate on distribution. Expeditions, such as that of the " Challenger," equipped, not for geographical exploration and discovery, but for the purpose of throwing light on problems of physical and biological science, have been sent out by our own and other Governments, and have obtained stores of information of the greatest value. For the first time, we are in possession of something like precise knowledge of the physical features of the deep seas, and of the living population of the floor of the ocean. The careful and exhaustive study of the phenomena presented by the accumulations of snow and ice, in polar and mountainous regions, which has taken place in our time, has not only revealed to the geologist an agent of denudation and transport, which has slowly and quietly produced effects, formerly confidently referred to diluvial catastrophes, but it has suggested new methods of accounting for various puzzling facts of distribution.

Palæontology, which treats of the extinct forms of life and their succession and distribution upon our globe, a branch of science which could hardly be said to exist a century ago, has undergone a wonderful development in our epoch. In some groups of animals and plants, the extinct representatives, already known, are more numerous and important than the living. There can be no doubt that the existing Fauna and Flora is but the last term of a long series of equally numerous contemporary species, which have succeeded one another, by the slow and gradual substitution of species for species, in the vast interval of time which has elapsed between the deposition of the earliest fossiliferous strata and the present day.

There is no reasonable ground for believing that the oldest remains yet obtained carry us even near the beginnings of life. The impressive warnings of Lyell against hasty speculations, based upon negative evidence, have been fully justified; time after time, highly organised types have been discovered in formations of an age in which the existence of such forms of life had been confidently declared to be impossible. The western territories of the United States alone have yielded a world of extinct animal forms, undreamed of fifty years ago. And, wherever sufficiently numerous series of the remains of any given group, which has endured for a long space of time, are carefully examined, their morphological relations are never in discordance with the requirements of the doctrine of evolution, and often afford convincing evidence of it. At the same time it has been shown that certain forms persist with very little change, from the oldest to the newest fossiliferous formations; and thus show that progressive development is a contingent, and not a necessary, result of the nature of living matter.

Geology is, as it were, the biology of our planet as a whole. In so far as it comprises the surface configuration and the inner structure of the earth, it answers to morphology; in so far as it studies changes of condition and their causes, it corresponds with physiology; in so far as it deals with the causes which have effected the progress of the earth from its earliest to its present state, it forms part of the general doctrine of evolution. An interesting contrast between the geology of the present day and that of half a century ago, is presented by the complete emancipation of the modern geologist from the controlling and per- verting influence of theology, all-powerful at the earlier date. As the geologist of my young days wrote, he had one eye upon fact, and the other on Genesis; at present, he wisely keeps both eyes on fact, and ignores the pentateuchal mythology altogether. The publication of the "Principles of Geology" brought upon its illustrious author a period of social ostracism; the instruction given to our children is based upon those principles. Whewell had the courage to attack Lyell's funda- mental assumption (which surely is a dictate of common sense) that we ought to exhaust known causes before seeking for the explanation of geo- logical phenomena in causes of which we have no experience. But geology has advanced to its present state by working from Lyell's [1] axiom; and, to this day, the record of the stratified rocks affords no proof that the intensity or the rapidity of action of the causes of change has ever varied between wider limits than those between which

---

[1] Perhaps I ought rather to say Buffon's axiom. For that great naturalist and writer embodied the principles of sound geology in a pithy phrase of the *Théorie de la Terre*: "Pour juger de ce qui est arrivé, et même de ce qui arrivera, nous n'avons qu'à examiner ce qui arrive."

the operations of Nature have taken place in the youngest geological epochs.

An incalculable benefit has accrued to geological science from the accurate and detailed surveys, which have now been executed by skilled geologists employed by the Governments of all parts of the civilised world. In geology, the study of large maps is as important as it is said to be in politics; and sections, on a true scale, are even more important, in so far as they are essential to the apprehension of the extraordinary insignificance of geological perturbations in relation to the whole mass of our planet. It should never be forgotten that what we call "catastrophes," are, in relation to the earth, changes, the equivalents of which would be well represented by the development of a few pimples, or the scratch of a pin, on a man's head. Vast regions of the earth's surface remain geologically unknown; but the area already fairly explored is many times greater than it was in 1837; and, in many parts of Europe and the United States, the structure of the superficial crust of the earth has been investigated with great minuteness.

The parallel between Biology and Geology, which I have drawn, is further illustrated by the modern growth of that branch of the science known as Petrology, which answers to Histology, and has made the microscope as essential an instrument to the geological as to the biological investigator.

The evidence of the importance of causes now in operation has been wonderfully enlarged by the study of glacial phænomena; by that of earthquakes and volcanoes; and by that of the efficacy of heat and cold, wind, rain, and rivers as agents of denudation and transport. On the other hand, the exploration of coral reefs and of the deposits now taking place at the bottom of the great oceans, has proved that, in animal and plant life, we have agents of reconstruction of a potency hitherto unsuspected.

There is no study better fitted than that of geology to impress upon men of general culture that conviction of the unbroken sequence of the order of natural phænomena, throughout the duration of the universe, which is the great, and perhaps the most important, effect of the increase of natural knowledge.

[I desire to express my obligations to Messrs. Smith, Elder and Co. for their courteous permission to reprint this essay from " The Reign of Queen Victoria."]

III

ON THE PHYSICAL BASIS OF LIFE[1]

[1868]

IN order to make the title of this discourse generally intelligible, I have translated the term "Protoplasm," which is the scientific name of the substance of which I am about to speak, by the words "the physical basis of life." I suppose that, to many, the idea that there is such a thing as a physical basis, or matter, of life may be novel—

[1] The substance of this paper was contained in a discourse which was delivered in Edinburgh on the evening of Sunday, the 8th of November, 1868—being the first of a series of Sunday evening addresses upon non-theological topics, instituted by the Rev. J. Cranbrook. Some phrases, which could possess only a transitory and local interest have been omitted ; instead of the newspaper report of the Archbishop of York's address, his Grace's subsequently published pamphlet *On the Limits of Philosophical Inquiry* is quoted ; and I have, here and there, endeavoured to express my meaning more fully and clearly than I seem to have done in speaking—if I may judge by sundry criticisms upon what I am supposed to have said, which have appeared. But in substance, and, so far as my recollection serves, in form, what is here written corresponds with what was there said.

so widely spread is the conception of life as a
something which works through matter, but is
independent of it; and even those who are aware
that matter and life are inseparably connected,
may not be prepared for the conclusion plainly
suggested by the phrase, "*the* physical basis or
matter of life," that there is some one kind of
matter which is common to all living beings, and
that their endless diversities are bound together
by a physical, as well as an ideal, unity. In fact,
when first apprehended, such a doctrine as this
appears almost shocking to common sense.

What, truly, can seem to be more obviously
different from one another, in faculty, in form, and
in substance, than the various kinds of living
beings? What community of faculty can there
be between the brightly-coloured lichen, which so
nearly resembles a mere mineral incrustation of
the bare rock on which it grows, and the painter,
to whom it is instinct with beauty, or the botanist,
whom it feeds with knowledge ?

Again, think of the microscopic fungus—a mere
infinitesimal ovoid particle, which finds space and
duration enough to multiply into countless millions
in the body of a living fly ; and then of the wealth
of foliage, the luxuriance of flower and fruit,
which lies between this bald sketch of a plant and
the giant pine of California, towering to the
dimensions of a cathedral spire, or the Indian fig,
which covers acres with its profound shadow, and

endures while nations and empires come and go around its vast circumference. Or, turning to the other half of the world of life, picture to yourselves the great Finner whale, hugest of beasts that live, or have lived, disporting his eighty or ninety feet of bone, muscle, and blubber, with easy roll, among waves in which the stoutest ship that ever left dockyard would flounder hopelessly; and contrast him with the invisible animalcules— mere gelatinous specks, multitudes of which could, in fact, dance upon the point of a needle with the same ease as the angels of the Schoolmen could, in imagination. With these images before your minds, you may well ask, what community of form, or structure, is there between the animalcule and the whale; or between the fungus and the fig-tree ? And, *à fortiori*, between all four ?

Finally, if we regard substance, or material composition, what hidden bond can connect the flower which a girl wears in her hair and the blood which courses through her youthful veins; or, what is there in common between the dense and resisting mass of the oak, or the strong fabric of the tortoise, and those broad disks of glassy jelly which may be seen pulsating through the waters of a calm sea, but which drain away to mere films in the hand which raises them out of their element ?

Such objections as these must, I think, arise in the mind of every one who ponders, for the first time, upon the conception of a single physical basis of life underlying all the diversities of vital existence; but I propose to demonstrate to you that, notwithstanding these apparent difficulties, a threefold unity—namely, a unity of power or faculty, a unity of form, and a unity of substantial composition—does pervade the whole living world.

No very abstruse argumentation is needed, in the first place to prove that the powers, or faculties, of all kinds of living matter, diverse as they may be in degree, are substantially similar in kind.

Goethe has condensed a survey of all powers of mankind into the well-known epigram :—

> "Warum treibt sich das Volk so und schreit ? Es will sich
>   ernähren
>   Kinder zeugen, und die nähren so gut es vermag.
>   *   *   *   *
>   Weiter bringt es kein Mensch, stell' er sich wie er auch
>   will."

In physiological language this means, that all the multifarious and complicated activities of man are comprehensible under three categories. Either they are immediately directed towards the maintenance and development of the body, or they effect transitory changes in the relative positions of parts of the body, or they tend towards the continuance of the species. Even those manifestations of intellect, of feeling, and of will, which we rightly name the higher faculties, are not excluded from this classification, inasmuch as to every one but the subject of them, they are known only as transitory changes in the relative positions of parts of the body. Speech, gesture, and every other form of human action are, in the long run, resolvable into muscular contraction, and muscular contraction is but a transitory change in the relative positions of the parts of a muscle. But the scheme which is large enough to embrace the activities of the highest form of life, covers all those of the lower creatures. The lowest plant, or animalcule, feeds, grows, and reproduces its kind. In addition, all animals manifest those transitory changes of form which we class under irritability and contractility ; and, it is more than probable, that when the vegetable world is thoroughly explored, we shall find all plants in possession of the same powers, at one time or other of their existence.

I am not now alluding to such phænomena, at once rare and conspicuous, as those exhibited by the leaflets of the sensitive plants, or the stamens of the barberry, but to much more widely spread, and at the same time, more subtle and hidden, manifestations of vegetable contractility. You are doubtless aware that the common nettle owes its stinging property to the innumerable stiff and needle-like, though exquisitely delicate, hairs which cover its surface. Each stinging-needle tapers from a broad base to a slender summit, which, though rounded at the end, is of such microscopic fineness that it readily penetrates, and breaks off in, the skin. The whole hair consists of a very delicate outer case of wood, closely applied to the inner surface of which is a layer of semifluid matter, full of innumerable granules of extreme minuteness. This semi-fluid lining is protoplasm, which thus constitutes a kind of bag, full of a limpid liquid, and roughly corresponding in form with the interior of the hair which it fills. When viewed with a sufficiently high magnifying power, the protoplasmic layer of the nettle hair is seen to be in a condition of unceasing activity. Local contractions of the whole thickness of its substance pass slowly and gradually from point to point, and give rise to the appearance of progressive waves, just as the bending of successive stalks of corn by a breeze produces the apparent billows of a cornfield.

But, in addition to these movements, and independently of them, the granules are driven, in relatively rapid streams, through channels in the protoplasm which seem to have a considerable amount of persistence. Most commonly, the currents in adjacent parts of the protoplasm take similar directions; and, thus, there is a general stream up one side of the hair and down the other. But this does not prevent the existence of partial currents which take different routes; and sometimes trains of granules may be seen coursing swiftly in opposite directions within a twenty-thousandth of an inch of one another; while, occasionally, opposite streams come into direct collision, and, after a longer or shorter struggle, one predominates. The cause of these currents seems to lie in contractions of the protoplasm which bounds the channels in which they flow, but which are so minute that the best microscopes show only their effects, and not themselves.

The spectacle afforded by the wonderful energies prisoned within the compass of the microscopic hair of a plant, which we commonly regard as a merely passive organism, is not easily forgotten by one who has watched its display, continued hour after hour, without pause or sign of weakening. The possible complexity of many other organic forms, seemingly as simple as the protoplasm of the nettle, dawns upon one; and the comparison of such a protoplasm to a body with an internal circulation, which has been put forward by an eminent physiologist, loses much of its startling character. Currents similar to those of the hairs of the nettle have been observed in a great multitude of very different plants, and weighty authorities have suggested that they probably occur, in more or less perfection, in all young vegetable cells. If such be the case, the wonderful noonday silence of a tropical forest is, after all, due only to the dulness of our hearing; and could our ears catch the murmur of these tiny Maelstroms, as they whirl in the innumerable myriads of living cells which constitute each tree, we should be stunned, as with the roar of a great city.

Among the lower plants, it is the rule rather than the exception, that contractility should be still more openly manifested at some periods of their existence. The protoplasm of *Algæ* and *Fungi* becomes, under many circumstances, partially, or completely, freed from its woody case, and exhibits movements of its whole mass, or is propelled by the contractility of one, or more, hair-like prolongations of its body, which are called vibratile cilia. And, so far as the conditions of the manifestation of the phænomena of contractility have yet been studied, they are the same for the plant as for the animal. Heat and electric shocks influence both, and in the same way, though it may be in different degrees. It is by no means my intention to suggest that there is no difference in faculty between the lowest plant and the highest, or between plants and animals. But the difference between the powers of the lowest plant, or animal, and those of the highest, is one of degree, not of kind, and depends, as Milne-Edwards long ago so well pointed out, upon the extent to which the principle of the division of labour is carried out in the living economy. In the lowest organism all parts are competent to perform all functions, and one and the same portion of protoplasm may

10

successfully take on the function of feeding, moving, or reproducing apparatus. In the highest, on the contrary, a great number of parts combine to perform each function, each part doing its allotted share of the work with great accuracy and efficiency, but being useless for any other purpose.

On the other hand, notwithstanding all the fundamental resemblances which exist between the powers of the protoplasm in plants and in animals, they present a striking difference (to which I shall advert more at length presently), in the fact that plants can manufacture fresh protoplasm out of mineral compounds, whereas animals are obliged to procure it ready made, and hence, in the long run, depend upon plants. Upon what condition this difference in the powers of the two great divisions of the world of life depends, nothing is at present known.

With such qualifications as arises out of the last-mentioned fact, it may be truly said that the acts of all living things are fundamentally one. Is any such unity predicable of their forms? Let us seek in easily verified facts for a reply to this question. If a drop of blood be drawn by pricking one's finger, and viewed with proper precautions, and under a sufficiently high microscopic power, there will be seen, among the innumerable multitude of little, circular, discoidal bodies, or corpuscles, which float in it and give it its colour, a comparatively small number of colourless corpuscles, of somewhat larger size and very irregular shape. If the drop of blood be kept at the temperature of the body, these colourless corpuscles will be seen to exhibit a marvellous activity, changing their forms with great rapidity, drawing in and thrusting out prolongations of their substance, and creeping about as if they were independent organisms.

The substance which is thus active is a mass of protoplasm, and its activity differs in detail, rather than in principle, from that of the protoplasm of the nettle. Under sundry circumstances the corpuscle dies and becomes distended into a round mass, in the midst of which is seen a smaller spherical body, which existed, but was more or less hidden, in the living corpuscle, and is called its *nucleus.* Corpuscles of essentially similar structure are to be found in the skin, in the lining of the mouth, and scattered through the whole framework of the body. Nay, more; in the earliest condition of the human organism, in that state in which it has but just become distinguishable from the egg in which it arises, it is nothing but an aggregation of such corpuscles, and every organ of the body was, once, no more than such an aggregation.

Thus a nucleated mass of protoplasm turns out to be what may be termed the structural unit of the human body. As a matter of fact, the body, in its earliest state, is a mere multiple of such units; and in its perfect condition, it is a multiple of such units, variously modified.

But does the formula which expresses the essential structural character of the highest animal cover all the rest, as the statement of its powers and faculties covered that of all others? Very nearly. Beast and fowl, reptile and fish, mollusk, worm, and polype, are all composed of structural units of the same character, namely, masses of protoplasm with a nucleus. There are sundry very low animals, each of which, structurally, is a mere colourless blood-corpuscle, leading an independent life. But, at the very bottom of the animal scale, even this simplicity becomes simplified, and all the phænomena of life are manifested by a particle of protoplasm without a nucleus. Nor are such organisms insignificant by reason of their want of complexity. It is a fair question whether the protoplasm of those simplest forms of life, which people an immense extent of the bottom of the sea, would not outweigh that of all the higher living beings which inhabit the land put together. And in ancient times, no less than at the present day, such living beings as these have been the greatest of rock builders.

What has been said of the animal world is no less true of plants. Imbedded in the protoplasm at the broad, or attached, end of the nettle hair, there lies a spheroidal nucleus. Careful examina-

tion further proves that the whole substance of
the nettle is made up of a repetition of such masses
of nucleated protoplasm, each contained in a
wooden case, which is modified in form, sometimes into a woody fibre, sometimes into a duct
or spiral vessel, sometimes into a pollen grain, or
an ovule. Traced back to its earliest state, the
nettle arises as the man does, in a particle
of nucleated protoplasm. And in the lowest
plants, as in the lowest animals, a single mass
of such protoplasm may constitute the whole
plant, or the protoplasm may exist without a
nucleus.

Under these circumstances it may well be asked,
how is one mass of non-nucleated protoplasm to
be distinguished from another? why call one
" plant " and the other " animal " ?

The only reply is that, so far as form is concerned, plants and animals are not separable, and
that, in many cases, it is a mere matter of convention whether we call a given organism an
animal or a plant. There is a living body called
Æthalium septicum, which appears upon decaying
vegetable substances, and, in one of its forms,
is common upon the surfaces of tan-pits. In this
condition it is, to all intents and purposes, a
fungus, and formerly was always regarded as
such ; but the remarkable investigations of De
Bary have shown that, in another condition, the
Æthalium is an actively locomotive creature, and

takes in solid matters, upon which, apparently, it feeds, thus exhibiting the most characteristic feature of animality. Is this a plant ; or is it an animal ? Is it both ; or is it neither ? Some decide in favour of the last supposition, and establish an intermediate kingdom, a sort of biological No Man's Land for all these question-able forms. But, as it is admittedly impossible to draw any distinct boundary line between this no man's land and the vegetable world on the one hand, or the animal, on the other, it appears to me that this proceeding merely doubles the diffi-culty which, before, was single.

Protoplasm, simple or nucleated, is the formal basis of all life. It is the clay of the potter : which, bake it and paint it as he will, remains clay, separated by artifice, and not by nature, from the commonest brick or sun-dried clod.

Thus it becomes clear that all living powers are cognate, and that all living forms are fundamen-tally of one character. The researches of the chemist have revealed a no less striking uni-formity of material composition in living matter.

In perfect strictness, it is true that chemical in-vestigation can tell us little or nothing, directly, of the composition of living matter, inasmuch as such matter must needs die in the act of analysis,—and upon this very obvious ground, objections, which I confess seem to me to be somewhat frivolous, have been raised to the drawing of any conclusions

whatever respecting the composition of actually
living matter, from that of the dead matter of
life, which alone is accessible to us. But objectors of this class do not seem to reflect that
it is also, in strictness, true that we know nothing
about the composition of any body whatever, as
it is. The statement that a crystal of calc-spar
consists of carbonate of lime, is quite true, if we
only mean that, by appropriate processes, it may be
resolved into carbonic acid and quicklime. If you
pass the same carbonic acid over the very quicklime thus obtained, you will obtain carbonate of
lime again; but it will not be calc-spar, nor anything like it. Can it, therefore, be said that
chemical analysis teaches nothing about the
chemical composition of calc-spar? Such a statement would be absurd; but it is hardly more so
than the talk one occasionally hears about the
uselessness of applying the results of chemical
analysis to the living bodies which have yielded
them.

One fact, at any rate, is out of reach of such
refinements, and this is, that all the forms of protoplasm which have yet been examined contain
the four elements, carbon, hydrogen, oxygen, and
nitrogen, in very complex union, and that they
behave similarly towards several reagents. To
this complex combination, the nature of which has
never been determined with exactness, the name
of Protein has been applied. And if we use this

term with such caution as may properly arise out of our comparative ignorance of the things for which it stands, it may be truly said, that all protoplasm is proteinaceous, or, as the white, or albumen, of an egg is one of the commonest examples of a nearly pure proteine matter, we may say that all living matter is more or less albuminoid.

Perhaps it would not yet be safe to say that all forms of protoplasm are affected by the direct action of electric shocks; and yet the number of cases in which the contraction of protoplasm is shown to be affected by this agency increases every day.

Nor can it be affirmed with perfect confidence, that all forms of protoplasm are liable to undergo that peculiar coagulation at a temperature of 40° —50° centigrade, which has been called "heat-stiffening," though Kühne's beautiful researches have proved this occurrence to take place in so many and such diverse living beings, that it is hardly rash to expect that the law holds good for all.

Enough has, perhaps, been said to prove the existence of a general uniformity in the character of the protoplasm, or physical basis, of life, in whatever group of living beings it may be studied. But it will be understood that this general uniformity by no means excludes any amount of special modifications of the fundamental substance. The mineral, carbonate of lime, assumes an immense diversity of characters, though no one doubts that, under all these Protean changes, it is one and the same thing.

And now, what is the ultimate fate, and what the origin, of the matter of life?

Is it, as some of the older naturalists supposed, diffused throughout the universe in molecules, which are indestructible and unchangeable in themselves; but, in endless transmigration, unite in innumerable permutations, into the diversified forms of life we know? Or, is the matter of life composed of ordinary matter, differing from it only in the manner in which its atoms are aggregated? Is it built up of ordinary matter, and again resolved into ordinary matter when its work is done?

Modern science does not hesitate a moment between these alternatives. Physiology writes over the portals of life—

"Debemur morti nos nostraque,"

with a profounder meaning than the Roman poet attached to that melancholy line. Under whatever disguise it takes refuge, whether fungus or oak, worm or man, the living protoplasm not only ultimately dies and is resolved into its mineral and lifeless constituents, but is always dying, and, strange as the paradox may sound, could not live unless it died.

In the wonderful story of the "Peau de Chagrin," the hero becomes possessed of a magical wild ass' skin, which yields him the means of gratifying all his wishes. But its surface represents the duration of the proprietor's life; and for every satisfied desire the skin shrinks in proportion to the intensity of fruition, until at length life and the last handbreadth of the *peau de chagrin*, disappear with the gratification of a last wish.

Balzac's studies had led him over a wide range of thought and speculation, and his shadowing forth of physiological truth in this strange story may have been intentional. At any rate, the matter of life is a veritable *peau de chagrin*, and for every vital act it is somewhat the smaller. All work implies waste, and the work of life results, directly or indirectly, in the waste of protoplasm.

Every word uttered by a speaker costs him some physical loss; and, in the strictest sense, he burns that others may have light—so much eloquence, so much of his body resolved into carbonic acid, water, and urea. It is clear that this process of expenditure cannot go on for ever. But, happily, the protoplasmic *peau de chagrin* differs from Balzac's in its capacity of being repaired, and brought back to its full size, after every exertion.

For example, this present lecture, whatever its intellectual worth to you, has a certain physical value to me, which is, conceivably, expressible by the number of grains of protoplasm and other bodily substance wasted in maintaining my vital processes during its delivery. My *peau de chagrin* will be distinctly smaller at the end of the discourse than it was at the beginning. By and by, I shall probably have recourse to the substance commonly called mutton, for the purpose of stretching it back to its original size. Now this mutton was once the living protoplasm, more or less modified, of another animal—a sheep. As I shall eat it, it is the same matter altered, not only by death, but by exposure to sundry artificial operations in the process of cooking.

But these changes, whatever be their extent, have not rendered it incompetent to resume its old functions as matter of life. A singular inward laboratory, which I possess, will dissolve a certain portion of the modified protoplasm; the solution so formed will pass into my veins; and the subtle influences to which it will then be subjected will convert the dead protoplasm into living protoplasm, and transubstantiate sheep into man.

Nor is this all. If digestion were a thing to be trifled with, I might sup upon lobster, and the matter of life of the crustacean would undergo the same wonderful metamorphosis into humanity. And were I to return to my own place by sea, and undergo shipwreck, the crustacean might, and probably would, return the compliment, and demonstrate our common nature by turning my protoplasm into living lobster. Or, if nothing better were to be had, I might supply my wants with mere bread, and I should find the protoplasm of the wheat-plant to be convertible into man, with no more trouble than that of the sheep, and with far less, I fancy, than that of the lobster.

Hence it appears to be a matter of no great moment what animal, or what plant, I lay under contribution for protoplasm, and the fact speaks volumes for the general identity of that substance in all living beings. I share this catholicity of assimilation with other animals, all of which, so far as we know, could thrive equally well on the protoplasm of any of their fellows, or of any plant ; but here the assimilative powers of the animal world cease. A solution of smelling-salts in water, with an infinitesimal proportion of some other saline matters, contains all the elementary bodies which enter into the composition of protoplasm ; but, as I need hardly say, a hogshead of that fluid would not keep a hungry man from starving, nor would it save any animal whatever from a like fate. An animal cannot make protoplasm, but must take it ready-made from some other animal, or some plant—the animal's highest feat of constructive chemistry being to convert dead protoplasm into that living matter of life which is appropriate to itself.

Therefore, in seeking for the origin of proto-plasm, we must eventually turn to the vegetable world. A fluid containing carbonic acid, water, and nitrogenous salts, which offers such a Barmecide feast to the animal, is a table richly spread to multitudes of plants; and, with a due supply of only such materials, many a plant will not only maintain itself in vigour, but grow and multiply until it has increased a million-fold, or a million million-fold, the quantity of protoplasm which it originally possessed; in this way building up the matter of life, to an indefinite extent, from the common matter of the universe.

Thus, the animal can only raise the complex substance of dead protoplasm to the higher power, as one may say, of living protoplasm; while the plant can raise the less complex substances— carbonic acid, water, and nitrogenous salts—to the same stage of living protoplasm, if not to the same level. But the plant also has its limitations. Some of the fungi, for example, appear to need higher compounds to start with; and no known plant can live upon the uncompounded elements of protoplasm. A plant supplied with pure carbon, hydrogen, oxygen, and nitrogen, phosphorus, sulphur, and the like, would as infallibly die as the animal in his bath of smelling-salts, though it would be surrounded by all the constituents of protoplasm. Nor, indeed, need the process of simplification of vegetable food be carried so far as this, in order to arrive at the limit of the plant's thaumaturgy. Let water, carbonic acid, and all the other needful constituents be supplied except nitrogenous salts, and an ordinary plant will still be unable to manufacture protoplasm.

Thus the matter of life, so far as we know it (and we have no right to speculate on any other), breaks up, in consequence of that continual death which is the condition of its manifesting vitality, into carbonic acid, water, and nitrogenous compounds, which certainly possess no properties but those of ordinary matter. And out of these same forms of ordinary matter, and from none which are simpler, the vegetable world builds up all the protoplasm which keeps the animal world a-going. Plants are the accumulators of the power which animals distribute and disperse.

But it will be observed, that the existence of the matter of life depends on the pre-existence of certain compounds; namely, carbonic acid, water, and certain nitrogenous bodies. Withdraw any one of these three from the world, and all vital phænomena come to an end. They are as necessary to the protoplasm of the plant, as the protoplasm of the plant is to that of the animal. Carbon, hydrogen, oxygen, and nitrogen are all lifeless bodies. Of these, carbon and oxygen unite in certain proportions and under certain conditions, to give rise to carbonic acid; hydrogen and oxygen produce water; nitrogen and other elements give rise to nitrogenous salts. These new compounds, like the elementary bodies of which they are composed, are lifeless.   But when they are brought together, under certain conditions, they give rise to the still more complex body, protoplasm, and this protoplasm exhibits the phænomena of life.

I see no break in this series of steps in molecular complication, and I am unable to understand why the language which is applicable to any one term of the series may not be used to any of the others.   We think fit to call different kinds of matter carbon, oxygen, hydrogen, and nitrogen, and to speak of the various powers and activities of these substances as the properties of the matter of which they are composed.

When hydrogen and oxygen are mixed in a certain proportion, and an electric spark is passed through them, they disappear, and a quantity of water, equal in weight to the sum of their weights, appears in their place.   There is not the slightest parity between the passive and active powers of the water and those of the oxygen and hydrogen which have given rise to it.   At 32° Fahrenheit, and far below that temperature, oxygen and hydrogen are elastic gaseous bodies, whose particles tend to rush away from one another with great force.   Water, at the same temperature, is a strong though brittle solid, whose particles tend to cohere into definite geometrical shapes, and sometimes build up frosty imitations of the most complex forms of vegetable foliage.

Nevertheless we call these, and many other

strange phænomena, the properties of the water, and we do not hesitate to believe that, in some way or another, they result from the properties of the component elements of the water. We do not assume that a something called "aquosity" entered into and took possession of the oxidated hydrogen as soon as it was formed, and then guided the aqueous particles to their places in the facets of the crystal, or amongst the leaflets of the hoar-frost. On the contrary, we live in the hope and in the faith that, by the advance of molecular physics, we shall by and by be able to see our way as clearly from the constituents of water to the properties of water, as we are now able to deduce the operations of a watch from the form of its parts and the manner in which they are put together.

Is the case in any way changed when carbonic acid, water, and nitrogenous salts disappear, and in their place, under the influence of pre-existing living protoplasm, an equivalent weight of the matter of life makes its appearance?

It is true that there is no sort of parity between the properties of the components and the properties of the resultant, but neither was there in the case of the water. It is also true that what I have spoken of as the influence of pre-existing living matter is something quite unintelligible; but does anybody quite comprehend the *modus operandi* of an electric spark, which traverses a mixture of oxygen and hydrogen?

What justification is there, then, for the assumption of the existence in the living matter of a something which has no representative, or correlative, in the not living matter which gave rise to it? What better philosophical status has "vitality" than "aquosity"? And why should "vitality" hope for a better fate than the other "itys" which have disappeared since Martinus Scriblerus accounted for the operation of the meat-jack by its inherent "meat-roasting quality," and scorned the "materialism" of those who explained the turning of the spit by a certain mechanism worked by the draught of the chimney.

If scientific language is to possess a definite and constant signification whenever it is employed, it seems to me that we are logically bound to apply to the protoplasm, or physical basis of life, the same conceptions as those which are held to be legitimate elsewhere. If the phænomena exhibited by water are its properties, so are those presented by protoplasm, living or dead, its properties.

If the properties of water may be properly said to result from the nature and disposition of its component molecules, I can find no intelligible ground for refusing to say that the properties of protoplasm result from the nature and disposition of its molecules.

But I bid you beware that, in accepting these conclusions, you are placing your feet on the first

11

rung of a ladder which, in most people's estimation, is the reverse of Jacob's, and leads to the
antipodes of heaven. It may seem a small thing
to admit that the dull vital actions of a fungus,
or a foraminifer, are the properties of their protoplasm, and are the direct results of the nature of
the matter of which they are composed. But if,
as I have endeavoured to prove to you, their protoplasm is essentially identical with, and most
readily converted into, that of any animal, I can
discover no logical halting-place between the
admission that such is the case, and the further
concession that all vital action may, with equal
propriety, be said to be the result of the molecular
forces of the protoplasm which displays it. And
if so, it must be true, in the same sense and to
the same extent, that the thoughts to which I am
now giving utterance, and your thoughts regarding
them, are the expression of molecular changes in
that matter of life which is the source of our other
vital phænomena.

Past experience leads me to be tolerably certain
that, when the propositions I have just placed
before you are accessible to public comment and
criticism, they will be condemned by many zealous
persons, and perhaps by some few of the wise and
thoughtful. I should not wonder if "gross and
brutal materialism" were the mildest phrase
applied to them in certain quarters. And, most

undoubtedly, the terms of the propositions are distinctly materialistic. Nevertheless two things are certain ; the one, that I hold the statements to be substantially true ; the other, that I, individually, am no materialist, but, on the contrary, believe materialism to involve grave philosophical error.

This union of materialistic terminology with the repudiation of materialistic philosophy I share with some of the most thoughtful men with whom I am acquainted. And, when I first undertook to deliver the present discourse, it appeared to me to be a fitting opportunity to explain how such a union is not only consistent with, but necessitated by, sound logic. I purposed to lead you through the territory of vital phænomena to the materialistic slough in which you find yourselves now plunged, and then to point out to you the sole path by which, in my judgment, extrication is possible.

An occurrence of which I was unaware until my arrival here last night renders this line of argument singularly opportune. I found in your papers the eloquent address "On the Limits of Philosophical Inquiry," which a distinguished prelate of the English Church delivered before the members of the Philosophical Institution on the previous day. My argument, also, turns upon this very point of the limits of philosphical inquiry ; and I cannot bring out my own views better than by contrasting them with those so plainly and, in the main, fairly stated by the Archbishop of York.

But I may be permitted to make a preliminary comment upon an occurrence that greatly astonished me. Applying the name of the "New Philosophy" to that estimate of the limits of philosophical inquiry which I, in common with many other men of science, hold to be just, the Archbishop opens his address by identifying this "New Philosophy" with the Positive Philosophy of M. Comte (of whom he speaks as its "founder"); and then proceeds to attack that philosopher and his doctrines vigorously.

Now, so far as I am concerned, the most reverend prelate might dialectically hew M. Comte in pieces, as a modern Agag, and I should not attempt to stay his hand. In so far as my study of what specially characterises the Positive Philosophy has led me, I find therein little or nothing of any scientific value, and a great deal which is as thoroughly antagonistic to the very essence of science as anything in ultramontane Catholicism. In fact, M. Comte's philosophy, in practice, might be compendiously described as Catholicism *minus* Christianity.

But what has Comtism to do with the "New Philosophy," as the Archbishop defines it in the following passage?

"Let me briefly remind you of the leading principles of this new philosophy.

"All knowledge is experience of facts acquired by the senses. The traditions of older philosophies have obscured our experience by mixing with it much that the senses cannot observe, and until these additions are discarded our knowledge is impure. Thus metaphysics tell us that one fact which we observe is a cause, and another is the effect of that cause ; but, upon a rigid analysis, we find that our senses observe nothing of cause or effect : they observe, first, that one fact succeeds another, and, after some opportunity, that this fact has never failed to follow —that for cause and effect we should substitute invariable succession. An older philosophy teaches us to define an object by distinguishing its essential from its accidental qualities : but experience knows nothing of essential and accidental ; she sees only that certain marks attach to an object, and, after many observations, that some of them attach invariably whilst others may at times be absent. . . . . As all knowledge is relative, the notion of anything being necessary must be banished with other traditions." [1]

There is much here that expresses the spirit of the " New Philosophy," if by that term be meant the spirit of modern science ; but I cannot but marvel that the assembled wisdom and learning of Edinburgh should have uttered no sign of dissent, when Comte was declared to be the founder of these doctrines. No one will accuse Scotchmen of habitually forgetting their great countrymen ; but it was enough to make David Hume turn in his grave, that here, almost within ear-shot of his house, an instructed audience should have listened, without a murmur, while his most characteristic doctrines were attributed to a

[1] *The Limits of Philosophical Inquiry*, pp. 4 and 5.

French writer of fifty years later date, in whose dreary and verbose pages we miss alike the vigour of thought and the exquisite clearness of style of the man whom I make bold to term the most acute thinker of the eighteenth century—even though that century produced Kant.

But I did not come to Scotland to vindicate the honour of one of the greatest men she has ever produced. My business is to point out to you that the only way of escape out of the "crass materialism" in which we just now landed, is the adoption and strict working-out of the very principles which the Archbishop holds up to reprobation.

Let us suppose that knowledge is absolute, and not relative, and therefore, that our conception of matter represents that which it really is. Let us suppose, further, that we do know more of cause and effect than a certain definite order of succession among facts, and that we have a knowledge of the necessity of that succession—and hence, of necessary laws—and I, for my part, do not see what escape there is from utter materialism and necessarianism. For it is obvious that our knowledge of what we call the material world is, to begin with, at least as certain and definite as that of the spiritual world, and that our acquaintance with law is of as old a date as our knowledge of spontaneity. Further, I take it to be demonstrable that it is utterly impossible to prove that anything what-

ever may not be the effect of a material and
necessary cause, and that human logic is equally
incompetent to prove that any act is really spontaneous. A really spontaneous act is one which,
by the assumption, has no cause ; and the attempt
to prove such a negative as this is, on the face of
the matter, absurd. And while it is thus a philosophical impossibility to demonstrate that any
given phænomenon is not the effect of a material
cause, any one who is acquainted with the history
of science will admit, that its progress has, in all
ages, meant, and now, more than ever, means, the
extension of the province of what we call matter
and causation, and the concomitant gradual banish-
ment from all regions of human thought of what
we call spirit and spontaneity.

I have endeavoured, in the first part of this discourse, to give you a conception of the direction
towards which modern physiology is tending ; and
I ask you, what is the difference between the conception of life as the product of a certain disposition of material molecules, and the old notion
of an Archæus governing and directing blind
matter within each living body, except this—that
here, as elsewhere, matter and law have devoured
spirit and spontaneity ? And as surely as every
future grows out of past and present, so will the
physiology of the future gradually extend the
realm of matter and law until it is co-extensive
with knowledge, with feeling, and with action.

The consciousness of this great truth weighs like a nightmare, I believe, upon many of the best minds of these days. They watch what they conceive to be the progress of materialism, in such fear and powerless anger as a savage feels, when, during an eclipse, the great shadow creeps over the face of the sun. The advancing tide of matter threatens to drown their souls ; the tightening grasp of law impedes their freedom ; they are alarmed lest man's moral nature be debased by the increase of his wisdom.

If the " New Philosophy " be worthy of the reprobation with which it is visited, I confess their fears seem to me to be well founded. While, on the contrary, could David Hume be consulted, I think he would smile at their perplexities, and chide them for doing even as the heathen, and falling down in terror before the hideous idols their own hands have raised.

For, after all, what do we know of this terrible " matter," except as a name for the unknown and hypothetical cause of states of our own consciousness ? And what do we know of that " spirit " over whose threatened extinction by matter a great lamentation is arising, like that which was heard at the death of Pan, except that it is also a name for an unknown and hypothetical cause, or condition, of states of consciousness ? In other words, matter and spirit are but names for the imaginary substrata of groups of natural phænomena.

And what is the dire necessity and "iron" law under which men groan? Truly, most gratuitously invented bugbears. I suppose if there be an "iron" law, it is that of gravitation; and if there be a physical necessity, it is that a stone, unsupported, must fall to the ground. But what is all we really know, and can know, about the latter phænomena? Simply, that, in all human experience, stones have fallen to the ground under these conditions; that we have not the smallest reason for believing that any stone so circumstanced will not fall to the ground; and that we have, on the contrary, every reason to believe that it will so fall. It is very convenient to indicate that all the conditions of belief have been fulfilled in this case, by calling the statement that unsupported stones will fall to the ground, "a law of Nature." But when, as commonly happens, we change *will* into *must*, we introduce an idea of necessity which most assuredly does not lie in the observed facts, and has no warranty that I can discover elsewhere. For my part, I utterly repudiate and anathematise the intruder. Fact I know; and Law I know; but what is this Necessity, save an empty shadow of my own mind's throwing?

But, if it is certain that we can have no knowledge of the nature of either matter or spirit, and that the notion of necessity is something illegitimately thrust into the perfectly legitimate conception of law, the materialistic position that there is nothing in the world but matter, force, and necessity, is as utterly devoid of justification as the most baseless of theological dogmas. The fundamental doctrines of materialism, like those of spiritualism, and most other " isms," lie outside "the limits of philosophical inquiry," and David Hume's great service to humanity is his irrefragable demonstration of what these limits are. Hume called himself a sceptic, and therefore others cannot be blamed if they apply the same title to him ; but that does not alter the fact that the name, with its existing implications, does him gross injustice.

If a man asks me what the politics of the inhabitants of the moon are, and I reply that I do not know ; that neither I, nor any one else, has any means of knowing ; and that, under these circumstances, I decline to trouble myself about the subject at all, I do not think he has any right to call me a sceptic. On the contrary, in replying thus, I conceive that I am simply honest and truthful, and show a proper regard for the economy of time. So Hume's strong and subtle intellect takes up a great many problems about which we are naturally curious, and shows us that they are essentially questions of lunar politics, in their essence incapable of being answered, and therefore not worth the attention of men who have work to do in the world. And he thus ends one of his essays :—

" If we take in hand any volume of Divinity, or school metaphysics, for instance, let us ask, *Does it contain any abstract reasoning concerning quantity or number?* No. *Does it contain any experimental reasoning concerning matter of fact and existence?* No. Commit it then to the flames ; for it can contain nothing but sophistry and illusion." [1]

Permit me to enforce this most wise advice. Why trouble ourselves about matters of which, however important they may be, we do know nothing, and can know nothing ? We live in a world which is full of misery and ignorance, and the plain duty of each and all of us is to try to make the little corner he can influence somewhat less miserable and somewhat less ignorant than it was before he entered it. To do this effectually it is necessary to be fully possessed of only two beliefs : the first, that the order of Nature is ascertainable by our faculties to an extent which is practically unlimited ; the second, that our volition [2] counts for something as a condition of the course of events.

Each of these beliefs can be verified experimentally, as often as we like to try. Each, therefore, stands upon the strongest foundation upon which any belief can rest, and forms one of our highest

---

[1] Hume's Essay " Of the Academical or Sceptical Philosophy," in the *Inquiry concerning the Human Understanding.*—[Many critics of this passage seem to forget that the subject-matter of Ethics and Æsthetics consists of matters of fact and existence.—1892].

[2] Or, to speak more accurately, the physical state of which volition is the expression.—[1892].

truths.   If we find that the ascertainment of the order of nature is facilitated by using one terminology, or one set of symbols, rather than another, it is our clear duty to use the former; and no harm can accrue, so long as we bear in mind, that we are dealing merely with terms and symbols.

In itself it is of little moment whether we express the phænomena of matter in terms of spirit; or the phænomena of spirit in terms of matter: matter may be regarded as a form of thought, thought may be regarded as a property of matter—each statement has a certain relative truth.   But with a view to the progress of science, the materialistic terminology is in every way to be preferred.   For it connects thought with the other phænomena of the universe, and suggests inquiry into the nature of those physical conditions, or concomitants of thought, which are more or less accessible to us, and a knowledge of which may, in future, help us to exercise the same kind of control over the world of thought, as we already possess in respect of the material world; whereas, the alternative, or spiritualistic, terminology is utterly barren, and leads to nothing but obscurity and confusion of ideas.

Thus there can be little doubt, that the further science advances, the more extensively and consistently will all the phænomena of Nature be represented by materialistic formulæ and symbols.

But the man of science, who, forgetting the limits of philosophical inquiry, slides from these formulæ and symbols into what is commonly understood by materialism, seems to me to place himself on a level with the mathematician, who should mistake the x's and y's with which he works his problems, for real entities—and with this further disadvantage, as compared with the mathematician, that the blunders of the latter are of no practical consequence, while the errors of systematic materialism may paralyse the energies and destroy the beauty of a life.

[I cannot say I have ever had to complain of lack of hostile criticism; but the preceding essay has come in for more than its fair share of that commodity. It may be well, therefore, for the general reader to study, in connection with it, the first chapter of the standard "Textbook of Physiology," by Dr. Foster, making fair allowance for the rapid progress of knowledge during the last quarter of a century.   1892.]

IV

ON DESCARTES' "DISCOURSE TOUCHING
THE METHOD OF USING ONE'S
REASON RIGHTLY AND OF SEEKING
SCIENTIFIC TRUTH"

[1870]

IT has been well said that "all the thoughts of
men, from the beginning of the world until now,
are linked together into one great chain ; " but the
conception of the intellectual filiation of mankind
which is expressed in these words may, perhaps,
be more fitly shadowed forth by a different
metaphor. The thoughts of men seem rather to
be comparable to the leaves, flowers, and fruit
upon the innumerable branches of a few great
stems, fed by commingled and hidden roots.
These stems bear the names of the half-a-dozen
men, endowed with intellects of heroic force and
clearness, to whom we are led, at whatever point
of the world of thought the attempt to trace its

history commences, just as certainly as the following up the small twigs of a tree to the branchlets
which bear them, and tracing the branchlets to
their supporting branches, brings us, sooner or
later, to the bole.

It seems to me that the thinker who, more than
any other, stands in the relation of such a stem
towards the philosophy and the science of the
modern world is Réné Descartes. I mean, that if
you lay hold of any characteristic product of
modern ways of thinking, either in the region of
philosophy, or in that of science, you find the spirit
of that thought, if not its form, to have been
present in the mind of the great Frenchman.

There are some men who are counted great
because they represent the actuality of their own
age, and mirror it as it is.   Such an one was
Voltaire, of whom it was epigrammatically said,
" he expressed everybody's thoughts better than
anybody." [1]   But there are other men who attain
greatness because they embody the potentiality of
their own day, and magically reflect the future.
They express the thoughts which will be everybody's two or three centuries after them.   Such
an one was Descartes.

Born in 1596, nearly three hundred years ago,
of a noble family in Touraine, Réné Descartes
grew up into a sickly and diminutive child, whose

---

[1] I forget who it was said of him ; "Il a plus que personne
l'esprit que tout le monde a."

keen wit soon gained him that title of "the
Philosopher," which, in the mouths of his noble
kinsmen, was more than half a reproach. The
best schoolmasters of the day, the Jesuits, educated him as well as a French boy of the
seventeenth century could be educated. And they
must have done their work honestly and well, for,
before his schoolboy days were over, he had
discovered that the most of what he had learned,
except in mathematics, was devoid of solid and
real value.

"Therefore," says he, in that 'Discourse'[1] which I
have taken for my text, "as soon as I was old enough to be
set free from the government of my teachers, I entirely forsook
the study of letters ; and determining to seek no other knowledge than that which I could discover within myself, or in the
great book of the world, I spent the remainder of my youth in
travelling ; in seeing courts and armies ; in the society of
people of different humours and conditions ; in gathering varied
experience ; in testing myself by the chances of fortune ; and in
always trying to profit by my reflections on what happened.
. . . And I always had an intense desire to learn how to
distinguish truth from falsehood, in order to be clear about my
actions, and to walk surefootedly in this life."

But "learn what is true, in order to do what is
right," is the summing up of the whole duty of
man, for all who are unable to satisfy their mental
hunger with the east wind of authority ; and to
those of us moderns who are in this position, it is
one of Descartes' great claims to our reverence as

[1] *Discours de la Méthode pour bien conduire sa Raison et
chercher la Vérité dans les Sciences.*

a spiritual ancestor, that, at three-and-twenty, he saw clearly that this was his duty, and acted up to his conviction. At two-and-thirty, in fact, finding all other occupations incompatible with the search after the knowledge which leads to action, and being possessed of a modest competence, he withdrew into Holland; where he spent nine years in learning and thinking, in such retirement that only one or two trusted friends knew of his whereabouts.

In 1637 the first-fruits of these long meditations were given to the world in the famous "Discourse touching the Method of using Reason rightly and of seeking Scientific Truth," which, at once an autobiography and a philosophy, clothes the deepest thought in language of exquisite harmony, simplicity, and clearness.

The central propositions of the whole "Discourse" are these. There is a path that leads to truth so surely, that any one who will follow it must needs reach the goal, whether his capacity be great or small. And there is one guiding rule by which a man may always find this path, and keep himself from straying when he has found it. This golden rule is—give unqualified assent to no propositions but those the truth of which is so clear and distinct that they cannot be doubted.

The enunciation of this great first commandment of science consecrated Doubt. It removed Doubt from the seat of penance among the

12

grievous sins to which it had long been condemned, and enthroned it in that high place among the primary duties, which is assigned to it by the scientific conscience of these latter days. Descartes was the first among the moderns to obey this commandment deliberately; and, as a matter of religious duty, to strip off all his beliefs and reduce himself to a state of intellectual nakedness, until such time as he could satisfy himself which were fit to be worn. He thought a bare skin healthier than the most respectable and well-cut clothing of what might, possibly, be mere shoddy.

When I say that Descartes consecrated doubt, you must remember that it was that sort of doubt which Goethe has called " the active scepticism, whose whole aim is to conquer itself; " [1] and not that other sort which is born of flippancy and ignorance, and whose aim is only to perpetuate itself, as an excuse for idleness and indifference. But it is impossible to define what is meant by scientific doubt better than in Descartes' own words. After describing the gradual progress of his negative criticism, he tells us :—

" For all that, I did not imitate the sceptics, who doubt only for doubting's sake, and pretend to be always undecided ; on the contrary, my whole intention was to arrive at a certainty, and to dig away the drift and the sand until I reached the rock or the clay beneath."

---

[1] " Eine thätige Skepsis ist die, welche unablässig bemüht ist sich selbst zu überwinden, und durch geregelte Erfahrung zu

And further, since no man of common sense when he pulls down his house for the purpose of rebuilding it, fails to provide himself with some shelter while the work is in progress; so, before demolishing the spacious, if not commodious, mansion of his old beliefs, Descartes thought it wise to equip himself with what he calls "*une morale par provision*," by which he resolved to govern his practical life until such time as he should be better instructed. The laws of this "provisional self-government" are embodied in four maxims, of which one binds our philosopher to submit himself to the laws and religion in which he was brought up; another, to act, on all those occasions which call for action, promptly and according to the best of his judgment, and to abide, without repining, by the result : a third rule is to seek happiness in limiting his desires, rather than in attempting to satisfy them; while the last is to make the search after truth the business of his life.

Thus prepared to go on living while he doubted, Descartes proceeded to face his doubts like a man. One thing was clear to him, he would not lie to himself—would, under no penalties, say, " I am sure " of that of which he was not sure ; but would go on digging and delving until he came to the solid adamant or, at worst, made sure there was

einer Art von bedingter Zuverlässigkeit zu gelangen." — *Maximen und Reflexionen*, 7te Abtheilung.

no adamant. As the record of his progress tells us, he was obliged to confess that life is full of delusions ; that authority may err ; that testimony may be false or mistaken ; that reason lands us in endless fallacies ; that memory is often as little trustworthy as hope ; that the evidence of the very senses may be misunderstood ; that dreams are real as long as they last, and that what we call reality may be a long and restless dream. Nay, it is conceivable that some powerful and malicious being may find his pleasure in deluding us, and in making us believe the thing which is not, every moment of our lives. What, then, is certain ? What even, if such a being exists, is beyond the reach of his powers of delusion ? Why, the fact that the thought, the present consciousness, exists. Our thoughts may be delusive, but they cannot be fictitious. As thoughts, they are real and existent, and the cleverest deceiver cannot make them otherwise.

Thus, thought is existence. More than that, so far as we are concerned, existence is thought, all our conceptions of existence being some kind or other of thought. Do not for a moment suppose that these are mere paradoxes or subtleties. A little reflection upon the commonest facts proves them to be irrefragable truths. For example, I take up a marble, and I find it to be a red, round, hard, single body. We call the redness, the roundness, the hardness, and the singleness,

" qualities " of the marble ; and it sounds, at first,
the height of absurdity to say that all these
qualities are modes of our own consciousness,
which cannot even be conceived to exist in the
marble.   But consider the redness, to begin with.
How does the sensation of redness arise ?   The
waves of a certain very attenuated matter, the
particles of which are vibrating with vast rapidity,
but with very different velocities, strike upon the
marble, and those which vibrate with one particular velocity are thrown off from its surface in all
directions.   The optical apparatus of the eye
gathers some of these together, and gives them such
a course that they impinge upon the surface of
the retina, which is a singularly delicate apparatus
connected with the termination of the fibres of
the optic nerve.   The impulses of the attenuated
matter, or ether, affect this apparatus and the
fibres of the optic nerve in a certain way ; and
the change in the fibres of the optic nerve produces yet other changes in the brain ; and these,
in some fashion unknown to us, give rise to the
feeling, or consciousness of redness.   If the
marble could remain unchanged, and either the
rate of vibration of the ether, or the nature of the
retina, could be altered, the marble would seem
not red, but some other colour.   There are many
people who are what are called colour-blind, being
unable to distinguish one colour from another.
Such an one might declare our marble to be

green; and he would be quite as right in saying
that it is green, as we are in declaring it to be
red. But then, as the marble cannot, in itself,
be both green and red, at the same time, this
shows that the quality "redness" must be in our
consciousness and not in the marble.

In like manner, it is easy to see that the roundness and the hardness are forms of our consciousness, belonging to the groups which we call
sensations of sight and touch. If the surface of
the cornea were cylindrical, we should have a
very different notion of a round body from that
which we possess now; and if the strength
of the fabric, and the force of the muscles, of the
body were increased a hundredfold, our marble
would seem to be as soft as a pellet of bread
crumbs.

Not only is it obvious that all these qualities
are in us, but, if you will make the attempt, you
will find it quite impossible to conceive of "blue-
ness," "roundness," and "hardness" as existing
without reference to some such consciousness as our
own. It may seem strange to say that even the
"singleness" of the marble is relative to us; but
extremely simple experiments will show that
such is veritably the case, and that our two
most trustworthy senses may be made to contra-
dict one another on this very point. Hold the
marble between the finger and thumb, and look
at it in the ordinary way. Sight and touch agree

that it is single.   Now squint, and sight tells you
that there are two marbles, while touch asserts
that there is only one.   Next, return the eyes to
their natural position, and, having crossed the
forefinger and the middle finger, put the marble
between their tips.   Then touch will declare that
there are two marbles, while sight says that there
is only one ; and touch claims our belief, when
we attend to it, just as imperatively as sight
does.

But it may be said, the marble takes up a certain space which could not be occupied, at the
same time, by anything else.   In other words, the
marble has the primary quality of matter, extension.   Surely this quality must be in the thing,
and not in our minds ?   But the reply must still
be ; whatever may, or may not, exist in the thing,
all that we can know of these qualities is a state
of consciousness.   What we call extension is a
consciousness of a relation between two, or more,
affections of the sense of sight, or of touch.   And
it is wholly inconceivable that what we call extension should exist independently of such consciousness as our own.   Whether, notwithstanding this
inconceivability, it does so exist, or not, is a point
on which I offer no opinion.   Thus, whatever our
marble may be in itself, all that we can know of it
is under the shape of a bundle of our own con-
sciousnesses.

Nor is our knowledge of anything we know or

feel more, or less, than a knowledge of states of consciousness. And our whole life is made up of such states. Some of these states we refer to a cause we call " self ; " others to a cause or causes which may be comprehended under the title of " not-self." But neither of the existence of " self," nor of that of " not-self," have we, or can we by any possibility have, any such unquestionable and immediate certainty as we have of the states of consciousness which we consider to be their effects. They are not immediately observed facts, but results of the application of the law of causation to those facts. Strictly speaking, the existence of a " self " and of a " not-self " are hypotheses by which we account for the facts of consciousness. They stand upon the same footing as the belief in the general trustworthiness of memory, and in the general constancy of the order of Nature—as hypothetical assumptions which cannot be proved, or known with that highest degree of certainty which is given by immediate consciousness ; but which, nevertheless, are of the highest practical value, inasmuch as the conclusions logically drawn from them are always verified by experience.

This, in my judgment, is the ultimate issue of Descartes' argument ; but it is proper for me to point out that we have left Descartes himself some way behind us. He stopped at the famous formula, " I think, therefore I am." Yet a little consideration will show this formula to be full of snares and verbal entanglements. In the first place, the " therefore " has no business there. The " I am " is assumed in the " I think," which is simply another way of saying " I am thinking." And, in the second place, " I think " is not one simple proposition, but three distinct assertions rolled into one. The first of these is, " something called I exists; " the second is, " something called thought exists; " and the third is, " the thought is the result of the action of the I."

Now, it will be obvious to you, that the only one of these three propositions which can stand the Cartesian test of certainty is the second. It cannot be doubted, for the very doubt is an existent thought. But the first and third, whether true or not, may be doubted, and have been doubted. For the assertor may be asked, How do you know that thought is not self-existent ; or that a given thought is not the effect of its antecedent thought, or of some external power ? And a diversity of other questions, much more easily put than answered. Descartes, determined as he was to strip off all the garments which the intellect weaves for itself, forgot this gossamer shirt of the " self " ; to the great detriment, and indeed ruin, of his toilet when he began to clothe himself again.

But it is beside my purpose to dwell upon the minor peculiarities of the Cartesian philosophy.

All I wish to put clearly before your minds thus far, is that Descartes, having commenced by declaring doubt to be a duty, found certainty in consciousness alone; and that the necessary outcome of his views is what may properly be termed Idealism; namely, the doctrine that, whatever the universe may be, all we can know of it is the picture presented to us by consciousness. This picture may be a true likeness—though how this can be is inconceivable; or it may have no more resemblance to its cause than one of Bach's fugues has to the person who is playing it; or than a piece of poetry has to the mouth and lips of a reciter. It is enough for all the practical purposes of human existence if we find that our trust in the representations of consciousness is verified by results; and that, by their help, we are enabled "to walk surefootedly in this life."

Thus the method, or path which leads to truth, indicated by Descartes, takes us straight to the Critical Idealism of his great successor Kant. It is that Idealism which declares the ultimate fact of all knowledge to be consciousness, or, in other words, a mental phænomenon; and therefore affirms the highest of all certainties, and indeed the only absolute certainty, to be the existence of mind. But it is also that Idealism which refuses to make any assertions, either positive or negative, as to what lies beyond consciousness. It accuses the subtle Berkeley of stepping beyond

the limits of knowledge when he declared that
a substance of matter does not exist; and of illogi-
cality, for not seeing that the arguments which he
supposed demolished the existence of matter were
equally destructive to the existence of soul.   And
it refuses to listen to the jargon of more recent
days about the "Absolute" and all the other hypostatised adjectives, the initial letters of the
names of which are generally printed in capital
letters; just as you give a Grenadier a bearskin
cap, to make him look more formidable than he is
by nature.

I repeat, the path indicated and followed by
Descartes, which we have hitherto been treading,
leads through doubt to that critical Idealism
which lies at the heart of modern metaphysical
thought.   But the "Discourse" shows us another,
and apparently very different, path, which leads,
quite as definitely, to that correlation of all the
phænomena of the universe with matter and
motion, which lies at the heart of modern physical
thought, and which most people call Materialism.

The early part of the seventeenth century, when
Descartes reached manhood, is one of the great
epochs of the intellectual life of mankind.   At that
time, physical science suddenly strode into the
arena of public and familiar thought, and openly
challenged not only Philosophy and the Church,
but that common ignorance which often passes by
the name of Common Sense.   The assertion of the

motion of the earth was a defiance to all three,
and Physical Science threw down her glove by
the hand of Galileo.

It is not pleasant to think of the immediate
result of the combat; to see the champion of
science, old, worn, and on his knees before the
Cardinal Inquisitor, signing his name to what he
knew to be a lie. And, no doubt, the Cardinals
rubbed their hands as they thought how well
they had silenced and discredited their adversary.
But two hundred years have passed, and however
feeble or faulty her soldiers, Physical Science sits
crowned and enthroned as one of the legitimate
rulers of the world of thought. Charity children
would be ashamed not to know that the earth
moves; while the Schoolmen are forgotten; and
the Cardinals—well, the Cardinals are at the
Œcumenical Council, still at their old business
of trying to stop the movement of the world.

As a ship, which having lain becalmed with
every stitch of canvas set, bounds away before the
breeze which springs up astern, so the mind of
Descartes, poised in equilibrium of doubt, not only
yielded to the full force of the impulse towards
physical science and physical ways of thought,
given by his great contemporaries, Galileo and
Harvey, but shot beyond them; and anticipated,
by bold speculation, the conclusions, which could
only be placed upon a secure foundation by the
labours of generations of workers.

Descartes saw that the discoveries of Galileo meant that the remotest parts of the universe were governed by mechanical laws; while those of Harvey meant that the same laws presided over the operations of that portion of the world which is nearest to us, namely, our own bodily frame. And crossing the interval between the centre and its vast circumference by one of the great strides of genius, Descartes sought to resolve all the phænomena of the universe into matter and motion, or forces operating according to law.[1] This grand conception, which is sketched in the "Discours," and more fully developed in the "Principes" and in the "Traité de l'Homme," he worked out with extraordinary power and knowledge ; and with the effect of arriving, in the last-named essay, at that purely mechanical view of vital phænomena towards which modern physiology is striving.

Let us try to understand how Descartes got into this path, and why it led him where it did. The mechanism of the circulation of the blood had evidently taken a great hold of his mind, as he describes it several times, at much length. After giving a full account of it in the "Discourse," and

[1] Au milieu de toutes ses erreurs, il ne faut pas méconnaître une grande idée, qui consiste à avoir tenté pour la première fois de ramener tous les phénomènes naturels à n'être qu'un simple dévelloppement des lois de la mécanique," is the weighty judgment of Biot, cited by Bouillier (*Histoire de la Philosophie Cartésienne*, t. i. p. 196).

erroneously ascribing the motion of the blood, not
to the contraction of the walls of the heart, but to
the heat which he supposes to be generated there,
he adds :—

"This motion, which I have just explained, is as much the
necessary result of the structure of the parts which one can
see in the heart, and of the heat which one may feel there with
one's fingers, and of the nature of the blood, which may be
experimentally ascertained ; as is that of a clock of the force,
the situation, and the figure, of its weight, and of its wheels."

But if this apparently vital operation were explicable as a simple mechanism, might not other
vital operations be reducible to the same category ? Descartes replies without hesitation in the
affirmative.

"The animal spirits," says he, "resemble a very subtle fluid,
or a very pure and vivid flame, and are continually generated in
the heart, and ascend to the brain as to a sort of reservoir.
Hence they pass into the nerves and are distributed to the
muscles, causing contraction, or relaxation, according to their
quantity."

Thus, according to Descartes, the animal body
is an automaton, which is competent to perform
all the animal functions in exactly the same way
as a clock or any other piece of mechanism. As
he puts the case himself :—

" In proportion as these spirits [the animal spirits] enter the
cavities of the brain, they pass thence into the pores of its
substance, and from these pores into the nerves ; where, according as they enter, or even only tend to enter, more or less, into
one than into another, they have the power of altering the figure

of the muscles into which the nerves are inserted, and by this means of causing all the limbs to move. Thus, as you may have seen in the grottoes and the fountains in royal gardens, the force with which the water issues from its reservoir is sufficient to move various machines, and even to make them play instruments, or pronounce words according to the diff. rent disposition of the pipes which lead the water.

"And, in truth, the nerves of the machine which I am describing may very well be compared to the pipes of these waterworks ; its muscles and its tendons to the other various engines and springs which seem to move them ; its animal spirits to the water which impels them, of which the heart is the fountain ; while the cavities of the brain are the central office. Moreover, respiration and other such actions as are natural and usual in the body, and which depend on the course of the spirits, are like the movements of a clock, or of a mill, which may be kept up by the ordinary flow of the water.

"The external objects which, by their mere presence, act upon the organs of the senses ; and which, by this means, determine the corporal machine to move in many different ways, according as the parts of the brain are arranged, are like the strangers who, entering into some of the grottoes of these waterworks, unconsciously cause the movements which take place in their presence. For they cannot enter without treading upon certain planks so arranged that, for example, if they approach a bathing Diana, they cause her to hide among the reeds ; and if they attempt to follow her, they see approaching a Neptune, who threatens them with his trident : or if they try some other way, they cause some other monster, who vomits water into their faces, to dart out ; or like contrivances, according to the fancy of the engineers who have made them. And lastly, when the *rational soul* is lodged in this machine, it will have its principal seat in the brain, and will take the place of the engineer, who ought to be in that part of the works with which all the pipes are connected, when he wishes to increase, or to slacken, or in some way to alter their movements." [1]

---

[1] *Traité de l'Homme* (Cousin's edition), p. 347.

And again still more strongly :—

" All the functions which I have attributed to this machine
(the body), as the digestion of food, the pulsation of the heart
and of the arteries ; the nutrition and the growth of the limbs ;
respiration, wakefulness, and sleep ; the reception of light,
sounds, odours, flavours, heat, and such like qualities, in the
organs of the external senses ; the impression of the ideas of
these in the organ of common sense and in the imagination ;
the retention, or the impression, of these ideas on the memory ;
the internal movements of the appetites and the passions ; and
lastly, the external movements of all the limbs, which follow so
aptly, as well the action of the objects which are presented to
the senses, as the impressions which meet in the memory, that
they imitate as nearly as possible those of a real man : [1] I desire,
I say, that you should consider that these functions in the
machine naturally proceed from the mere arrangement of its
organs, neither more nor less than do the movements of a clock,
or other automaton, from that of its weights and its wheels ; so
that, so far as these are concerned, it is not necessary to conceive
any other vegetative or sensitive soul, nor any other principle of
motion, or of life, than the blood and the spirits agitated by
the fire which burns continually in the heart, and which is no
wise essentially different from all the fires which exist in
inanimate bodies." [2]

The spirit of these passages is exactly that of
the most advanced physiology of the present day;
all that is necessary to make them coincide with
our present physiology in form, is to represent the
details of the working of the animal machinery in

[1] Descartes pretends that he does not apply his views to the
human body, but only to an imaginary machine which, if it
could be constructed, would do all that the human body does ;
throwing a sop to Cerberus unworthily ; and uselessly, because
Cerberus was by no means stupid enough to swallow it.

[2] *Traité de l'Homme,* p. 427.

modern language, and by the aid of modern conceptions.

Most undoubtedly, the digestion of food in the
human body is a purely chemical process ; and the
passage of the nutritive parts of that food into the
blood, a physical operation. Beyond all question,
the circulation of the blood is simply a matter of
mechanism, and results from the structure and
arrangement of the parts of the heart and vessels,
from the contractility of those organs, and from
the regulation of that contractility by an automatically acting nervous apparatus. The progress
of physiology has further shown, that the contractility of the muscles and the irritability of the
nerves are purely the results of the molecular
mechanism of those organs ; and that the regular
movements of the respiratory, alimentary, and
other internal organs are governed and guided, as
mechanically, by their appropriate nervous centres.
The even rhythm of the breathing of every one of
us depends upon the structural integrity of a particular region of the medulla oblongata, as much
as the ticking of a clock depends upon the integrity of the escapement. You may take away
the hands of a clock and break up its striking
machinery, but it will still tick ; and a man may
be unable to feel, speak, or move, and yet he will
breathe.

Again, in entire accordance with Descartes'
affirmation, it is certain that the modes of motion

13

which constitute the physical basis of light, sound, and heat, are transmuted into affections of nervous matter by the sensory organs. These affections are, so to speak, a kind of physical ideas, which are retained in the central organs, constituting what might be called physical memory, and may be combined in a manner which answers to association and imagination, or may give rise to muscular contractions, in those "reflex actions" which are the mechanical representatives of volition.

Consider what happens when a blow is aimed at the eye.[1] Instantly, and without our knowledge or will, and even against the will, the eyelids close. What is it that happens? A picture of the rapidly-advancing fist is made upon the retina at the back of the eye. The retina changes this picture into an affection of a number of the fibres of the optic nerve; the fibres of the optic nerve affect certain parts of the brain; the brain, in consequence, affects those particular fibres of the seventh nerve which go to the orbicular muscle of the eyelids; the change in these nerve-fibres causes the muscular fibres to alter their dimensions, so as to become shorter and broader; and the result is the closing of the slit between the two lids, round which these fibres are disposed. Here is a pure mechanism, giving rise to a purposive action, and strictly comparable to that by which Descartes

[1] Compare *Traité des Passions*, Art. xlii. and xvi..

supposes his waterwork Diana to be moved. But
we may go further, and inquire whether our
volition, in what we term voluntary action, ever
plays any other part than that of Descartes'
engineer, sitting in his office, and turning this
tap or the other, as he wishes to set one or
another machine in motion, but exercising no
direct influence upon the movements of the
whole.

Our voluntary acts consist of two parts: firstly,
we desire to perform a certain action; and,
secondly, we somehow set a-going a machinery
which does what we desire. But so little do we
directly influence that machinery, that nine-tenths
of us do not even know of its existence. Suppose
one wills to raise one's arm and whirl it round.
Nothing is easier. But the majority of us do not
know that nerves and muscles are concerned in
this process; and the best anatomist among us
would be amazingly perplexed, if he were called
upon to direct the succession, and the relative
strength, of the multitudinous nerve-changes,
which are the actual causes of this very simple
operation. So again in speaking. How many of us
know that the voice is produced in the larynx,
and modified by the mouth? How many among
these instructed persons understand how the
voice is produced and modified? And what living
man, if he had unlimited control over all the
nerves supplying the mouth and larynx of another

person, could make him pronounce a sentence?
Yet, if one has anything to say, what is easier
than to say it?   We desire the utterance of certain words : we touch the spring of the word-
machine, and they are spoken.   Just as Descartes'
engineer, when he wanted a particular hydraulic
machine to play, had only to turn a tap, and what
he wished was done.   It is because the body is a
machine that education is possible.   Education is
the formation of habits, a superinducing of an
artificial organisation upon the natural organisation of the body ; so that acts, which at first
required a conscious effort, eventually became unconscious and mechanical.   If the act which
primarily requires a distinct consciousness and
volition of its details, always needed the same
effort, education would be an impossibility.

According to Descartes, then, all the functions
which are common to man and animals are performed by the body as a mere mechanism, and he
looks upon consciousness as the peculiar distinction of the " *chose pensante*," of the "rational soul,"
which in man (and in man only, in Descartes'
opinion) is superadded to the body.   This rational
soul he conceived to be lodged in the pineal gland,
as in a sort of central office; and here, by the intermediation of the animal spirits, it became aware
of what was going on in the body, or influenced
the operations of the body.   Modern physiologists
do not ascribe so exalted a function to the little

pineal gland,[1] but, in a vague sort of way, they adopt Descartes' principle, and suppose that the soul is lodged in the cortical part of the brain—at least this is commonly regarded as the seat and instrument of consciousness.

Descartes has clearly stated what he conceived to be the difference between spirit and matter. Matter is substance which has extension, but does not think ; spirit is substance which thinks, but has no extension. It is very hard to form a definite notion of what this phraseology means, when it is taken in connection with the location of the soul in the pineal gland ; and I can only represent it to myself as signifying that the soul is a mathematical point, having place but not extension, within the limits of the pineal body. Not only has it place, but it must exert force ; for, according to this hypothesis, it is competent, when it wills, to change the course of the animal spirits, which consist of matter in motion. Thus the soul becomes a centre of force. But, at the same time, the distinction between spirit and matter vanishes ; inasmuch as matter, according to a tenable hypothesis, may be nothing but a multitude of centres of force. The case is worse if we adopt the modern vague notion that consciousness is seated in the grey matter of the cerebrum, generally ; for,

---

[1] Which, however, as the remains of a Cyclopean eye possessed by some remote ancestor of the *Vertebrata*, has lost none of its interest. [1892.]

as the grey matter has extension, that which is lodged in it must also have extension. And thus we are led, in another way, to lose spirit in matter.

In truth, Descartes' physiology, like the modern physiology of which it anticipates the spirit, leads straight to Materialism, so far as that title is rightly applicable to the doctrine that we have no knowledge of any thinking substance, apart from extended substance ; and that thought is as much a function of matter as motion is. Thus we arrive at the singular result that, of the two paths opened up to us in the "Discourse upon Method," the one leads, by way of Berkeley and Hume, to Kant and Idealism ; while the other leads, by way of De La Mettrie and Priestley, to modern physiology and Materialism.[1] Our stem divides into two main branches, which grow in opposite ways, and bear flowers which look as different as they can well be. But each branch is sound and healthy, and has as much life and vigour as the other.

If a botanist found this state of things in a new plant, I imagine that he might be inclined to think that his tree was monœcious—that the

[1] Bouillier, into whose excellent *History of the Cartesian Philosophy* I had not looked when this passage was written, says, very justly, that Descartes "a merité le titre de père de la physique, aussi bien que celui de père de la metaphysique moderne" (t. i., p. 197). See also Kuno Fischer's *Geschichte der neuen Philosophie*, Bd. i. ; and the very remarkable work of Lange *Geschichte des Materialismus.*—A good translation of the latter would be a great service to philosophy in England. [It now exists, 1892.]

flowers were of different sexes, and that, so far from setting up a barrier between the two branches of the tree, the only hope of fertility lay in bringing them together. I may be taking too much of a naturalist's view of the case, but I must confess that this is exactly my notion of what is to be done with metaphysics and physics. Their differences are complementary, not antagonistic; and thought will never be completely fruitful until the one unites with the other. Let me try to explain what I mean. I hold, with the Materialist, that the human body, like all living bodies, is a machine, all the operations of which will, sooner or later, be explained on physical principles. I believe that we shall, sooner or later, arrive at a mechanical equivalent of consciousness, just as we have arrived at a mechanical equivalent of heat. If a pound weight falling through a distance of a foot gives rise to a definite amount of heat, which may properly be said to be its equivalent; the same pound weight falling through a foot on a man's hand gives rise to a definite amount of feeling, which might with equal propriety be said to be its equivalent in consciousness.[1] And as we already know that there is a certain parity between the intensity of a pain and the strength of one's desire to get rid

---

[1] For all the qualifications which need to be made here, I refer the reader to the thorough discussion of the nature of the relation between nerve-action and consciousness in Mr. Herbert Spencer's *Principles of Psychology*, p. 115 *et seq.*

of that pain ; and, secondly, that there is a certain
correspondence between the intensity of the heat,
or mechanical violence, which gives rise to the
pain, and the pain itself; the possibility of the
establishment of a correlation between mechanical
force and volition becomes apparent. And the
same conclusion is suggested by the fact that,
within certain limits, the intensity of the mechanical force we exert is proportioned to the intensity
of our desire to exert it.

Thus I am prepared to go with the Materialists
wherever the true pursuit of the path of Descartes
may lead them; and I am glad, on all occasions,
to declare my belief that their fearless development of the materialistic aspect of these matters
has had an immense, and a most beneficial,
influence upon physiology and psychology. Nay,
more, when they go farther than I think they are
entitled to do—when they introduce Calvinism
into science and declare that man is nothing but
a machine, I do not see any particular harm in
their doctrines, so long as they admit that which
is a matter of experimental fact—namely, that it
is a machine capable of adjusting itself within
certain limits.

I protest that if some great Power would agree
to make me always think what is true and do
what is right, on condition of being turned into
a sort of clock and wound up every morning
before I got out of bed, I should instantly close

with the offer.   The only freedom I care about is
the freedom to do right ; the freedom to do wrong
I am ready to part with on the cheapest terms to
any one who will take it of me.   But when the
Materialists stray beyond the borders of their
path and begin to talk about there being nothing
else in the universe but Matter and Force and
Necessary Laws, and all the rest of *their* "grena-
diers," I decline to follow them.   I go back to the
point from which we started, and to the other
path of Descartes.   I remind you that we have
already seen clearly and distinctly, and in a
manner which admits of no doubt, that all our
knowledge is a knowledge of states of consciousness.
"Matter" and "Force" are, as far as we can know,
mere names for certain forms of consciousness.
"Necessary" means that of which we cannot conceive the contrary.   "Law" means a rule which
we have always found to hold good, and which we
expect always will hold good.   Thus it is an
indisputable truth that what we call the material
world is only known to us under the forms of the
ideal world ; and, as Descartes tells us, our knowledge of the soul[1] is more intimate and certain
than our knowledge of the body.   If I say that
impenetrability is a property of matter, all that I
can really mean is that the consciousness I call
extension, and the consciousness I call resistance,

[1] Taken as the sum of states of consciousness of the individual.
[1892.]

constantly accompany one another. Why and how they are thus related is a mystery. And if I say that thought is a property of matter, all that I can mean is that actually or possibly, the consciousness of extension and that of resistance accompany all other sorts of consciousness. But, as in the former case, why they are thus associated is an insoluble mystery.

From all this it follows that what I may term legitimate materialism, that is, the extension of the conceptions and of the methods of physical science to the highest as well as the lowest phæ-nomena of vitality, is neither more nor less than a sort of shorthand Idealism; and Descartes' two paths meet at the summit of the mountain, though they set out on opposite sides of it.

The reconciliation of physics and metaphysics lies in the acknowledgment of faults upon both sides; in the confession by physics that all the phænomena of Nature are, in their ultimate ana-lysis, known to us only as facts of consciousness; in the admisson by metaphysics, that the facts of consciousness are, practically, interpretable only by the methods and the formulæ of physics : and, finally, in the observance by both metaphysical and physical thinkers of Descartes' maxim— assent to no proposition the matter of which is not so clear and distinct that it cannot be doubted.

When you did me the honour to ask me to deliver this address, I confess I was perplexed what topic to select. For you are emphatically and distinctly a *Christian* body; while science and philosophy, within the range of which lie all the topics on which I could venture to speak, are neither Christian, nor Unchristian, but are Extra-christian, and have a world of their own, which to use language which will be very familiar to your ears just now, is not only " unsectarian," but is altogether " secular." The arguments which I have put before you to-night, for example, are not inconsistent, so far as I know, with any form of theology.

After much consideration, I thought that I might be most useful to you, if I attempted to give you some vision of this Extrachristian world, as it appears to a person who lives a good deal in it; and if I tried to show you by what methods the dwellers therein try to distinguish truth from falsehood, in regard to some of the deepest and most difficult problems that beset humanity, " in order to be clear about their actions, and to walk surefootedly in this life," as Descartes says.

It struck me that if the execution of my project came anywhere near the conception of it, you would become aware that the philosophers and the men of science are not exactly what they are sometimes represented to you to be; and that their methods and paths do not lead so

perpendicularly downwards as you are occasionally told they do. And I must admit, also, that a
particular and personal motive weighed with me,
—namely, the desire to show that a certain discourse,[1] which brought a great storm about my
head some time ago, contained nothing but the
ultimate development of the views of the father of
modern philosophy. I do not know if I have
been quite wise in allowing this last motive to
weigh with me. They say that the most dangerous thing one can do in a thunderstorm is to
shelter oneself under a great tree, and the history
of Descartes' life shows how narrowly he escaped
being riven by the lightnings, which were more
destructive in his time than in ours.

Descartes lived and died a good Catholic, and
prided himself upon having demonstrated the
existence of God and of the soul of man. As a
reward for his exertions, his old friends the Jesuits
put his works upon the "Index," and called him
an Atheist; while the Protestant divines of
Holland declared him to be both a Jesuit and an
Atheist. His books narrowly escaped being
burned by the hangman; the fate of Vanini was
dangled before his eyes; and the misfortunes of
Galileo so alarmed him, that he well-nigh renounced the pursuits by which the world has so
greatly benefited, and was driven into subterfuges
and evasions which were not worthy of him.

[1] See above, *The Physical Basis of Life.*

"Very cowardly," you may say; and so it was. But you must make allowance for the fact that, in the seventeenth century, not only did heresy mean possible burning, or imprisonment, but the very suspicion of it destroyed a man's peace, and rendered the calm pursuit of truth difficult or impossible. I fancy that Descartes was a man to care more about being worried and disturbed, than about being burned outright; and, like many other men, sacrificed for the sake of peace and quietness, what he would have stubbornly maintained against downright violence. However this may be, let those who are sure they would have done better throw stones at him. I have no feelings but those of gratitude and reverence for the man who did what he did, when he did; and a sort of shame that any one should repine against taking a fair share of such treatment as the world thought good enough for him.

Finally, it occurs to me that, such being my feeling about the matter, it may be useful to all of us if I ask you, "What is yours? Do you think that the Christianity of the seventeenth century looks nobler and more attractive for such treatment of such a man?" You will hardly reply that it does. But if it does not, may it not be well if all of you do what lies within your power to prevent the Christianity of the nineteenth century from repeating the scandal?

There are one or two living men, who, a couple

of centuries hence, will be remembered as Descartes is now, because they have produced great thoughts which will live and grow as long as mankind lasts.

If the twenty-first century studies their history, it will find that the Christianity of the middle of the nineteenth century recognised them only as objects of vilification. It is for you and such as you, Christian young men, to say whether this shall be as true of the Christianity of the future as it is of that of the present. I appeal to you to say " No," in your own interest, and in that of the Christianity you profess.

In the interest of Science, no appeal is needful; as Dante sings of Fortune—

> " Quest' è colei, ch'è tanto posta in croce
> Pur da color, che le dovrian dar lode
> Dandole biasmo a torto e mala voce.
> Ma ella s' è beata, e ciò non ode :
> Con l' altre prime creature lieta
> Volve sua spera, e beata si gode : " [1]

so, whatever evil voices may rage, Science, secure among the powers that are eternal, will do her work and be blessed.

---

[1] " And this is she who's put on cross so much
Even by them who ought to give her praise,
Giving her wrongly ill repute and blame.
But she is blessed, and she hears not this :
She, with the other primal creatures, glad
Revolves her sphere, and blessed joys herself."

Inferno, vii. 90—95 (W. M. Rossetti's Translation).

V

ON THE HYPOTHESIS THAT ANIMALS
ARE AUTOMATA, AND ITS HISTORY

[1874]

THE first half of the seventeenth century is one of
the great epochs of biological science. For though
suggestions and indications of the conceptions
which took definite shape, at that time, are to be
met with in works of earlier date, they are little
more than the shadows which coming truth casts
forward; men's knowledge was neither extensive
enough, nor exact enough, to show them the solid
body of fact which threw these shadows.

But, in the seventeenth century, the idea that
the physical processes of life are capable of being
explained in the same way as other physical
phenomena, and, therefore, that the living body
is a mechanism, was proved to be true for certain
classes of vital actions; and, having thus taken

firm root in irrefragable fact, this conception has
not only successfully repelled every assault which
has been made upon it, but has steadily grown in
force and extent of application, until it is now the
expressed or implied fundamental proposition of
the whole doctrine of scientific Physiology.

If we ask to whom mankind are indebted for
this great service, the general voice will name
William Harvey. For, by his discovery of the
circulation of the blood in the higher animals, by
his explanation of the nature of the mechanism
by which that circulation is effected, and by his
no less remarkable, though less known, investigations of the process of development, Harvey solidly
laid the foundations of all those physical explanations of the functions of sustentation and
reproduction which modern physiologists have
achieved.

But the living body is not only sustained and
reproduced : it adjusts itself to external and
internal changes; it moves and feels. The
attempt to reduce the endless complexities of
animal motion and feeling to law and order is, at
least, as important a part of the task of the
physiologist as the elucidation of what are sometimes called the vegetative processes. Harvey
did not make this attempt himself; but the
influence of his work upon the man who did make
it is patent and unquestionable. This man was
René Descartes, who, though by many years

Harvey's junior, died before him; and yet in his short span of fifty-four years, took an undisputed place, not only among the chiefs of philosophy, but amongst the greatest and most original of mathematicians; while, in my belief, he is no less certainly entitled to the rank of a great and original physiologist; inasmuch as he did for the physiology of motion and sensation that which Harvey had done for the circulation of the blood, and opened up that road to the mechanical theory of these processes, which has been followed by all his successors.

Descartes was no mere speculator, as some would have us believe: but a man who knew of his own knowledge what was to be known of the facts of anatomy and physiology in his day. He was an unwearied dissector and observer; and it is said, that, on a visitor once asking to see his library, Descartes led him into a room set aside for dissections, and full of specimens under examination. "There," said he, "is my library."

I anticipate a smile of incredulity when I thus champion Descartes' claim to be considered a physiologist of the first rank. I expect to be told that I have read into his works what I find there, and to be asked, Why is it that we are left to discover Descartes' deserts at this time of day, more than two centuries after his death? How is it that Descartes is utterly ignored in some of

14

the latest works which treat expressly of the
subject in which he is said to have been so
great ?

It is much easier to ask such questions than to
answer them, especially if one desires to be on good
terms with one's contemporaries; but, if I must
give an answer, it is this : The growth of physical
science is now so prodigiously rapid, that those
who are actively engaged in keeping up with the
present, have much ado to find time to look at the
past, and even grow into the habit of neglecting it.
But, natural as this result may be, it is none the
less detrimental. The intellect loses, for there is
assuredly no more effectual method of clearing up
one's own mind on any subject than by talking
it over, so to speak, with men of real power and
grasp, who have considered it from a totally
different point of view. The parallax of time
helps us to the true position of a conception, as
the parallax of space helps us to that of a star.
And the moral nature loses no less. It is well to
turn aside from the fretful stir of the present and
to dwell with gratitude and respect upon the
services of those "mighty men of old who have
gone down to the grave with their weapons of
war," but who, while they yet lived, won splendid
victories over ignorance. It is well, again, to reflect that the fame of Descartes filled all Europe,
and his authority overshadowed it, for a century ;
while now, most of those who know his name

think of him, either as a person who had some preposterous notions about vortices and was deservedly annihilated by the great Sir Isaac Newton; or as the apostle of an essentially vicious method of deductive speculation; and that, nevertheless, neither the chatter of shifting opinion, nor the silence of personal oblivion, has in the slightest degree affected the growth of the great ideas of which he was the instrument and the mouthpiece.

It is a matter of fact that the greatest physiologist of the eighteenth century, Haller, in treating of the functions of nerve, does little more than reproduce and enlarge upon the ideas of Descartes. It is a matter of fact that David Hartley, in his remarkable work the "Essay on Man," expressly, though still insufficiently, acknowledges the resemblance of his fundamental conceptions to those of Descartes; and I shall now endeavour to show that a series of propositions, which constitute the foundation and essence of the modern physiology of the nervous system, are fully expressed and illustrated in the works of Descartes.

I. *The brain is the organ of sensation, thought, and emotion; that is to say, some change in the condition of the matter of this organ is the invariable antecedent of the state of consciousness to which each of these terms is applied.*

In the " Principes de la Philosophie " (§ 169),
Descartes says :—[1]

" Although the soul is united to the whole body, its principal
functions are, nevertheless, performed in the brain ; it is here
that it not only understands and imagines, but also feels ; and
this is effected by the intermediation of the nerves, which extend
in the form of delicate threads from the brain to all parts of the
body, to which they are attached in such a manner, that we can
hardly touch any part of the body without setting the extremity
of some nerve in motion.   This motion passes along the nerve
to that part of the brain which is the common sensorium, as I
have sufficiently explained in my ' Treatise on Dioptrics ;' and
the movements which thus travel along the nerves, as far as that
part of the brain with which the soul is closely joined and
united, cause it, by reason of their diverse characters, to have
different thoughts.   And it is these different thoughts of the
soul, which arise immediately from the movements that are
excited by the nerves in the brain, which we properly term our
feelings, or the perceptions of our senses."

Elsewhere,[2] Descartes, in arguing that the seat
of the passions is not (as many suppose) the heart,
but the brain, uses the following remarkable
language :—

" The opinion of those who think that the soul receives its
passions in the heart, is of no weight, for it is based upon the
fact that the passions cause a change to be felt in that organ ;
and it is easy to see that this change is felt, as if it were in the

---

[1] I quote, here and always, Cousin's edition of the works of
Descartes, as most convenient for reference.   It is entitled
Œuvres complètes de Descartes, publiées, par Victor Cousin.
1824.

[2] *Les Passions de l'Âme,* Article xxxiii.

heart, only by the intermediation of a little nerve which descends from the brain to it; just as pain is felt, as if it were in the foot, by the intermediation of the nerves of the foot; and the stars are perceived, as if they were in the heavens, by the intermediation of their light and of the optic nerves. So that it is no more necessary for the soul to exert its functions immediately in the heart, to feel its passions there, than it is necessary that it should be in the heavens to see the stars there."

This definite allocation of all the phenomena of consciousness to the brain as their organ, was a step the value of which it is difficult for us to appraise, so completely has Descartes' view incorporated itself with every-day thought and common language. A lunatic is said to be "crack-brained" or "touched in the head," a confused thinker is "muddle-headed," while a clever man is said to have "plenty of brains"; but it must be remembered that at the end of the last century a considerable, though much over-estimated, anatomist, Bichat, so far from having reached the level of Descartes, could gravely argue that the apparatuses of organic life are the sole seat of the passions, which in no way affect the brain, except so far as it is the agent by which the influence of the passions is transmitted to the muscles.[1]

Modern physiology, aided by pathology, easily demonstrates that the brain is the seat of all forms of consciousness, and fully bears out Descartes' explanation of the reference of those sensations in

[1] *Recherches physiologiques sur la Vie et la Mort.* Par Xav. Bichat. Art. Sixième.

the viscera which accompany intense emotion, to these organs. It proves, directly, that those states of consciousness which we call sensations are the immediate consequent of a change in the brain excited by the sensory nerves; and, on the well-known effects of injuries, of stimulants, and of narcotics, it bases the conclusion that thought and emotion are, in like manner, the consequents of physical antecedents.

II. *The movements of animals are due to the change of form of muscles, which shorten and become thicker; and this change of form in a muscle arises from a motion of the substance contained within the nerves which go to the muscle.*

In the " Passions de l'Âme," Art. vii., Descartes writes :—

"Moreover, we know that all the movements of the limbs depend on the muscles, and that these muscles are opposed to one another in such a manner, that when one of them shortens, it draws along the part of the body to which it is attached, and so gives rise to a simultaneous elongation of the muscle which is opposed to it. Then, if it happens, afterwards, that the latter shortens, it causes the former to elongate, and draws towards itself the part to which it is attached. Lastly, we know that all these movements of the muscles, as all the senses, depend on the nerves, which are like little threads or tubes, which all come from the brain, and, like it, contain a certain very subtle air or wind, termed the animal spirits."

The property of muscle mentioned by Descartes

now goes by the general name of contractility,
but his definition of it remains untouched. The
long-continued controversy whether contractile
substance, speaking generally, has an inherent
power of contraction, or whether it contracts only
in virtue of an influence exerted by nerve, is now
settled in Haller's favour; but Descartes' statement of the dependence of muscular contraction
on nerve holds good for the higher forms of muscle,
under normal circumstances; so that, although
the structure of the various modifications of contractile matter has been worked out with astonishing minuteness—although the delicate physical
and chemical changes which accompany muscular
contraction have been determined to an extent of
which Descartes could not have dreamed, and
have quite upset his hypothesis that the cause of
the shortening and thickening of the muscle is
the flow of animal spirits into it from the nerves—
the important and fundamental part of his statement remains perfectly true.

The like may be affirmed of what he says about
nerve. We know now that nerves are not exactly
tubes, and that "animal spirits" are myths; but
the exquisitely refined methods of investigation
of Dubois-Reymond and of Helmholz have no less
clearly proved that the antecedent of ordinary
muscular contraction is a motion of the molecules
of the nerve going to the muscle; and that this
motion is propagated with a measurable, and by

no means great, velocity, through the substance of the nerve towards the muscle.

With the progress of research, the term "animal spirits" gave way to "nervous fluid," and "nervous fluid" has now given way to "molecular motion of nerve-substance." Our conceptions of what takes place in nerve have altered in the same way as our conceptions of what takes place in a conducting wire have altered, since electricity was shown to be not a fluid, but a mode of molecular motion. The change is of vast importance, but it does not affect Descartes' fundamental idea, that a change in the substance of a motor nerve propagated towards a muscle is the ordinary cause of muscular contraction.

III. *The sensations of animals are due to a motion of the substance of the nerves which connect the sensory organs with the brain.*

In "La Dioptrique" (Discours Quatrième), Descartes explains, more fully than in the passage cited above, his hypothesis of the mode of action of sensory nerves :—

"It is the little threads of which the inner substance of the nerves is composed which subserve sensation. You must conceive that these little threads, being inclosed in tubes, which are always distended and kept open by the animal spirits which they contain, neither press upon nor interfere with one another and are extended from the brain to the extremities of all the mem-

bers which are sensitive—in such a manner, that the slightest
touch which excites the part of one of the members to which a
thread is attached, gives rise to a motion of the part of the brain
whence it arises, just as by pulling one of the ends of a stretched
cord, the other end is instantaneously moved. . . . And we
must take care not to imagine that, in order to feel, the soul
needs to behold certain images sent by the objects of sense to
the brain, as our philosophers commonly suppose ; or, at least,
we must conceive these images to be something quite different
from what they suppose them to be.   For, as all they suppose is
that these images ought to resemble the objects which they represent, it is impossible for them to show how they can be
formed by the objects received by the organs of the external
senses and transmitted to the brain.   And they have had no
reason for supposing the existence of these images except this ;
seeing that the mind is readily excited by a picture to conceive
the object which is depicted, they have thought that it must be
excited in the same way to conceive those objects which affect
our senses by little pictures of them formed in the head ; instead
of which we ought to recollect that there are many things besides images which may excite the mind, as, for example, signs
and words, which have not the least resemblance to the objects
which they signify." [1]

Modern physiology amends Descartes' conception
of the mode of action of sensory nerves in
detail, by showing that their structure is the same
as that of motor nerves ; and that the changes
which take place in them, when the sensory organs
with which they are connected are excited, are of

---

[1] Locke (*Human Understanding*, Book II., chap. viii. 37)
uses Descartes' illustration for the same purpose, and warns us
that " most of the ideas of sensation are no more the likeness of
something existing without us than the names that stand for
them are the likeness of our ideas, which yet, upon hearing, they
are apt to excite in us," a declaration which paved the way for
Berkeley.

just the same nature as those which occur in motor nerves, when the muscles to which they are distributed are made to contract : there is a molecular change which, in the case of the sensory nerve, is propagated towards the brain. But the great fact insisted upon by Descartes, that no likeness of external things is, or can be, transmitted to the mind by the sensory organs ; on the contrary, that, between the external cause of a sensation and the sensation, there is interposed a mode of motion of nervous matter, of which the state of consciousness is no likeness, but a mere symbol, is of the profoundest importance. It is the physiological foundation of the doctrine of the relativity of knowledge, and a more or less complete idealism is a necessary consequence of it.

For of two alternatives one must be true. Either consciousness is the function of a something distinct from the brain, which we call the soul, and a sensation is the mode in which this soul is affected by the motion of a part of the brain ; or there is no soul, and a sensation is something generated by the mode of motion of a part of the brain. In the former case, the phenomena of the senses are purely spiritual affections ; in the latter, they are something manufactured by the mechanism of the body, and as unlike the causes which set that mechanism in motion, as the sound of a repeater is unlike the pushing of the spring which gives rise to it.

The nervous system stands between consciousness and the assumed external world, as an
interpreter who can talk with his fingers stands
between a hidden speaker and a man who is stone
deaf—and Realism is equivalent to a belief on the
part of the deaf man, that the speaker must also
be talking with his fingers. "Les extrêmes se
touchent;" the shibboleth of materialists that
"thought is a secretion of the brain," is the
Fichtean doctrine that "the phenomenal universe is the creation of the Ego," expressed in
other language.

IV. *The motion of the matter of a sensory nerve
may be transmitted through the brain to
motor nerves, and thereby give rise to contraction of the muscles to which these motor
nerves are distributed ; and this reflection
of motion from a sensory into a motor
nerve may take place without volition, or
even contrary to it.*

In stating these important truths, Descartes
defined that which we now term " reflex action."
Indeed he almost uses the term itself, as he talks
of the "animal spirits" as "réfléchis,"[1] from the
sensory into the motor nerves. And that this use
of the word " reflected " was no mere accident, but
that the importance and appropriateness of the

---

[1] *Passions de l'Âme*, Art. xxxvi.

idea it suggests was fully understood by Descartes'
contemporaries, is apparent from a passage in
Willis's well-known essay, " De Animâ Brutorum,"
published in 1672, in which, in giving an account
of Descartes' views, he speaks of the animal spirits
being diverted into motor channels, " velut undulatione reflexâ."[1]

Nothing can be clearer in statement, or in
illustration, than the view of reflex action which
Descartes gives in the "Passions de l'Âme,"
Art. xiii.

After recapitulating the manner in which sensory
impressions transmitted by the sensory nerves to
the brain give rise to sensation, he proceeds :—

"And in addition to the different feelings excited in the
soul by these different motions of the brain, the animal spirits,
without the intervention of the soul, may take their course
towards certain muscles, rather than towards others, and thus
move the limbs, as I shall prove by an example. If some one
moves his hand rapidly towards our eyes, as if he were going to
strike us, although we know that he is a friend, that he does it
only in jest, and that he will be very careful to do us no harm,
nevertheless it will be hard to keep from winking. And this
shows, that it is not by the agency of the soul that the eyes
shut, since this action is contrary to that volition which is the

---

[1] " Quamcumque Bruti actionem, velut automati mechanici
motum artificialem, in eo consistere quod se primò sensibile
aliquod spiritus animales afficiens, eosque introrsum convertens,
sensionem excitat, à qua mox iidem spiritus, velut undulatione
reflexâ denuo retrorsum commoti atque pro concinno ipsius
fabricæ organorum, et partium ordine, in certos nervos muscul-
osque determinati, respectivos *membrorum motus* perficiunt."—
WILLIS : *De Animâ Brutorum*, p. 5, ed. 1763.

only, or at least the chief, function of the soul ; but it is because the mechanism of our body is so disposed, that the motion of the hand towards our eyes excites another movement in our brain, and this sends the animal spirits into those muscles which cause the eyelids to close."

Since Descartes' time, experiment has eminently enlarged our knowledge of the details of reflex action. The discovery of Bell has enabled us to follow the tracks of the sensory and motor impulses, along distinct bundles of nerve fibres ; and the spinal cord, apart from the brain, has been proved to be a great centre of reflex action; but the fundamental conception remains as Descartes left it, and it is one of the pillars of nerve physiology at the present day.

V. *The motion of any given portion of the matter of the brain excited by the motion of a sensory nerve, leaves behind a readiness to be moved in the same way, in that part. Anything which resuscitates the motion gives rise to the appropriate feeling. This is the physical mechanism of memory.*

Descartes imagined that the pineal body (a curious appendage to the upper side of the brain, the function of which, if it have any, is wholly unknown) [1] was the instrument through which the soul received impressions from, and communicated them to, the brain. And he thus endeavours to

[1] See above : p. 189, *note.*

explain what happens when one tries to recollect
something :—

"Thus when the soul wills to remember anything, this
volition, causing the [pineal] gland to incline itself in different
directions, drives the [animal] spirits towards different regions
of the brain, until they reach that part in which are the traces,
which the object which it desires to remember has left.   These
traces are produced thus : those pores of the brain through
which the [animal] spirits have previously been driven, by
reason of the presence of the object, have thereby acquired a
tendency to be opened by the animal spirits which return towards
them more easily than other pores, so that the animal spirits,
impinging on these pores, enter them more readily than
others.   By this means they excite a particular movement in
the pineal gland, which represents the object to the soul, and
causes it to know what it is which it desired to recollect." [1]

That memory is dependent upon some condition
of the brain is a fact established by many considerations—among the most important of which
are the remarkable phenomena of aphasia.   And
that the condition of the brain on which memory
depends, is largely determined by the repeated
occurrence of that condition of its molecules, which
gives rise to the idea of the thing remembered, is
no less certain.   Every boy who learns his lesson
by repeating it exemplifies the fact.   Descartes,
as we have seen, supposes that the pores of a
given part of the brain are stretched by the
animal spirits, on the occurrence of a sensation,
and that the part of the brain thus stretched,

[1] *Les Passions de l'Âme*, xlii.

being imperfectly elastic, does not return to exactly its previous condition, but remains more distensible than it was before. Hartley supposes that the vibrations, excited by a sensory, or other, impression, do not die away, but are represented by smaller vibrations or "vibratiuncules," the permanency and intensity of which are in relation with the frequency of repetition of the primary vibrations. Haller has substantially the same idea, but contents himself with the general term "mutationes," to express the cerebral change which is the cause of a state of consciousness. These "mutationes" persist for a long time after the cause which gives rise to them has ceased to operate, and are arranged in the brain according to the order of coexistence and succession of their causes. And he gives these persistent "mutationes" the picturesque name of *vestigia rerum*, "quæ non in mente sed in ipso corpore et in medulla quidem cerebri ineffabili modo incredibiliter minutis notis et copia infinita, inscriptæ sunt."[1] I do not know that any modern theory of the physical conditions of memory differs essentially from these, which are all children—*mutatis mutandis*—of the Cartesian doctrine. Physiology is, at present, incompetent to say anything positively about the matter, or to go farther than the expression of the high probability, that every molecular change which gives rise to a state of

[1] Haller, *Primæ Lineæ*, ed. iii. *Sensus interni*, dlvii.

consciousness, leaves a more or less persistent structural modification, through which the same molecular change may be regenerated by other agencies than the cause which first produced it.

Thus far, the prepositions respecting the physiology of the nervouss ystem which are stated by Descartes have simply been more clearly defined, more fully illustrated, and, for the most part, demonstrated, by modern physiological research. But there remains a doctrine to which Descartes attached great weight, so that full acceptance of it became a sort of note of a thoroughgoing Cartesian, but which, nevertheless, is so opposed to ordinary prepossessions that it attained more general notoriety, and gave rise to more discussion, than almost any other Cartesian hypothesis. It is the doctrine that brute animals are mere machines or automata, devoid not only of reason, but of any kind of consciousness, which is stated briefly in the " Discours de la Méthode," and more fully in the "Réponses aux Quatrièmes Objections," and in the correspondence with Henry More.[1]

The process of reasoning by which Descartes arrived at this startling conclusion is well shown in the following passage of the " Réponses : "—

"But as regards the souls of beasts, although this is not the place for considering them, and though, without a general

[1] *Réponse de M. Descartes à M. Morus.* 1649. *Œuvres,* tome x. p. 204. "Mais le plus grand de tous les préjugés que nous ayons retenus de notre enfance, est celui de croire que les bêtes pensent," etc

exposition of physics, I can say no more on this subject than I have already said in the fifth part of my Treatise on Method ; yet, I will further state, here, that it appears to me to be a very remarkable circumstance that no movement can take place, either in the bodies of beasts, or even in our own, if these bodies have not in themselves all the organs and instruments by means of which the very same movements would be accomplished in a machine. So that, even in us, the spirit, or the soul, does not directly move the limbs, but only determines the course of that very subtle liquid which is called the animal spirits, which, running continually from the heart by the brain into the muscles, is the cause of all the movements of our limbs, and often may cause many different motions, one as easily as the other.

"And it does not even always exert this determination ; for among the movements which take place in us, there are many which do not depend on the mind at all, such as the beating of the heart, the digestion of food, the nutrition, the respiration of those who sleep ; and even in those who are awake, walking, singing, and other similar actions, when they are performed without the mind thinking about them. And, when one who falls from a height throws his hands forward to save his head, it is in virtue of no ratiocination that he performs this action ; it does not depend upon his mind, but takes place merely because his senses being affected by the present danger, some change arises in his brain which determines the animal spirits to pass thence into the nerves, in such a manner as is required to produce this motion, in the same way as in a machine, and without the mind being able to hinder it. Now since we observe this in ourselves, why should we be so much astonished if the light reflected from the body of a wolf into the eye of a sheep has the same force to excite in it the motion of flight ?

"After having observed this, if we wish to learn by reasoning, whether certain movements of beasts are comparable to those which are effected in us by the operation of the mind, or, on the contrary, to those which depend only on the animal spirits and the disposition of the organs, it is necessary to consider the difference between the two, which I have explained in the fifth part of the Discourse on Method (for I do not think that any

15

others are discoverable), and then it will easily be seen, that all
the actions of beasts are similar only to those which we perform
without the help of our minds.   For which reason we shall be
forced to conclude, that we know of the existence in them of no
other principle of motion than the disposition of their organs
and the continual affluence of animal spirits produced by the
heat of the heart, which attenuates and subtilises the blood ; and,
at the same time, we shall acknowledge that we have had no
reason for assuming any other principle, except that, not having
distinguished these two principles of motion, and seeing that
the one, which depends only on the animal spirits and the
organs, exists in beasts as well as in us, we have hastily concluded that the other, which depends on mind and on thought,
was also possessed by them."

Descartes' line of argument is perfectly clear.
He starts from reflex action in man, from the
unquestionable fact that, in ourselves, co-ordinate,
purposive, actions may take place, without the
intervention of consciousness or volition, or even
contrary to the latter.   As actions of a certain
degree of complexity are brought about by mere
mechanism, why may not actions of still greater
complexity be the result of a more refined
mechanism ?   What proof is there that brutes are
other than a superior race of marionettes, which
eat without pleasure, cry without pain, desire
nothing, know nothing, and only simulate
intelligence as a bee simulates a mathematician ? [1]

The Port Royalists adopted the hypothesis that

[1] Malebranche states the view taken by orthodox Cartesians in
1689 very forcibly : "Ainsi dans les chiens, les chats, et les
autres animaux, il n'y a ny intelligence, ny âme spirituelle
comme on l'entend ordinairement.   Ils mangent sans plaisir ; ils

brutes are machines, and are said to have carried its practical applications so far as to treat domestic animals with neglect, if not with actual cruelty. As late as the middle of the eighteenth century, the problem was discussed very fully and ably by Bouillier, in his " Essai philosophique sur l'Âme des Bêtes," while Condillac deals with it in his " Traité des Animaux ; " but since then it has received little attention. Nevertheless, modern research has brought to light a great multitude of facts, which not only show that Descartes' view is defensible, but render it far more defensible than it was in his day.

It must be premised, that it is wholly impossible absolutely to prove the presence or absence of consciousness in anything but one's own brain, though, by analogy, we are justified in assuming its existence in other men. Now if, by some accident, a man's spinal cord is divided, his limbs are paralysed, so far as his volition is concerned, below the point of injury ; and he is incapable of experiencing all those states of consciousness which, in his uninjured state, would be excited by irritation of those nerves which come off below the injury. If the spinal cord is divided in the

crient sans douleur ; ils croissent sans le sçavoir ; ils ne désirent rien ; ils ne connoissent rien ; et s'ils agissent avec adresse et d'une manière qui marque l'intelligence, c'est que Dieu les faisant pour les conserver, il a conformé leurs corps de telle manière, qu'ils évitent organiquement, sans le sçavoir, tout ce qui peut les detruire et qu'ils semblent craindre." (*Feuillet de Conches. Méditations Métaphysiques et Correspondance de N. Malebranche. Neuvième Méditation.* 1841.)

middle of the back, for example, the skin of the feet may be cut, or pinched, or burned, or wetted with vitriol, without any sensation of touch, or of pain, arising in consciousness. So far as the man is concerned, therefore, the part of the central nervous system which lies beyond the injury is cut off from consciousness. It must indeed be admitted, that, if any one think fit to maintain that the spinal cord below the injury is conscious, but that it is cut off from any means of making its consciousness known to the other consciousness in the brain, there is no means of driving him from his position by logic. But assuredly there is no way of proving it, and in the matter of consciousness, if in anything, we may hold by the rule, " De non apparentibus et de non existentibus eadem est ratio." However near the brain the spinal cord is injured, consciousness remains intact, except that the irritation of parts below the injury is no longer represented by sensation. On the other hand, pressure upon the anterior division of the brain, or extensive injuries to it, abolish consciousness. Hence, it is a highly probable conclusion, that consciousness in man depends upon the integrity of the anterior division of the brain, while the middle and hinder divisions of the brain,[1] and the rest of the nervous centres, have nothing to do with it. And it is further highly probable,

---

[1] Not to be confounded with the anterior middle and hinder parts of the hemispheres of the cerebrum.

that what is true for man is true for other vertebrated animals.

We may assume, then, that in a living vertebrated animal, any segment of the cerebro-spinal axis (or spinal cord and brain) separated from that anterior division of the brain which is the organ of consciousness, is as completely incapable of giving rise to consciousness as we know it to be incapable of carrying out volitions. Nevertheless, this separated segment of the spinal cord is not passive and inert. On the contrary, it is the seat of extremely remarkable powers. In our imaginary case of injury, the man would, as we have seen, be devoid of sensation in his legs, and would have not the least power of moving them. But, if the soles of his feet were tickled, the legs would be drawn up just as vigorously as they would have been before the injury. We know exactly what happens when the soles of the feet are tickled; a molecular change takes place in the sensory nerves of the skin, and is propagated along them and through the posterior roots of the spinal nerves, which are constituted by them, to the grey matter of the spinal cord. Through that grey matter the molecular motion is reflected into the anterior roots of the same nerves, constituted by the filaments which supply the muscles of the legs, and, travelling along these motor filaments, reaches the muscles, which at once contract, and cause the limbs to be drawn up.

In order to move the legs in this way, a definite co-ordination of muscular contractions is necessary ; the muscles must contract in a certain order and with duly proportioned force; and moreover, as the feet are drawn away from the source of irritation, it may be said that the action has a final cause, or is purposive.

Thus it follows, that the grey matter of the segment of the man's spinal cord, though it is devoid of consciousness, nevertheless responds to a simple stimulus by giving rise to a complex set of muscular contractions, co-ordinated towards a definite end, and serving an obvious purpose.

If the spinal cord of a frog is cut across, so as to provide us with a segment separated from the brain, we shall have a subject parallel to the injured man, on which experiments can be made without remorse ; as we have a right to conclude that a frog's spinal cord is not likely to be con-scious, when a man's is not.

Now the frog behaves just as the man did. The legs are utterly paralysed, so far as voluntary movement is concerned ; but they are vigorously drawn up to the body when any irritant is applied to the foot.   But let us study our frog a little farther.   Touch the skin of the side of the body with a little acetic acid, which gives rise to all the signs of great pain in an uninjured frog.   In this case, there can be no pain, because the appli-cation is made to a part of the skin supplied with

nerves which come off from the cord below the
point of section; nevertheless, the frog lifts up
the limb of the same side, and applies the foot to
rub off the acetic acid; and, what is still more
remarkable, if the limb be held so that the frog
cannot use it, it will, by and by, move the limb of
the other side, turn it across the body, and use it
for the same rubbing process. It is impossible
that the frog, if it were in its entirety and could
reason, should perform actions more purposive
than these: and yet we have most complete
assurance that, in this case, the frog is not acting
from purpose, has no consciousness, and is a mere
insensible machine.

But now suppose that, instead of making a
section of the cord in the middle of the body, it
had been made in such a manner as to separate
the hindermost division of the brain from the
rest of the organ, and suppose the foremost two-
thirds of the brain entirely taken away. The
frog is then absolutely devoid of any spontaneity;
it sits upright in the attitude which a frog
habitually assumes; and it will not stir unless it
is touched; but it differs from the frog which I
have just described in this, that, if it be thrown
into the water, it begins to swim, and swims just
as well as the perfect frog does. But swimming
requires the combination and successive co-ordination of a great number of muscular actions. And
we are forced to conclude, that the impression

made upon the sensory nerves of the skin of the frog by the contact with the water into which it is thrown, causes the transmission to the central nervous apparatus of an impulse which sets going a certain machinery by which all the muscles of swimming are brought into play in due co-ordination. If the frog be stimulated by some irritating body, it jumps or walks as well as the complete frog can do. The simple sensory impression, acting through the machinery of the cord, gives rise to these complex combined movements.

It is possible to go a step farther. Suppose that only the anterior division of the brain—so much of it as lies in front of the " optic lobes "— is removed. If that operation is performed quickly and skilfully, the frog may be kept in a state of full bodily vigour for months, or it may be for years; but it will sit unmoved. It sees nothing : it hears nothing. It will starve sooner than feed itself, although food put into its mouth is swallowed. On irritation, it jumps or walks; if thrown into the water it swims. If it be put on the hand, it sits there, crouched, perfectly quiet, and would sit there for ever. If the hand be inclined very gently and slowly, so that the frog would naturally tend to slip off, the creature's fore paws are shifted on to the edge of the hand, until he can just prevent himself from falling. If the turning of the hand be slowly continued, he mounts up with great care and deliberation, putting first one leg forward and then another, until he balances himself with perfect precision upon the edge; and if the turning of the hand is continued, he goes through the needful set of muscular operations, until he comes to be seated in security, upon the back of the hand. The doing of all this requires a delicacy of co-ordination, and a precision of adjustment of the muscular apparatus of the body, which are only comparable to those of a rope-dancer. To the ordinary influences of light, the frog, deprived of its cerebral hemispheres, appears to be blind. Nevertheless, if the animal be put upon a table, with a book at some little distance between it and the light, and the skin of the hinder part of its body is then irritated, it will jump forward, avoiding the book by passing to the right or left of it. Therefore, although the frog appears to have no sensation of light, visible objects act through its brain upon the motor mechanism of its body.[1]

It is obvious, that had Descartes been acquainted with these remarkable results of modern research, they would have furnished him with far more powerful arguments than he possessed in favour of his view of the automatism of brutes. The

[1] See the remarkable essay of Göltz, *Beiträge zur Lehre von den Functionen der Nervencentren des Frosches*, published in 1869. I have repeated Göltz's experiments, and obtained the same results.

habits of a frog, leading its natural life, involve
such simple adaptations to surrounding conditions,
that the machinery which is competent to do so
much without the intervention of consciousness,
might well do all. And this argument is vastly
strengthened by what has been learned in recent
times of the marvellously complex operations
which are performed mechanically, and to all
appearance without consciousness, by men, when,
in consequence of injury or disease, they are
reduced to a condition more or less comparable to
that of a frog, in which the anterior part of the
brain has been removed. A case has recently
been published by an eminent French physician,
Dr. Mesnet, which illustrates this condition so
remarkably, that I make no apology for dwelling
upon it at considerable length.[1]

A sergeant of the French army, F——, twenty-
seven years of age, was wounded during the battle
of Bazeilles, by a ball which fractured his left
parietal bone. He ran his bayonet through the
Prussian soldier who wounded him, but almost
immediately his right arm became paralysed;
after walking about two hundred yards, his right
leg became similarly affected, and he lost his
senses. When he recovered them, three weeks

[1] "De l'Automatisme de la Mémoire et du Souvenir, dans le
Somnambulisme pathologique."   Par le Dr. E. Mesnet, Médecin
de l'Hôpital Saint-Antoine.   L'Union Médicale, Juillet 21 et 23,
1874. My attention was first called to a summary of this
remarkable case, which appeared in the Journal des Débats for
the 7th of August, 1874, by my friend General Strachey, F.R.S.

afterwards, in hospital at Mayence, the right half of the body was completely paralysed, and remained in this condition for a year. At present, the only trace of the paralysis which remains is a slight weakness of the right half of the body. Three or four months after the wound was inflicted, periodical disturbances of the functions of the brain made their appearance, and have continued ever since. The disturbances last from fifteen to thirty hours; the intervals at which they occur being from fifteen to thirty days.

For four years, therefore, the life of this man has been divided into alternating phases—short abnormal states intervening between long normal states.

In the periods of normal life, the ex-sergeant's health is perfect; he is intelligent and kindly, and performs, satisfactorily, the duties of a hospital attendant. The commencement of the abnormal state is ushered in by uneasiness and a sense of weight about the forehead, which the patient compares to the constriction of a circle of iron; and, after its termination, he complains, for some hours, of dulness and heaviness of the head. But the transition from the normal to the abnormal state takes place in a few minutes, without convulsions or cries, and without anything to indicate the change to a bystander. His movements remain free and his expression calm, except for a contraction of the brow, an incessant movement of the eyeballs, and a chewing motion of the jaws. The eyes are wide open, and their pupils dilated. If the man happens to be in a place to which he is accustomed, he walks about as usual; but, if he is in a new place, or if obstacles are intentionally placed in his way, he stumbles gently against them, stops, and then, feeling over the objects with his hands, passes on one side of them. He offers no resistance to any change of direction which may be impressed upon him, or to the forcible acceleration or retardation of his movements. He eats, drinks, smokes, walks about, dresses and undresses himself, rises and goes to bed at the accustomed hours. Nevertheless, pins may be run into his body, or strong electric shocks sent through it, without causing the least indication of pain; no odorous substance, pleasant or unpleasant, makes the least impression; he eats and drinks with avidity whatever is offered, and takes asafœtida, or vinegar, or quinine, as readily as water; no noise affects him; and light influences him only under certain conditions. Dr. Mesnet remarks, that the sense of touch alone seems to persist, and indeed to be more acute and delicate than in the normal state : and it is by means of the nerves of touch, almost exclusively, that his organism is brought into relation with the external world. Here a difficulty arises. It is clear from the facts detailed, that the nervous apparatus by which, in the normal state, sensations of touch are excited, is that by which external influences determine the movements of the body, in the abnormal state. But does the state of consciousness, which we term a tactile sensation, accompany the operation of this nervous apparatus in the abnormal state? or is consciousness utterly absent, the man being reduced to an insensible mechanism?

It is impossible to obtain direct evidence in favour of the one conclusion or the other; all that can be said is, that the case of the frog shows that the man may be devoid of any kind of consciousness.

A further difficult problem is this. The man is insensible to sensory impressions made through the ear, the nose, the tongue, and, to a great extent, the eye; nor is he susceptible of pain from causes operating during his abnormal state. Nevertheless, it is possible so to act upon his tactile apparatus, as to give rise to those molecular changes in his sensorium, which are ordinarily the causes of associated trains of ideas. I give a striking example of this process in Dr. Mesnet's words :—

"Il se promenait dans le jardin, sous un massif d'arbres, on lui remet à la main sa canne qu'il avait laissé tomber quelques minutes avant. Il la palpe, promène à plusieurs reprises la main sur la poignée coudée de sa canne—devient attentif—semble prêter l'oreille—et, tout-à-coup, appelle 'Henri!' Puis, 'Les voilà! Ils sont au moins une vingtaine! à nous deux, nous en

viendrons à bout ! '   Et alors portant la main derrière son dos
comme pour prendre une cartouche, il fait le mouvement de
charger son arme, se couche dans l'herbe à plat ventre, la tête
cachée par un arbre, dans la position d'un tirailleur, et suit
l'arme épaulée, tous les mouvements de l'ennemi qu'il croit voir
à courte distance."

In a subsequent abnormal period, Dr. Mesnet
caused the patient to repeat this scene by placing
him in the same conditions.   Now, in this case,
the question arises whether the series of actions
constituting this singular pantomime was accompanied by the ordinary states of consciousness, the
appropriate train of ideas, or not ?   Did the man
dream that he was skirmishing ? or was he in the
condition of one of Vaucauson's automata—a
senseless mechanism worked by molecular changes
in his nervous system ?   The analogy of the frog
shows that the latter assumption is perfectly justifiable.

The ex-sergeant has a good voice, and had, at
one time, been employed as a singer at a café.   In
one of his abnormal states he was observed to
begin humming a tune. He then went to his
room, dressed himself carefully, and took up some
parts of a periodical novel, which lay on his bed,
as if he were trying to find something.   Dr.
Mesnet, suspecting that he was seeking his music,
made up one of these into a roll and put it
into his hand. He appeared satisfied, took his
cane and went down stairs to the door.   Here
Dr. Mesnet turned him round, and he walked

quite contentedly, in the opposite direction, towards the room of the concierge. The light of the sun shining through a window now happened to fall upon him, and seemed to suggest the foot-lights of the stage on which he was accustomed to make his appearance. He stopped, opened his roll of imaginary music, put himself into the atti-tude of a singer, and sang, with perfect execution, three songs, one after the other. After which he wiped his face with his handkerchief and drank, without a grimace, a tumbler of strong vinegar and water which was put into his hand.

An experiment which may be performed upon the frog deprived of the fore part of its brain, well known as Göltz's "Quak-versuch," affords a parallel to this performance. If the skin of a certain part of the back of such a frog is gently stroked with the finger, it immediately croaks. It never croaks unless it is so stroked, and the croak always follows the stroke, just as the sound of a repeater follows the touching of the spring. In the frog, this "song" is innate—so to speak *à priori*—and depends upon a mechanism in the brain governing the vocal apparatus, which is set at work by the molecular change set up in the sensory nerves of the skin of the back by the contact of a foreign body.

In man there is also a vocal mechanism, and the cry of an infant is in the same sense innate and *à priori*, inasmuch as it depends on an organic relation between its sensory nerves and the nervous mechanism which governs the vocal apparatus. Learning to speak, and learning to sing, are processes by which the vocal mechanism is set to new tunes. A song which has been learned has its molecular equivalent, which potentially represents it in the brain, just as a musical box, wound up, potentially represents an overture. Touch the stop and the overture begins; send a molecular impulse along the proper afferent nerve and the singer begins his song.

Again, the manner in which the frog, though apparently insensible to light, is yet, under some circumstances, influenced by visual images, finds a singular parallel in the case of the ex-sergeant.

Sitting at a table, in one of his abnormal states, he took up a pen, felt for paper and ink, and began to write a letter to his general, in which he recommended himself for a medal, on account of his good conduct and courage. It occurred to Dr. Mesnet to ascertain experimentally how far vision was concerned in this act of writing. He therefore interposed a screen between the man's eyes and his hands; under these circumstances he went on writing for a short time, but the words became illegible, and he finally stopped, without manifesting any discontent. On the withdrawal of the screen he began to write again where he had left off. The substitution of water for ink in the inkstand had a similar result. He stopped,

looked at his pen, wiped it on his coat, dipped it
in the water, and began again with the same effect.

On one occasion, he began to write upon the
topmost of ten superimposed sheets of paper.
After he had written a line or two, this sheet was
suddenly drawn away. There was a slight expression of surprise, but he continued his letter
on the second sheet exactly as if it had been the
first. This operation was repeated five times, so
that the fifth sheet contained nothing but the
writer's signature at the bottom of the page.
Nevertheless, when the signature was finished,
his eyes turned to the top of the blank sheet, and
he went through the form of reading over what
he had written, a movement of the lips accom-
panying each word; moreover, with his pen, he put
in such corrections as were needed, in that part of
the blank page which corresponded with the
position of the words which required correction,
in the sheets which had been taken away. If the
five sheets had been transparent, therefore, they
would, when superposed, have formed a properly
written and corrected letter.

Immediately after he had written his letter,
F——got up, walked down to the garden, made
himself a cigarette, lighted and smoked it. He
was about to prepare another, but sought in vain
for his tobacco-pouch, which had been purposely
taken away. The pouch was now thrust before
his eyes and put under his nose, but he neither

16

saw nor smelt it; yet, when it was placed in his hand, he at once seized it, made a fresh cigarette, and ignited a match to light the latter. The match was blown out, and another lighted match placed close before his eyes, but he made no attempt to take it; and, if his cigarette was lighted for him, he made no attempt to smoke. All this time the eyes were vacant, and neither winked, nor exhibited any contraction of the pupils. From these and other experiments, Dr. Mesnet draws the conclusion that his patient sees some things and not others; that the sense of sight is accessible to all things which are brought into relation with him by the sense of touch, and, on the contrary, insensible to things which lie outside this relation. He sees the match he holds and does not see any other.

Just so the frog "sees" the book which is in the way of his jump, at the same time that isolated visual impressions take no effect upon him.[1]

---

[1] Those who have had occasion to become acquainted with the phenomena of somnambulism and of mesmerism, will be struck with the close parallel which they present to the proceedings of F. in his abnormal state. But the great value of Dr. Mesnet's observations lies in the fact that the abnormal condition is traceable to a definite injury to the brain, and that the circumstances are such as to keep us clear of the cloud of voluntary and involuntary fictions in which the truth is too often smothered in such cases. In the unfortunate subjects of such abnormal conditions of the brain, the disturbance of the sensory and intellectual faculties is not unfrequently accompanied by a perturbation of the moral nature, which may manifest itself in a most astonishing love of lying for its own sake. And, in this respect, also, F.'s case is singularly instruct-

As I have pointed out, it is impossible to prove that F—— is absolutely unconscious in his abnormal state, but it is no less impossible to prove the contrary; and the case of the frog goes a long way to justify the assumption that, in the abnormal state, the man is a mere insensible machine.

If such facts as these had come under the knowledge of Descartes, would they not have formed an apt commentary upon that remarkable passage in the " Traité de l'Homme," which I have quoted elsewhere, but which is worth repetition ?—

" All the functions which I have attributed to this machine (the body), as the digestion of food, the pulsation of the heart and of the arteries ; the nutrition and the growth of the limbs ; respiration, wakefulness, and sleep ; the reception of light, sounds, odours, flavours, heat, and such like qualities, in the organs of the external senses ; the impression of the ideas of these in the organ of common sensation and in the imagination ;

---

ive, for though, in his normal state, he is a perfectly honest man, in his abnormal condition he is an inveterate thief, stealing and hiding away whatever he can lay hands on, with much dexterity, and with an absurd indifference as to whether the property is his own or not. Hoffman's terrible conception of the "Doppelt-gänger" is realised by men in this state—who live two lives, in the one of which they may be guilty of the most criminal acts, while, in the other, they are eminently virtuous and respectable. Neither life knows anything of the other. Dr. Mesnet states that he has watched a man in his abnormal state elaborately prepare to hang himself, and has let him go on until asphyxia set in, when he cut him down. But on passing into the normal state the would-be suicide was wholly ignorant of what had happened. The problem of responsibility is here as complicated as that of the prince-bishop, who swore as a prince and not as a bishop. " But, highness, if the prince is damned, what will become of the bishop ? ' said the peasant.

the retention or the impression of these ideas on the memory ;
the internal movements of the appetites and the passions ; and
lastly the external movements of all the limbs, which follow so
aptly, as well the action of the objects which are presented to
the senses, as the impressions which meet in the memory, that
they imitate as nearly as possible those of a real man ; I desire,
I say, that you should consider that these functions in the
machine naturally proceed from the mere arrangement of its
organs, neither more nor less than do the movements of a clock,
or other automaton, from that of its weights and its wheels ; so
that, so far as these are concerned, it is not necessary to conceive any other vegetative or sensitive soul, nor any other
principle of motion or of life, than the blood and the spirits
agitated by the fire which burns continually in the heart, and
which is no wise essentially different from all the fires which
exist in inanimate bodies."

And would Descartes not have been justified in
asking why we need deny that animals are
machines, when men, in a state of unconsciousness,
perform, mechanically, actions as complicated and
as seemingly rational as those of any animals ?

But though I do not think that Descartes'
hypothesis can be positively refuted, I am not disposed to accept it. The doctrine of continuity is
too well established for it to be permissible to me
to suppose that any complex natural phenomenon
comes into existence suddenly, and without being
preceded by simpler modifications ; and very
strong arguments would be needed to prove that
such complex phenomena as those of consciousness, first make their appearance in man. We
know, that, in the individual man, consciousness
grows from a dim glimmer to its full light, whether

we consider the infant advancing in years, or the adult emerging from slumber and swoon. We know, further, that the lower animals possess, though less developed, that part of the brain which we have every reason to believe to be the organ of consciousness in man; and as, in other cases, function and organ are proportional, so we have a right to conclude it is with the brain; and that the brutes, though they may not possess our intensity of consciousness, and though, from the absence of language, they can have no trains of thoughts, but only trains of feelings, yet have a consciousness which, more or less distinctly, foreshadows our own.

I confess that, in view of the struggle for existence which goes on in the animal world, and of the frightful quantity of pain with which it must be accompanied, I should be glad if the probabilities were in favour of Descartes' hypothesis; but, on the other hand, considering the terrible practical consequences to domestic animals which might ensue from any error on our part, it is as well to err on the right side, if we err at all, and deal with them as weaker brethren, who are bound, like the rest of us, to pay their toll for living, and suffer what is needful for the general good. As Hartley finely says, "We seem to be in the place of God to them;" and we may justly follow the precedents He sets in nature in our dealings with them.

But though we may see reason to disagree with

Descartes' hypothesis that brutes are unconscious machines, it does not follow that he was wrong in regarding them as automata. They may be more or less conscious, sensitive, automata; and the view that they are such conscious machines is that which is implicitly, or explicitly, adopted by most persons. When we speak of the actions of the lower animals being guided by instinct and not by reason, what we really mean is that, though they feel as we do, yet their actions are the results of their physical organisation. We believe, in short, that they are machines, one part of which (the nervous system) not only sets the rest in motion, and co-ordinates its movements in relation with changes in surrounding bodies, but is provided with special apparatus, the function of which is the calling into existence of those states of consciousness which are termed sensations, emotions, and ideas. I believe that this generally accepted view is the best expression of the facts at present known.

It is experimentally demonstrable—any one who cares to run a pin into himself may perform a sufficient demonstration of the fact—that a mode of motion of the nervous system is the immediate antecedent of a state of consciousness. All but the adherents of "Occasionalism," or of the doctrine of "Pre-established Harmony" (if any such now exist), must admit that we have as much reason for regarding the mode of motion of the nervous system as the cause of the state of consciousness, as we have for regarding any event as the cause of another. How the one phenomenon causes the other we know, as much or as little, as in any other case of causation; but we have as much right to believe that the sensation is an effect of the molecular change, as we have to believe that motion is an effect of impact; and there is as much propriety in saying that the brain evolves sensation, as there is in saying that an iron rod, when hammered, evolves heat.

As I have endeavoured to show, we are justified in supposing that something analogous to what happens in ourselves takes place in the brutes, and that the affections of their sensory nerves give rise to molecular changes in the brain, which again give rise to, or evolve, the corresponding states of consciousness. Nor can there be any reasonable doubt that the emotions of brutes, and such ideas as they possess, are similarly dependent upon molecular brain changes. Each sensory impression leaves behind a record in the structure of the brain—an " ideagenous " molecule, so to speak, which is competent, under certain conditions, to reproduce, in a fainter condition, the state of consciousness which corresponds with that sensory impression; and it is these " ideagenous molecules " which are the physical basis of memory.

It may be assumed, then, that molecular changes in the brain are the causes of all the states of consciousness of brutes. Is there any evidence that these states of consciousness may, conversely, cause those molecular changes which give rise to muscular motion ? I see no such evidence. The frog walks, hops, swims, and goes through his gymnastic performances quite as well without consciousness, and consequently without volition, as with it ; and, if a frog, in his natural state, possesses anything corresponding with what we call volition, there is no reason to think that it is anything but a concomitant of the molecular changes in the brain which form part of the series involved in the production of motion.

The consciousness of brutes would appear to be related to the mechanism of their body simply as a collateral product of its working, and to be as completely without any power of modifying that working as the steam-whistle which accompanies the work of a locomotive engine is without influence upon its machinery. Their volition, if they have any, is an emotion indicative of physical changes, not a cause of such changes.

This conception of the relations of states of consciousness with molecular changes in the brain— of *psychoses* with *neuroses*—does not prevent us from ascribing free will to brutes. For an agent is free when there is nothing to prevent him from doing that which he desires to do. If a greyhound chases a hare, he is a free agent, because his action is in entire accordance with his strong desire to catch the hare ; while so long as he is held back by the leash he is not free, being prevented by external force from following his inclination. And the ascription of freedom to the greyhound under the former circumstances is by no means inconsistent with the other aspect of the facts of the case—that he is a machine impelled to the chase, and caused, at the same time, to have the desire to catch the game by the impression which the rays of light proceeding from the hare make upon his eyes, and through them upon his brain.

Much ingenious argument has at various times been bestowed upon the question : How is it possible to imagine that volition, which is a state of consciousness, and, as such, has not the slightest community of nature with matter in motion, can act upon the moving matter of which the body is composed, as it is assumed to do in voluntary acts ? But if, as is here suggested, the voluntary acts of brutes—or, in other words, the acts which they desire to perform—are as purely mechanical as the rest of their actions, and are simply accompanied by the state of consciousness called volition, the inquiry, so far as they are concerned, becomes superfluous. Their volitions do not enter into the chain of causation of their actions at all.

The hypothesis that brutes are conscious automata is perfectly consistent with any view that may be held respecting the often discussed and curious question whether they have souls or not ; and, if they have souls, whether those souls are immortal or not. It is obviously harmonious with the most literal adherence to the text of Scripture concerning " the beast that perisheth "; but it is not inconsistent with the amiable conviction ascribed by Pope to his " untutored savage," that when he passes to the happy hunting-grounds in the sky, " his faithful dog shall bear him company." If the brutes have consciousness and no souls, then it is clear that, in them, consciousness is a direct function of material changes; while, if they possess immaterial subjects of consciousness, or souls, then, as consciousness is brought into existence only as the consequence of molecular motion of the brain, it follows that it is an indirect product of material changes. The soul stands related to the body as the bell of a clock to the works, and consciousness answers to the sound which the bell gives out when it is struck.

Thus far I have strictly confined myself to the problem with which I proposed to deal at starting —the automatism of brutes. The question is, I believe, a perfectly open one, and I feel happy in running no risk of either Papal or Presbyterian condemnation for the views which I have ventured to put forward. And there are so very few interesting questions which one is, at present, allowed to

think out scientifically—to go as far as reason
leads, and stop where evidence comes to an end—
without speedily being deafened by the tattoo of
"the drum ecclesiastic"—that I have luxuriated
in my rare freedom, and would now willingly
bring this disquisition to an end if I could hope
that other people would go no farther. Unfortunately, past experience debars me from entertaining any such hope, even if

> " . . . . that drum's discordant sound
> Parading round and round and round,"

were not, at present, as audible to me as it was
to the mild poet who ventured to express his
hatred of drums in general, in that well-known
couplet.

It will be said, that I mean that the conclusions
deduced from the study of the brutes are applicable
to man, and that the logical consequences of such
application are fatalism, materialism, and atheism
—whereupon the drums will beat the *pas de
charge*.

One does not do battle with drummers; but I
venture to offer a few remarks for the calm consideration of thoughtful persons, untrammelled by
foregone conclusions, unpledged to shore-up totter-
ing dogmas, and anxious only to know the true
bearings of the case.

It is quite true that, to the best of my judgment, the argumentation which applies to brutes

holds equally good of men; and, therefore, that all states of consciousness in us, as in them, are immediately caused by molecular changes of the brain-substance. It seems to me that in men, as in brutes, there is no proof that any state of consciousness is the cause of change in the motion of the matter of the organism. If these positions are well based, it follows that our mental conditions are simply the symbols in consciousness of the changes which takes place automatically in the organism; and that, to take an extreme illustration, the feeling we call volition is not the cause of a voluntary act, but the symbol of that state of the brain which is the immediate cause of that act. We are conscious automata, endowed with free will in the only intelligible sense of that much-abused term—inasmuch as in many respects we are able to do as we like—but none the less parts of the great series of causes and effects which, in unbroken continuity, composes that which is, and has been, and shall be—the sum of existence.

As to the logical consequences of this conviction of mine, I may be permitted to remark that logical consequences are the scarecrows of fools and the beacons of wise men. The only question which any wise man can ask himself, and which any honest man will ask himself, is whether a doctrine is true or false. Consequences will take care of themselves; at most their importance can only justify us in testing with extra care the reasoning process from which they result.

So that if the view I have taken did really and logically lead to fatalism, materialism, and atheism, I should profess myself a fatalist, materialist, and atheist; and I should look upon those who, while they believed in my honesty of purpose and intellectual competency, should raise a hue and cry against me, as people who by their own admission preferred lying to truth, and whose opinions therefore were unworthy of the smallest attention.

But, as I have endeavoured to explain on other occasions, I really have no claim to rank myself among fatalistic, materialistic, or atheistic philosophers. Not among fatalists, for I take the conception of necessity to have a logical, and not a physical foundation; not among materialists, for I am utterly incapable of conceiving the existence of matter if there is no mind in which to picture that existence; not among atheists, for the problem of the ultimate cause of existence is one which seems to me to be hopelessly out of reach of my poor powers. Of all the senseless babble I have ever had occasion to read, the demonstrations of these philosophers who undertake to tell us all about the nature of God would be the worst, if they were not surpassed by the still greater absurdities of the philosophers who try to prove that there is no God.

And if this personal disclaimer should not be enough, let me further point out that a great many persons whose acuteness and learning will not be contested, and whose Christian piety, and, in some cases, strict orthodoxy, are above suspicion, have held more or less definitely the view that man is a conscious automaton.

It is held, for example, in substance, by the whole school of predestinarian theologians, typified by St. Augustine, Calvin, and Jonathan Edwards— the great work of the latter on the will showing in this, as in other cases, that the growth of physical science has introduced no new difficulties of principle into theological problems, but has merely given visible body, as it were, to those already existed.

Among philosophers, the pious Geulincx and the whole school of occasionalist Cartesians held this view; the orthodox Leibnitz invented the term "automate spirituel," and applied it to man ; the fervent Christian, Hartley, was one of the chief advocates and best expositors of the doctrine ; while another zealous apologist of Christianity in a sceptical age, and a contemporary of Hartley, Charles Bonnet, the Genevese naturalist, has embodied the doctrine in language of such precision and simplicity, that I will quote the little-known passage of his "Essai de Psychologie" at length :—

"Another Hypothesis concerning the Mechanism of Ideas [1]

"Philosophers accustomed to judge of things by that which they are in themselves, and not by their relation to received ideas, would not be shocked if they met with the proposition that the soul is a mere spectator of the movements of its body ; that the latter performs of itself all that series of actions which constitutes life : that it moves of itself : that it is the body alone which reproduces ideas, compares and arranges them ; which forms reasonings, imagines and executes plans of all kinds, etc. This hypothesis, though perhaps of an excessive boldness, nevertheless deserves some consideration.

"It is not to be denied that Supreme Power could create an automaton which should exactly imitate all the external and internal actions of man.

"I understand by external actions, all those movements which pass under our eyes : I term internal actions, all the motions which in the natural state cannot be observed because they take place in the interior of the body—such as the movements of digestion, circulation, sensation, etc. Moreover, I include in this category the movements which give rise to ideas, whatever be their nature.

"In the automaton which we are considering everything would be precisely determined. Everything would occur according to the rules of the most admirable mechanism : one state would succeed another state, one operation would lead to another operation, according to invariable laws ; motion would become alternately cause and effect, effect and cause ; reaction would answer to action, and reproduction to production.

"Constructed with definite relations to the activity of the beings which compose the world, the automaton would receive impressions from it, and, in faithful correspondence thereto, it would execute a corresponding series of motions.

"Indifferent towards any determination, it would yield

---

[1] *Essai de Psychologie*, chap. xxvii.

equally to all, if the first impressions did not, so to speak, wind up the machine and decide its operations and its course.

"The series of movements which this automaton could execute would distinguish it from all others formed on the same model, but which, not having been placed in similar circumstances, would not have experienced the same impressions, or would not have experienced them in the same order.

"The senses of the automaton, set in motion by the objects presented to it, would communicate their motion to the brain, the chief motor apparatus of the machine. This would put in action the muscles of the hands and feet, in virtue of their secret connection with the senses. These muscles, alternately contracted and dilated, would approximate or remove the automaton from the objects, in the relation which they would bear to the conservation or the destruction of the machine.

"The motions of perception and sensation which the objects would have impressed on the brain, would be preserved in it by the energy of its mechanism. They would become more vivid according to the actual condition of the automaton, considered in itself and relatively to the objects.

"Words being only the motions impressed on the organ of hearing and that of voice, the diversity of these movements, their combination, the order in which they would succeed one another, would represent judgments, reasoning, and all the operations of the mind.

"A close correspondence between the organs of the senses, either by the opening into one another of their nervous ramifications, or by interposed springs (*ressorts*), would establish such a connection in their working, that, on the occasion of the movements impressed on one of these organs, other movements would be excited, or would become more vivid in some of the other senses.

"Give the automaton a soul which contemplates its movements, which believes itself to be the author of them, which has different volitions on the occasion of the different movements, and you will on this hypothesis construct a man.

"But would this man be free? Can the feeling of our liberty, this feeling which is so clear and so distinct and so vivid as to persuade us that we are the authors of our actions, be conciliated with this hypothesis? If it removes the difficulty which attends the conception of the action of the soul on the body, on the other hand it leaves untouched that which meets us in endeavouring to conceive the action of the body on the soul."

But if Leibnitz, Jonathan Edwards, and Hartley —men who rank among the giants of the world of thought—could see no antagonism between the doctrine under discussion and Christian orthodoxy, is it not just possible that smaller folk may be wrong in making such a coil about "logical consequences"? And, seeing how large a share of this clamour is raised by the clergy of one denomination or another, may I say, in conclusion, that it really would be well if ecclesiastical persons would reflect that ordination, whatever deep-seated graces it may confer, has never been observed to be followed by any visible increase in the learning or the logic of its subject. Making a man a Bishop, or entrusting him with the office of ministering to even the largest of Presbyterian congregations, or setting him up to lecture to a Church congress, really does not in the smallest degree augment such title to respect as his opinions may intrinsically possess. And when such a man presumes on an authority which was conferred upon him for other purposes to sit in judgment upon matters his incompetence to deal with which is patent, it is permissible to ignore his sacerdotal pretensions, and to tell him, as one

17

would tell a mere common, unconsecrated, lay-
man : that it is not necessary for any man to
occupy himself with problems of this kind unless
he so choose ; life is filled full enough by the performance of its ordinary and obvious duties.   But
that, if a man elect to become a judge of these
grave questions ; still more, if he assume the
responsibility of attaching praise or blame to his
fellow-men for the conclusions at which they
arrive touching them, he will commit a sin more
grievous than most breaches of the Decalogue,
unless he avoid a lazy reliance upon the information that is gathered by prejudice and filtered
through passion, unless he go back to the prime
sources of knowledge—the facts of Nature, and
the thoughts of those wise men who for generations past have been her best interpreters.

VI

ADMINISTRATIVE NIHILISM

[1871]

To me, and, as I trust, to the great majority of those whom I address, the great attempt to educate the people of England which has just been set afoot, is one of the most satisfactory and hopeful events in our modern history. But it is impossible, even if it were desirable, to shut our eyes to the fact, that there is a minority, not inconsiderable in numbers, nor deficient in supporters of weight and authority, in whose judgment all this legislation is a step in the wrong direction, false in principle, and consequently sure to produce evil in practice.

The arguments employed by these objectors are of two kinds. The first is what I will venture to term the caste argument; for, if logically carried out, it would end in the separation of the people of this country into castes, as permanent and as sharply defined, if not as numerous, as those of India. It is maintained that the whole fabric of society will be destroyed if the poor, as well as the rich, are educated ; that anything like sound and good education will only make them discontented with their station and raise hopes which, in the great majority of cases, will be bitterly disappointed. It is said : There must be hewers of wood and drawers of water, scavengers and coalheavers, day labourers and domestic servants, or the work of society will come to a standstill. But, if you educate and refine everybody, nobody will be content to assume these functions, and all the world will want to be gentlemen and ladies.

One hears this argument most frequently from the representatives of the well-to-do middle class ; and, coming from them, it strikes me as peculiarly inconsistent, as the one thing they admire, strive after, and advise their own children to do, is to get on in the world, and, if possible, rise out of the class in which they were born into that above them. Society needs grocers and merchants as much as it needs coalheavers ; but if a merchant accumulates wealth and works his way to a baronetcy, or if the son of a greengrocer becomes a lord chancellor, or an archbishop, or, as a successful soldier, wins a peerage, all the world admires them ; and looks with pride upon the social system which renders such achievements possible.

Nobody suggests that there is anything wrong in their being discontented with their station; or that, in their cases society suffers by men of ability reaching the positions for which Nature has fitted them.

But there are better replies than those of the *tu quoque* sort to the caste agument. In the first place, it is not true that education, as such, unfits men for rough and laborious, or even disgusting, occupations. The life of a sailor is rougher and harder than that of nine landsmen out of ten, and yet, as every ship's captain knows, no sailor was ever the worse for possessing a trained intelligence. The life of a medical practitioner, especially in the country, is harder and more laborious than that of most artisans, and he is constantly obliged to do things, which, in point of pleasantness, cannot be ranked above scavengering—yet he always ought to be, and he frequently is, a highly educated man. In the second place, though it may be granted that the words of the catechism, which require a man to do his duty in the station to which it has pleased God to call him, give an admirable definition of our obligation to ourselves and to society; yet the question remains, how is any given person to find out what is the particular station to which it has pleased God to call him? A new-born infant does not come into the world labelled scavenger, shopkeeper, bishop or duke. One mass of red pulp is just like another to all outward appearance. And it is only by finding out what his faculties are good for, and seeking, not for the sake of gratifying a paltry vanity, but as the highest duty to himself and to his fellow-men, to put himself into the position in which they can attain their full development, that the man discovers his true station.   That which is to be lamented, I fancy, is not that society should do its utmost to help capacity to ascend from the lower strata to the higher, but that it has no machinery by which to facilitate the descent of incapacity from the higher strata to the lower.   In that noble romance, the "Republic" (which is now, thanks to the Master of Balliol, as intelligible to us all as if it had been written in our mother tongue), Plato makes Socrates say that he should like to inculcate upon the citizens of his ideal state just one "royal lie."

" 'Citizens,' we shall say to them in our tale—'You are brothers, yet God has framed you differently. Some of you have the power of command, and these He has composed of gold, wherefore also they have the greatest honour ; others of silver, to be auxiliaries ; others again, who are to be husbandmen and craftsmen, He has made of brass and iron ; and the species will generally be preserved in the children. But as you are of the same original family, a golden parent will sometimes have a silver son, or a silver parent a golden son. And God proclaims to the rulers, as a first principle, that before all they should watch over their offspring, and see what elements mingle with their nature ; for if the son of a golden or silver parent has an admixture of brass and iron, then nature orders a transposition of ranks, and the eye of the ruler must not be pitiful towards his child because he has to descend in the scale and become a husbandman or artisan ; just as there may be others sprung from the artisan class, who are raised to honour, and become guardians and auxiliaries. For an oracle says that when a man of brass and iron guards the State, it will then be destroyed.' " [1]

Time, whose tooth gnaws away everything else, is powerless against truth ; and the lapse of more than two thousand years has not weakened the force of these wise words. Nor is it necessary that, as Plato suggests, society should provide functionaries expressly charged with the perform- ance of the difficult duty of picking out the men of brass from those of silver and gold. Educate, and the latter will certainly rise to the top ; re- move all those artificial props by which the brass and iron folk are kept at the top, and, by a law as sure as that of gravitation, they will gradually sink to the bottom. We have all known noble lords who would have been coachmen, or gamekeepers, or billiard-markers, if they had not been kept afloat by our social corks ; we have all known men among the lowest ranks, of whom every one has said, " What might not that man have become, if he had only had a little education ? "

And who that attends, even in the most super- ficial way, to the conditions upon which the stability of modern society—and especially of a society like ours, in which recent legislation has placed sovereign authority in the hands of the

---

[1] *The Dialogues of Plato.* Translated into English, with Analysis and Introduction, by B. Jowett, M.A. Vol. ii. p. 243.

masses, whenever they are united enough to wield
their power—can doubt that every man of high
natural ability, who is both ignorant and miserable, is as great a danger to society as a rocket
without a stick is to the people who fire it?
Misery is a match that never goes out; genius, as
an explosive power, beats gunpowder hollow; and
if knowledge, which should give that power guidance, is wanting, the chances are not small that
the rocket will simply run a-muck among friends
and foes. What gives force to the socialistic
movement which is now stirring European society
to its depths, but a determination on the part of
the naturally able men among the proletariat, to
put an end, somehow or other, to the misery and
degradation in which a large proportion of their
fellows are steeped? The question, whether the
means by which they purpose to achieve this end
are adequate or not, is at this moment the most
important of all political questions—and it is
beside my present purpose to discuss it. All I
desire to point out is, that if the chance of the
controversy being decided calmly and rationally,
and not by passion and force, looks miserably
small to an impartial bystander, the reason is that
not one in ten thousand of those who constitute
the ultimate court of appeal, by which questions
of the utmost difficulty, as well as of the most
momentous gravity, will have to be decided,
is prepared by education to comprehend the

real nature of the suit brought before their tribunal.

Finally, as to the ladies and gentlemen question, all I can say is, would that every woman-child born into this world were trained to be a lady, and every man-child a gentleman! But then I do not use those much-abused words by way of distinguishing people who wear fine clothes, and live in fine houses, and talk aristocratic slang, from those who go about in fustian, and live in back slums, and talk gutter slang. Some inborn plebeian blindness, in fact, prevents me from understanding what advantage the former have over the latter. I have never even been able to understand why pigeon-shooting at Hurlingham should be refined and polite, while a rat-killing match in Whitechapel is low; or why "What a lark" should be coarse, when one hears "How awfully jolly" drop from the most refined lips twenty times in an evening.

Thoughtfulness for others, generosity, modesty, and self-respect, are the qualities which make a real gentleman, or lady, as distinguished from the veneered article which commonly goes by that name. I by no means wish to express any sentimental preference for Lazarus against Dives, but, on the face of the matter, one does not see why the practice of these virtues should be more difficult in one state of life than another; and any one who has had a wide experience among all sorts and conditions of men, will, I think, agree with me that they are as common in the lower ranks of life as in the higher.

Leaving the caste argument aside then, as inconsistent with the practice of those who employ it, as devoid of any justification in theory, and as utterly mischievous if its logical consequences were carried out, let us turn to the other class of objectors. To these opponents, the Education Act is only one of a number of pieces of legislation to which they object on principle ; and they include under like condemnation the Vaccination Act, the Contagious Diseases Act, and all other sanitary Acts ; all attempts on the part of the State to prevent adulteration, or to regulate injurious trades ; all legislative interference with anything that bears directly or indirectly on commerce, such as shipping, harbours, railways, roads, cab-fares, and the carriage of letters ; and all attempts to promote the spread of knowledge by the establishment of teaching bodies, examining bodies, libraries, or museums, or by the sending out of scientific expeditions ; all endeavours to advance art by the establishment of schools of design, or picture galleries ; or by spending money upon an architectural public building when a brick box would answer the purpose. According to their views, not a shilling of public money must be bestowed upon a public park or pleasure-ground ; not sixpence upon the relief of starvation,

or the cure of disease. Those who hold these
views support them by two lines of argument.
They enforce them deductively by arguing from
an assumed axiom, that the State has no right to
do anything but protect its subjects from aggression. The State is simply a policeman, and its
duty is neither more nor less than to prevent
robbery and murder and enforce contracts. It is
not to promote good, nor even to do anything to
prevent evil, except by the enforcement of
penalties upon those who have been guilty of
obvious and tangible assaults upon purses or
persons. And, according to this view, the proper
form of government is neither a monarchy, an
aristocracy, nor a democracy, but an *astynomocracy*,
or police government. On the other hand, these
views are supported *à posteriori*, by an induction
from observation, which professes to show that
whatever is done by a Government beyond these
negative limits, is not only sure to be done badly,
but to be done much worse than private enterprise
would have done the same thing.

I am by no means clear as to the truth of the
latter proposition. It is generally supported by
statements which prove clearly enough that the
State does a great many things very badly. But
this is really beside the question. The State
lives in a glass house; we see what it tries to do,
and all its failures, partial or total, are made the
most of. But private enterprise is sheltered under

good opaque bricks and mortar. The public rarely knows what it tries to do, and only hears of failures when they are gross and patent to all the world. Who is to say how private enterprise would come out if it tried its hand at State work ? Those who have had most experience of joint-stock companies and their management, will probably be least inclined to believe in the innate superiority of private enterprise over State management. If continental bureaucracy and centralisation be fraught with multitudinous evils, surely English beadleocracy and parochial ob-struction are not altogether lovely. If it be said that, as a matter of political experience, it is found to be for the best interests, including the healthy and free development, of a people, that the State should restrict itself to what is absolutely neces-sary, and should leave to the voluntary efforts of individuals as much as voluntary effort can be got to do, nothing can be more just. But, on the other hand, it seems to me that nothing can be less justifiable than the dogmatic assertion that State interference, beyond the limits of home and foreign police, must, under all circumstances, do harm.

Suppose, however, for the sake of argument, that we accept the proposition that the functions of the State may be properly summed up in the one great negative commandment,—" Thou shalt not allow any man to interfere with the liberty of any other man,"—I am unable to see that the logical consequence is any such restriction of the power of Government, as its supporters imply. If my next-door neighbour chooses to have his drains in such a state as to create a poisonous atmosphere, which I breathe at the risk of typhoid and diphtheria, he restricts my just freedom to live just as much as if he went about with a pistol, threatening my life; if he is to be allowed to let his children go unvaccinated, he might as well be allowed to leave strychnine lozenges about in the way of mine ; and if he brings them up untaught and untrained to earn their living, he is doing his best to restrict my freedom, by increasing the burden of taxation for the support of gaols and workhouses, which I have to pay.

The higher the state of civilisation, the more completely do the actions of one member of the social body influence all the rest, and the less possible is it for any one man to do a wrong thing without interfering, more or less, with the freedom of all his fellow-citizens. So that, even upon the narrowest view of the functions of the State, it must be admitted to have wider powers than the advocates of the police theory are disposed to admit.

It is urged, I am aware, that if the right of the State to step beyond the assigned limits is admitted at all, there is no stopping ; and that the principle which justifies the State in enforcing vaccination or education, will also justify it in prescribing my religious belief, or my mode of carrying on my trade or profession; in determining the number of courses I have for dinner. or the pattern of my waistcoat.

But surely the answer is obvious that, on similar grounds, the right of a man to eat when he is hungry might be disputed, because if you once allow that he may eat at all, there is no stopping him until he gorges himself, and suffers all the ills of a surfeit.   In practice, the man leaves off when reason tells him he has had enough; and, in a properly organised State, the Government, being nothing but the corporate reason of the community, will soon find out when State interference has been carried far enough.   And, so far as my acquaintance with those who carry on the business of Government goes, I must say that I find them far less eager to interfere with the people, than the people are to be interfered with.   And the reason is obvious.   The people are keenly sensible of particular evils, and, like a man suffering from pain, desire an immediate remedy.   The statesman, on the other hand, is like the physician, who knows that he can stop the pain at once by an opiate; but who also knows that the opiate may do more harm than good in the long run.   In three cases out of four the wisest thing he can do is to wait, and leave the case to nature.   But in the fourth case, in which the symptoms are unmistakable, and the cause of the disease distinctly known, prompt remedy saves a life. Is the fact that a wise physician will give as little medicine as possible any argument for his abstaining from giving any at all ?

But the argument may be met directly. It may be granted that the State, or corporate authority of the people, might with perfect propriety order my religion, or my waistcoat, if as good grounds could be assigned for such an order as for the command to educate my children. And this leads us to the question which lies at the root of the whole discussion—the question, namely, upon what foundation does the authority of the State rest, and how are the limits of that authority to be determined ?

One of the oldest and profoundest of English philosophers, Hobbes of Malmesbury writes thus:—

"The office of the sovereign, be it monarch or an assembly, consisteth in the end for which he was entrusted with the sovereign power, namely, the procuration of *the safety* of the people : to which he is obliged by the law of nature, and to render an account thereof to God, the author of that law, and to none but Him. But by safety, here, is not meant a bare preservation, but also all other contentments of life, which every man by lawful industry, without danger or hurt to the commonwealth, shall acquire to himself."

At first sight this may appear to be a statement of the police-theory of government, pure and simple ; but it is not so. For Hobbes goes on to say :—

"And this is intended should be done, not by care applied to individuals, further than their protection from injuries, when they shall complain; but by a general providence contained in public instruction both of doctrine and example; and in the making and executing of good laws to which individual persons may apply their own cases." [1]

To a witness of the civil war between Charles I. and the Parliament, it is not wonderful that the dissolution of the bonds of society which is involved in such strife should appear to be "the greatest evil that can happen in this life;" and all who have read the " Leviathan " know to what length Hobbes's anxiety for the preservation of the authority of the representative of the sovereign power, whatever its shape, leads him. But the justice of his conception of the duties of the sovereign power does not seem to me to be invalidated by his monstrous doctrines respecting the sacredness of that power.

To Hobbes, who lived during the break-up of the sovereign power by popular force, society appeared to be threatened by everything which weakened that power ; but, to John Locke, who witnessed the evils which flow from the attempt of the sovereign power to destroy the rights of the people by fraud and violence, the danger lay in the other direction.

The safety of the representative of the sovereign power itself is to Locke a matter of very small

[1] *Leviathan*, Molesworth's ed. p. 322.

moment, and he contemplates its abolition when it ceases to do its duty, and its replacement by another, as a matter of course. The great champion of the revolution of 1688 could do no less. Nor is it otherwise than natural that he should seek to limit, rather than to enlarge, the powers of the State, though in substance he entirely agrees with Hobbes's view of its duties :—

"But though men," says he, "when they enter into society, give up the equality, liberty, and executive power they had in the state of nature, into the hands of the society, to be so far disposed of by the Legislature as the good of society shall require ; yet it being only with an intention in every one the better to preserve himself, his liberty and property (for no rational creature can be supposed to change his condition with an intention to be worse), the power of the society, or legislation, constituted by them can never be supposed to extend further than the common good, but is obliged to secure every one's property by providing against those three defects above mentioned, that made the state of nature so unsafe and uneasy. And so, whoever has the legislative or supreme power of any commonwealth, is bound to govern by established standing laws, promulgated and known to the people, and not by extemporary decrees ; by indifferent and upright judges, who are to decide controversies by those laws : and to employ the force of the community at home only in the execution of such laws ; or abroad, to prevent or redress foreign injuries, and secure the community from inroads and invasion. And all this to be directed to no other end than the peace, safety, and public good of the people." [1]

Just as in the case of Hobbes, so in that of Locke, it may at first sight appear from this passage that the latter philosopher's views of the

[1] Locke's Essay, *Of Civil Government*, § 131.

18

functions of Government incline to the negative, rather than the positive, side. But a further study of Locke's writings will at once remove this misconception. In the famous " Letter concerning Toleration," Locke says :—

"The commonwealth seems to me to be a society of men constituted only for the procuring, preserving, and *advancing* their own civil interests.

"Civil interests I call life, liberty, health, and indolency of body ; and the possession of outward things, such as money, lands, houses, furniture, and the like.

" It is the duty of the civil magistrate, by the impartial execution of equal laws, to secure unto all the people in general, and to every one of his subjects in particular, the just possession of those things belonging to this life.

" . . . The whole jurisdiction of the magistrate reaches only to these civil concernments. . . . All civil power, right, and dominion, is bounded and confined to the only care of promoting these things."

Elsewhere in the same "Letter," Locke lays down the proposition that if the magistrate understand washing a child "to be profitable to the curing or preventing any disease that children are subject unto, and esteem the matter weighty enough to be taken care of by a law, in that case he may order it to be done."

Locke seems to differ most widely from Hobbes by his strong advocacy of a certain measure of toleration in religious matters. But the reason why the civil magistrate ought to leave religion alone is, according to Locke, simply this, that " true and saving religion consists in the inward persuasion of the mind." And since "such is the nature of the understanding that it cannot be compelled to the belief of anything by outward force," it is absurd to attempt to make men religious by compulsion. I cannot discover that Locke fathers the pet doctrine of modern Liberalism, that the toleration of error is a good thing in itself, and to be reckoned among the cardinal virtues ; on the contrary, in this very " Letter on Toleration" he states in the clearest language that " No opinion contrary to human society, or to those moral rules which are necessary to the preservation of civil society, are to be tolerated by the magistrate." And the practical corollary which he draws from this proposition is that there ought to be no toleration for either Papists or Atheists.

After Locke's time the negative view of the functions of Government gradually grew in strength, until it obtained systematic and able expression in Wilhelm von Humboldt's " Ideen," [1] the essence of which is the denial that the State has a right to be anything more than chief policeman. And, of late years, the belief in the efficacy of doing nothing, thus formulated, has acquired considerable popularity for several reasons. In the first place, men's speculative convictions have become less and less real ; their tolerance is large

---

[1] An English translation has been published under the title of *Essay on the Sphere and Duties of Government.*

because their belief is small; they know that the State had better leave things alone unless it has a clear knowledge about them; and, with reason, they suspect that the knowledge of the governing power may stand no higher than the very low watermark of their own.

In the second place, men have become largely absorbed in the mere accumulation of wealth; and as this is a matter in which the plainest and strongest form of self-interest is intensely concerned, science (in the shape of Political Economy) has readily demonstrated that self-interest may be safely left to find the best way of attaining its ends. Rapidity and certainty of intercourse between different countries, the enormous development of the powers of machinery, and general peace (however interrupted by brief periods of warfare), have changed the face of commerce as completely as modern artillery has changed that of war. The merchant found himself as much burdened by ancient protective measures as the soldier by his armour—and negative legislation has been of as much use to the one as the stripping off of breast-plates, greaves, and buff-coat to the other. But because the soldier is better without his armour it does not exactly follow that it is desirable that our defenders should strip themselves stark naked; and it is not more apparent why *laissez-faire*—great and beneficial as it may be in all that relates to the accumulation of wealth—

should be the one great commandment which the State is to obey in all other matters; and especially in those in which the justification of *laissez-faire*, namely, the keen insight given by the strong stimulus of direct personal interest, in matters clearly understood, is entirely absent.

Thirdly, to the indifference generated by the absence of fixed beliefs, and to the confidence in the efficacy of *laissez-faire*, apparently justified by experience of the value of that principle when applied to the pursuit of wealth, there must be added that nobler and better reason for a profound distrust of legislative interference, which animates Von Humboldt and shines forth in the pages of Mr. Mill's famous Essay on Liberty—I mean the just fear lest the end should be sacrificed to the means; lest freedom and variety should be drilled and disciplined out of human life in order that the great mill of the State should grind smoothly.

One of the profoundest of living English philosophers, who is at the same time the most thoroughgoing and consistent of the champions of astynomocracy, has devoted a very able and ingenious essay [1] to the drawing out of a comparison between the process by which men have advanced from the savage state to the highest civilisation, and that by which an animal passes from the condition of an almost shapeless and

---

[1] *The Social Organism:* Essays. Second Series.

structureless germ, to that in which it exhibits a
highly complicated structure and a corresponding
diversity of powers.   Mr. Spencer says with great
justice—

"That they gradually increase in mass ; that they become,
little by little, more complex ; that, at the same time, their
parts grow more mutually dependent ; and that they continue to
live and grow as wholes, while successive generations of their
units appear and disappear,—are broad peculiarities which
bodies politic display, in common with all living bodies, and in
which they and living bodies differ from everything else."

In a very striking passage of this essay Mr.
Spencer shows with what singular closeness a
parallel between the development of a nervous
system, which is the governing power of the body
in the series of animal organisms, and that of
government, in the series of social organisms, can
be drawn :—

"Strange as the assertion will be thought," says Mr. Spencer,
"our Houses of Parliament discharge in the social economy
functions that are, in sundry respects, comparable to those dis-
charged by the cerebral masses in a vertebrate animal. . . . .
The cerebrum co-ordinates the countless heterogeneous considerations which affect the present and future welfare of the individual as a whole ; and the Legislature co-ordinates the countless
heterogeneous considerations which affect the immediate and
remote welfare of the whole community.   We may describe the
office of the brain as that of *averaging* the interests of life,
physical, intellectual, moral, social ; and a good brain is one in
which the desires answering to their respective interests are so
balanced, that the conduct they jointly dictate sacrifices none of
them.   Similarly we may describe the office of Parliament as
that of *averaging* the interests of the various classes in a com-

munity ; and a good Parliament is one in which the parties
answering to these respective interests are so balanced, that their
united legislation concedes to each class as much as consists with
the claims of the rest."

All this appears to be very just. But if the
resemblances between the body physiological and
the body politic are any indication, not only of
what the latter is, and how it has become what it
is, but of what it ought to be, and what it is tending to become, I cannot but think that the real
force of the analogy is totally opposed to the
negative view of State function.

Suppose that, in accordance with this view,
each muscle were to maintain that the nervous
system had no right to interfere with its contraction, except to prevent it from hindering the
contraction of another muscle ; or each gland, that
it had a right to secrete, so long as its secretion
interfered with no other ; suppose every separate
cell left free to follow its own " interest," and
laissez-faire lord of all, what would become of
the body physiological ?

The fact is that the sovereign power of the
body thinks for the physiological organism, acts
for it, and rules the individual components with a
rod of iron. Even the blood-corpuscles can't hold
a public meeting without being accused of " con-
gestion "—and the brain, like other despots whom
we have known, calls out at once for the use of
sharp steel against them. As in Hobbes's

" Leviathan," the representative of the sovereign
authority in the living organism, though he
derives all his powers from the mass which he
rules, is above the law. The questioning of his
authority involves death, or that partial death
which we call paralysis. Hence, if the analogy of
the body politic with the body physiological
counts for anything, it seems to me to be in
favour of a much larger amount of governmental
interference than exists at present, or than I,
for one, at all desire to see. But, tempting as
the opportunity is, I am not disposed to build
up any argument in favour of my own case upon
this analogy, curious, interesting, and in many
respects close, as it is, for it takes no cognisance
of certain profound and essential differences
between the physiological and the political
bodies.

Much as the notion of a " social contract " has
been ridiculed, it nevertheless seems to be clear
enough, that all social organisation whatever
depends upon what is substantially a contract,
whether expressed or implied, between the members of the society. No society ever was, or ever
can be, really held together by force. It may seem
a paradox to say that a slaveholder does not make
his slaves work by force, but by agreement. And
yet it is true. There is a contract between the
two which, if it were written out, would run in
these terms :—" I undertake to feed, clothe, house,

and not to kill, flog, or otherwise maltreat you, Quashie, if you perform a certain amount of work." Quashie, seeing no better terms to be had, accepts the bargain, and goes to work accordingly. A highwayman who garrotes me, and then clears out my pockets, robs me by force in the strict sense of the words; but if he puts a pistol to my head and demands my money or my life, and I, preferring the latter, hand over my purse, we have virtually made a contract, and I perform one of the terms of that contract. If, nevertheless, the highwayman subsequently shoots me, everybody will see that, in addition to the crimes of murder and theft, he has been guilty of a breach of contract.

A despotic Government, therefore, though often a mere combination of slaveholding and highway robbery, nevertheless implies a contract between governor and governed, with voluntary submission on the part of the latter; and *à fortiori*, all other forms of government are in like case.

Now a contract between any two men implies a restriction of the freedom of each in certain particulars. The highwayman gives up his freedom to shoot me, on condition of my giving up my freedom to do as I like with my money : I give up my freedom to kill Quashie, on condition of Quashie's giving up his freedom to be idle. And the essence and foundation of every social organisation, whether simple or complex, is the

fact that each member of the society voluntarily
renounces his freedom in certain directions, in
return for the advantages which he expects from
association with the other members of that society.
Nor are constitutions, laws, or manners, in ultimate
analysis, anything but so many expressed or implied contracts between the members of a society
to do this, or abstain from that.

It appears to me that this feature constitutes
the difference between the social and the physiological organism. Among the higher physiological
organisms, there is none which is developed by
the conjunction of a number of primitively independent existences into a complex whole. The
process of social organisation appears to be comparable, not so much to the process of organic
development, as to the synthesis of the chemist,
by which independent elements are gradually built
up into complex aggregations—in which each
element retains an independent individuality,
though held in subordination to the whole. The
atoms of carbon and hydrogen, oxygen, nitrogen,
which enter into a complex molecule, do not lose
the powers originally inherent in them, when they
unite to form that molecule, the properties of
which express those forces of the whole aggregation
which are not neutralised and balanced by one
another. Each atom has given up something,
in order that the atomic society, or molecule, may
subsist. And as soon as any one or more of the

atoms thus associated resumes the freedom which
it has renounced, and follows some external attraction, the molecule is broken up, and all the peculiar
properties which depended upon its constitution
vanish.

Every society, great or small, resembles such
a complex molecule, in which the atoms are represented by men, possessed of all those multifarious attractions and repulsions which are manifested in their desires and volitions, the unlimited
power of satisfying which, we call freedom. The
social molecule exists in virtue of the renunciation of more or less of this freedom by every
individual. It is decomposed, when the attraction
of desire leads to the resumption of that freedom,
the suppression of which is essential to the existence of the social molecule. And the great
problem of that social chemistry we call politics,
is to discover what desires of mankind may be
gratified, and what must be suppressed, if the
highly complex compound, society, is to avoid
decomposition. That the gratification of some of
men's desires shall be renounced is essential to
order ; that the satisfaction of others shall be permitted is no less essential to progress ; and the
business of the sovereign authority—which is, or
ought to be, simply a delegation of the people
appointed to act for its good—appears to me
to be, not only to enforce the renunciation of
the anti-social desires, but, wherever it may be

necessary, to promote the satisfaction of those which are conducive to progress. ·

The great metaphysician, Immanuel Kant, who is at his greatest when he discusses questions which are not metaphysical, wrote, nearly a century ago, a wonderfully instructive essay entitled "A Conception of Universal History in relation to Universal Citizenship," [1] from which I will borrow a few pregnant sentences :—

"The means of which Nature has availed herself, in order to bring about the development of all the capacities of man, is the antagonism of those capacities to social organisation, so far as the latter does in the long run necessitate their definite correlation. By antagonism, I here mean the unsocial sociability of mankind—that is, the combination in them of an impulse to enter into society, with a thorough spirit of opposition which constantly threatens to break up this society. The ground of this lies in human nature. Man has an inclination to enter into society, because in that state he feels that he becomes more a man, or, in other words, that his natural faculties develop. But he has also a great tendency to isolate himself, because he is, at the same time, aware of the unsocial peculiarity of desiring to have everything his own way ; and thus, being conscious of an inclination to oppose others, he is naturally led to expect opposition from them.

"Now it is this opposition which awakens all the dormant powers of men, stimulates them to overcome their inclination to be idle, and, spurred by the love of honour, or power, or wealth, to make themselves a place among their fellows, whom they can neither do with, nor do without.

---

[1] *Idee zu einer allgemeinen Geschichte in weltbürgerlicher Absicht*, 1784. This paper has been translated by De Quincey, and attention has been recently drawn to its "signal merits" by the Editor of the *Fortnightly Review* in his Essay on Condorcet. (*Fortnightly Review*, No. xxxviii. N.S. pp. 136, 137.)

"Thus they make the first steps from brutishness towards culture, of which the social value of man is the measure. Thus all talents become gradually developed, taste is formed, and by continual enlightenment the foundations of a way of thinking are laid, which gradually changes the mere rude capacity of moral perception into determinate practical principles; and thus society, which is originated by a sort of pathological compulsion, becomes metamorphosed into a moral unity." (*Loc. cit.* p. 147.)

"All the culture and art which adorn humanity, the most refined social order, are produced by that unsociability which is compelled by its own existence to discipline itself, and so by enforced art to bring the seeds implanted by Nature into full flower." (*Loc. cit.* p. 148.)

In these passages, as in others of this remarkable tract, Kant anticipates the application of the "struggle for existence" to politics, and indicates the manner in which the evolution of society has resulted from the constant attempt of individuals to strain its bonds. If individuality has no play, society does not advance; if individuality breaks out of all bounds, society perishes.

But when men living in society once become aware that their welfare depends upon two opposing tendencies of equal importance—the one restraining, the other encouraging, individual freedom—the question "What are the functions of Government?" is translated into another— namely, "What ought we men, in our corporate capacity, to do, not only in the way of restraining that free individuality which is inconsistent with the existence of society, but in encouraging that

free individuality which is essential to the evolution of the social organisation? The formula
which truly defines the function of Government
must contain the solution of both the problems
involved, and not merely of one of them.

Locke has furnished us with such a formula,
in the noblest, and at the same time briefest,
statement of the purpose of Government known
to me:—

"THE END OF GOVERNMENT IS THE GOOD OF MANKIND." [1]

But the good of mankind is not a something
which is absolute and fixed for all men, whatever
their capacities or state of civilisation. Doubtless it is possible to imagine a true " Civitas Dei,"
in which every man's moral faculty shall be such
as leads him to control all those desires which
run counter to the good of mankind, and to
cherish only those which conduce to the welfare
of society; and in which every man's native intellect shall be sufficiently strong, and his culture
sufficiently extensive, to enable him to know
what he ought to do and to seek after. And,
in that blessed State, police will be as much a
superfluity as every other kind of government.

But the eye of man has not beheld that State,
and is not likely to behold it for some time to

---

[1] *Of Civil Government*, § 229.

come. What we do see, in fact, is that States are made up of a considerable number of the ignorant and foolish, a small proportion of genuine knaves, and a sprinkling of capable and honest men, by whose efforts the former are kept in a reasonable state of guidance, and the latter of repression. And, such being the case, I do not see how any limit whatever can be laid down as to the extent to which, under some circumstances, the action of Government may be rightfully carried.

Was our own Government wrong in suppressing Thuggee in India? If not, would it be wrong in putting down any enthusiast who attempted to set up the worship of Astarte in the Haymarket? Has the State no right to put a stop to gross and open violations of common decency? And if the State has, as I believe it has, a perfect right to do all these things, are we not bound to admit, with Locke, that it may have a right to interfere with "Popery" and "Atheism," if it be really true that the practical consequences of such beliefs can be proved to be injurious to civil society? The question where to draw the line between those things with which the State ought, and those with which it ought not, to interfere, then, is one which must be left to be decided separately for each individual case. The difficulty which meets the statesman is the same as that which meets us all in individual life, in which our abstract rights are generally clear enough, though it is frequently extremely hard to say at what point it is wise to cease our attempts to enforce them.

The notion that the social body should be organised in such a manner as to advance the welfare of its members, is as old as political thought; and the schemes of Plato, More, Robert Owen, St. Simon, Comte, and the modern socialists, bear witness that, in every age, men whose capacity is of no mean order, and whose desire to benefit their fellows has rarely been excelled, have been strongly, nay, enthusiastically, convinced that Government may attain its end— the good of the people—by some more effectual process than the very simple and easy one of putting its hands in its pockets, and letting them alone.

It may be, that all the schemes of social organisation which have hitherto been propounded are impracticable follies. But if this be so the fact proves, not that the idea which underlies them is worthless, but only that the science of politics is in a very rudimentary and imperfect state. Politics, as a science, is not older than astronomy; but though the subject-matter of the latter is vastly less complex than that of the former, the theory of the moon's motions is not quite settled yet.

Perhaps it may help us a little way towards getting clearer notions of what the State may and

what it may not do, if, assuming the truth of
Locke's maxim that "The end of Government is
the good of mankind," we consider a little what
the good of mankind is.

I take it that the good of mankind means the
attainment, by every man, of all the happiness
which he can enjoy without diminishing the
happiness of his fellow men.[1]

If we inquire what kinds of happiness come
under this definition, we find those derived from
the sense of security or peace; from wealth, or
commodity, obtained by commerce; from Art—
whether it be architecture, sculpture, painting,
music, or literature; from knowledge, or science;
and, finally, from sympathy, or friendship. No
man is injured, but the contrary, by peace.
No man is any the worse off because another
acquires wealth by trade, or by the exercise of
a profession; on the contrary, he cannot have
acquired his wealth, except by benefiting others
to the full extent of what they considered to be
its value; and his wealth is no more than fairy
gold if he does not go on benefiting others in

---

[1] "Hic est itaque finis ad quem tendo, talem scilicet Naturam
acquirere, et ut multi mecum eam acquirant, conari hoc est de
mea felicitate etiam operam dare, ut alii multi idem atque ego
intelligant, ut eorum intellectus et cupiditas prorsus cum meo
intellectu et cupiditate conveniant: atque hoc fiat, necesse
est tantum de Natura intelligere, quantum sufficit ad talem
naturam acquirendam; deinde formare talem societatem qualis
est desideranda, ut quam plurimi quam facillime et secure
eo perveniant."—B. Spinoza, *De Intellectûs Emendatione Trac-
tatus.*

the same way. A thousand men may enjoy the pleasure derived from a picture, a symphony, or a poem, without lessening the happiness of the most devoted connoisseur. The investigation of Nature is an infinite pasture-ground, where all may graze, and where the more bite, the longer the grass grows, the sweeter is its flavour, and the more it nourishes. If I love a friend, it is no damage to me, but rather a pleasure, if all the world also love him and think of him as highly as I do.

It appears to be universally agreed, for the reasons already mentioned, that it is unnecessary and undesirable for the State to attempt to promote the acquisition of wealth by any direct interference with commerce. But there is no such agreement as to the further question whether the State may not promote the acquisition of wealth by indirect means. For example, may the State make a road, or build a harbour, when it is quite clear that by so doing it will open up a productive district, and thereby add enormously to the total wealth of the community? And if so, may the State, acting for the general good, take charge of the means of communication between its members, or of the postal and telegraph services? I have not yet met with any valid argument against the propriety of the State doing what our Government does in this matter; except the assumption, which remains to be proved, that Government will manage these things worse than private enterprise would do. Nor is there any agreement upon the still more important question whether the State ought, or ought not, to regulate the distribution of wealth. If it ought not, then all legislation which regulates inheritance—the Statute of Mortmain, and the like—is wrong in principle; and, when a rich man dies, we ought to return to the state of Nature, and have a scramble for his property. If, on the other hand, the authority of the State is legitimately employed in regulating these matters, then it is an open question, to be decided entirely by evidence as to what tends to the highest good of the people, whether we keep our present laws, or whether we modify them. At present the State protects men in the possession and enjoyment of their property, and defines what that property is. The justification for its so doing is that its action promotes the good of the people. If it can be clearly proved that the abolition of property would tend still more to promote the good of the people, the State will have the same justification for abolishing property that it now has for maintaining it.

Again, I suppose it is universally agreed that it would be useless and absurd for the State to attempt to promote friendship and sympathy between man and man directly. But I see no reason why, if it be otherwise expedient, the State

may not do something towards that end indirectly.
For example, I can conceive the existence of an
Established Church which should be a blessing
to the community.   A Church in which, week by
week, services should be devoted, not to the itera-
tion of abstract propositions in theology, but to
the setting before men's minds of an ideal of true,
just, and pure living ; a place in which those who
are weary of the burden of daily cares, should find
a moment's rest in the contemplation of the higher
life which is possible for all, though attained by so
few ; a place in which the man of strife and of
business should have time to think how small,
after all, are the rewards he covets compared with
peace and charity.   Depend upon it, if such a
Church existed, no one would seek to dis-
establish it.

Whatever the State may not do, however, it is
universally agreed that it may take charge of the
maintenance of internal and external peace.   Even
the strongest advocate of administrative nihilism
admits that Government may prevent aggression
of one man on another.   But this implies the
maintenance of an army and navy, as much as of a
body of police ; it implies a diplomatic as well as
a detective force ; and it implies, further, that the
State, as a corporate whole, shall have distinct
and definite views as to its wants, powers, and
obligations.

For independent States stand in the same

relation to one another as men in a state of nature, or unlimited freedom. Each endeavours to get all it can, until the inconvenience of the state of war suggests either the formation of those express contracts we call treaties, or mutual consent to those implied contracts which are expressed by international law. The moral rights of a State rest upon the same basis as those of an individual. If any number of States agree to observe a common set of international laws, they have, in fact, set up a sovereign authority or supra-national government, the end of which, like that of all governments, is the good of mankind; and the possession of as much freedom by each State, as is consistent with the attainment of that end. But there is this difference : that the government thus set up over nations is ideal, and has no concrete representative of the sovereign power ; whence the only way of settling any dispute finally is to fight it out. Thus the supra-national society is continually in danger of returning to the state of nature, in which contracts are void ; and the possibility of this contingency justifies a government in restricting the liberty of its subjects in many ways that would otherwise be unjustifiable.

Finally, with respect to the advancement of science and art. I have never yet had the good fortune to hear any valid reason alleged why that corporation of individuals we call the State may not do what voluntary effort fails in doing, either from want of intelligence or lack of will. And here it cannot be alleged that the action of the State is always hurtful. On the contrary, in every country in Europe, universities, public libraries, picture galleries, museums, and laboratories, have been established by the State, and have done infinite service to the intellectual and moral progress and the refinement of mankind.

A few days ago I received from one of the most eminent members of the Institut of France a pamphlet entitled " Pourquoi la France n'a pas trouvé d'hommes supérieurs au moment du péril." The writer, M. Pasteur, has no doubt that the cause of the astounding collapse of his countrymen is to be sought in the miserable neglect of the higher branches of culture, which has been one of the many disgraces of the Second Empire, if not of its predecessors.

"Au point où nous sommes arrivés de ce qu'on appelle la *civilisation moderne*, la culture des sciences dans leur expression la plus élevée est peut-être plus nécessaire encore à l'état moral d'une nation qu'à sa prospérité matérielle.

"Les grandes découvertes, les méditations de la pensée dans les arts, dans les sciences et dans les lettres, en un mot les travaux désintéressés de l'esprit dans tous les genres, les centres d'enseignement propres à les faire connaître, introduisent dans le corps social tout entier l'esprit philosophique ou scientifique, cet esprit de discernement qui soumet tout à une raison sévère, condamne l'ignorance, dissipe les préjugés et les erreurs. Ils élèvent le niveau intellectuel, le sentiment moral ; par eux, l'idée divine elle-même se répand et s'exalte. . . . Si, au moment du péril suprême, la France n'a pas trouvé des hommes supérieurs pour mettre en œuvre ses ressources et

le courage de ses enfants, il faut l'attribuer, j'en ai la conviction, à ce que la France s'est désintéressée, depuis un demi-siècle,
des grands travaux de la pensée, particulièrement dans les
sciences exactes."

Individually, I have no love for academies on
the continental model, and still less for the system
of decorating men of distinction in science, letters,
or art, with orders and titles, or enriching them
with sinecures. What men of science want is only
a fair day's wages for more than a fair day's work;
and most of us, I suspect, would be well content if,
for our days and nights of unremitting toil, we
could secure the pay which a first-class Treasury
clerk earns without any obviously trying strain
upon his faculties. The sole order of nobility
which, in my judgment, becomes a philosopher, is
that rank which he holds in the estimation of his
fellow-workers, who are the only competent judges
in such matters. Newton and Cuvier lowered
themselves when the one accepted an idle knight-
hood, and the other became a baron of the empire.
The great men who went to their graves as
Michael Faraday and George Grote seem to
me to have understood the dignity of knowledge
better when they declined all such meretricious
trappings.

But it is one thing for the State to appeal to
the vanity and ambition which are to be found in
philosophical as in other breasts, and another to
offer men who desire to do the hardest of work for

the most modest of tangible rewards, the means of making themselves useful to their age and generation. And this is just what the State does when it founds a public library or museum, or provides the means of scientific research by such grants of money as that administered by the Royal Society.

It is one thing, again, for the State to take all the higher education of the nation into its own hands; it is another to stimulate and to aid, while they are yet young and weak, local efforts to the same end. The Midland Institute, Owens College in Manchester, the newly-instituted Science College in Newcastle, are all noble products of local energy and munificence. But the good they are doing is not local—the commonwealth, to its uttermost limits, shares in the benefits they confer; and I am at a loss to understand upon what principle of equity the State, which admits the principle of payment on results, refuses to give a fair equivalent for these benefits; or on what principle of justice the State, which admits the obligation of sharing the duty of primary education with a locality, denies the existence of that obligation when the higher education is in question.

To sum up: If the positive advancement of the peace, wealth, and the intellectual and moral development of its members, are objects which the Government, as the representative of the corporate authority of society, may justly strive

after, in fulfilment of its end—the good of mankind; then it is clear that the Government may
undertake to educate the people.   For education
promotes peace by teaching men the realities of
life and the obligations which are involved in
the very existence of society; it promotes intellectual development, not only by training the
individual intellect, but by sifting out from the
masses of ordinary or inferior capacities, those
who are competent to increase the general welfare by occupying higher positions; and, lastly,
it promotes morality and refinement, by teaching
men to discipline themselves, and by leading
them to see that the highest, as it is the only
permanent, content is to be attained, not by
grovelling in the rank and steaming valleys of
sense, but by continual striving towards those
high peaks, where, resting in eternal calm, reason
discerns the undefined but bright ideal of the
highest Good—" a cloud by day, a pillar of fire
by night."

VII

ON THE
NATURAL INEQUALITY OF MEN

[1890]

THE political speculations set forth in Rousseau's "Discours sur l'origine de l'inégalité parmi les hommes," and in the more noted essay, "Du Contrat Social," which were published, the former in 1754 and the latter eight years later, are, for the most part, if not wholly, founded upon conceptions with the origination of which he had nothing to do. The political, like the religious, revolutionary intellectual movement of the eighteenth century in France came from England. Hobbes, primarily, and Locke, secondarily (Rousseau was acquainted with the writings of both), supplied every notion of fundamental importance which is to be found in the works which I have mentioned. But the skill of a master of the literary art and the fervour of a prophet combined to embellish and intensify the new presentation of old speculations; which had the further good fortune to address itself to a public as ripe and ready as Balak himself to accept the revelations of any seer whose prophecies were to its mind.

Missionaries, whether of philosophy or of religion, rarely make rapid way, unless their preachings fall in with the prepossessions of the multitude of shallow thinkers, or can be made to serve as a stalking-horse for the promotion of the practical aims of the still larger multitude, who do not profess to think much, but are quite certain they want a great deal. Rousseau's writings are so admirably adapted to touch both these classes that the effect they produced, especially in France, is easily intelligible. For, in the middle of the eighteenth century, French society (not perhaps so different as may be imagined from other societies before and since) presented two large groups of people who troubled themselves about politics—in any sense other than that of personal or party intrigue. There was an upper stratum of luxurious idlers, jealously excluded from political action and consequently ignorant of practical affairs, with no solid knowledge or firm principles of any sort; but, on the other hand, open-minded to every novelty which could be apprehended without too much trouble, and exquisitely appreciative of close deductive reasoning and clear exposition. Such a public naturally welcomed Rousseau's brilliant developments of plausible first principles by the help of that *à priori* method which saves so much troublesome investigation.[1] It just suited the "philosophes," male and female, interchanging their airy epigrams in salons, which had about as much likeness to the Academy or to the Stoa, as the "philosophes" had to the philosophers of antiquity.

I do not forget the existence of men of the type of Montesquieu or D'Argenson in the France of the eighteenth century, when I take this as a fair representation of the enlightened public of that day. The unenlightened public, on the other hand, the people who were morally and physically debased by sheer hunger; or those, not so far dulled or infuriated by absolute want, who yet were maddened by the wrongs of every description inflicted upon them by a political system, which so far as its proper object, the welfare of the

[1] In his famous work on *Ancient Law* the late Sir Henry Maine has remarked, with great justice, that Rousseau's philosophy "still possesses singular fascination for the looser thinkers of every country;" that "it helped most powerfully to bring about the grosser disappointments of which the first French Revolution was fertile," and that "it gave birth, or intense stimulus, to the vices of mental habit all but universal at the time, disdain of positive law, impatience of experience, and the preference of *à priori* to all other reasoning" (pp. 89-92). I shall often have to quote *Ancient Law*. The first edition of this admirable book was published in 1861, but now, after twenty-nine years of growing influence on thoughtful men, it seems to be forgotten, or wilfully ignored, by the ruck of political speculators. It is enough to make one despair of the future that Demos and the Bourbons seem to be much alike in their want of capacity for either learning or forgetting.

people, was concerned was effete and powerless; the subjects of a government smitten with paralysis for everything but the working of iniquity and the generation of scandals; these naturally hailed with rapture the appearance of the teacher who clothed passion in the garb of philosophy; and preached the sweeping away of injustice by the perpetration of further injustice, as if it were nothing but the conversion of sound theory into practice.

It is true that any one who has looked below the surface [1] will hardly be disposed to join in the cry which is so often raised against the "philosophes" that their "infidel and levelling" principles brought about the French Revolution. People, with political eyes in their heads, like the Marquis d'Argenson, saw that the Revolution was inevitable before Rousseau wrote a line. In truth, the Bull "Unigenitus," the interested restiveness of the Parliaments and the extravagances and profligacy of the Court had a great deal more influence in generating the catastrophe than all the "philosophes" that ever put pen to paper. But, undoubtedly, Rousseau's extremely attractive and

---

[1] Those who desire to do so with ease and pleasure should read M. Rocquain's *L'Esprit révolutionnaire en France avant la Révolution.* It is really a luminous book, which ought to be translated for the benefit of our rising public men, who, having had the advantage of a public school education, are so often unable to read French with comfort. For deeper students there is, of course, the great work of M. Taine, *Les Origines de la France contemporaine.* [An excellent condensed English version of M. Rocquain's book, by Miss J. D Hunting, was published in 1891.]

widely read writings did a great deal to give a colour of rationality to those principles of '89 [1] which, even after the lapse of a century, are considered by a good many people to be the Magna Charta of the human race. "Liberty, Equality, and Fraternity," is still the war-cry of those, and they are many, who think, with Rousseau, that human sufferings must needs be the consequence of the artificial arrangements of society and can all be alleviated or removed by political changes.

The intellectual impulse which may thus be fairly enough connected with the name of the Genevese dreamer has by no means spent itself in the century and a half which has elapsed since it was given. On the contrary, after a period of comparative obscurity (at least outside France), Rousseauism has gradually come to the front again, and at present promises to exert once more a very grave influence on practical life. The two essays to which I have referred are, to all appearance, very little known to the present generation of those who have followed in Rousseau's track. None the less is it true that his teachings, filtered

[1] Sir H. Maine observes that the "strictly juridical axiom" of the lawyers of the Antonine era ("omnes homines naturâ æquales sunt"), after passing through the hands of Rousseau, and being adopted by the founders of the Constitution of the United States, returned to France endowed with vastly greater energy and dignity, and that "of all 'the principles of 1789' it is the one which has been least strenuously assailed, which has most thoroughly leavened modern opinion, and which promises to modify most deeply the constitution of societies, and the politics of States" (*Ancient Law*. p. 96)

through innumerable channels and passing under other names, are still regarded as the foundations of political science by the existing representatives of the classes who were so much attracted by them when they were put forth. My friend, Mr. John Morley, who probably knows more about Rousseau and his school than anybody else,[1] must have been entertained (so far as amusement is possible to the subject of the process of "heckling") when Rousseau's *plats*, the indigestibility of which he exposed so many years ago, were set before him as a wholesome British dish; the situation had a certain piquancy, which no one would appreciate more keenly.

I happened to be very much occupied upon subjects of a totally different character, and had no mind to leave them, when the narrative of this occurrence and some letters to which it gave rise, appeared in the "Times." But I have very long entertained the conviction that the revived Rousseauism of our day is working sad mischief, leading astray those who have not the time, even when they possess the ability, to go to the root of the superficially plausible doctrines which are disseminated among them. And I thought it was

---

[1] If I had not reason to think that Mr. Morley's *Rousseau*, and Sir Henry Maine's *Ancient Law*, especially the admirable chapters III. and IV., must be unknown to many political writers and speakers, and *à fortiori* to the general public, there would be no excuse for the present essay, which simply restates the case which they have so exhaustively treated.

my duty to see whether some thirty years' training
in the art of making difficult questions intelligible
to audiences without much learning, but with that
abundance of keen practical sense which characterises English workmen of the better class, would
enable me to do something towards the counter-
action of the fallacious guidance which is offered
to them. Perhaps I may be permitted to add
that the subject was by no means new to me.
Very curious cases of communal organisation and
difficult questions involving the whole subject of
the rights of property come before those whose
duty it is to acquaint themselves with the condition
of either sea or freshwater fisheries, or with the
administration of Fishery Laws. For a number
of years it was my fate to discharge such duties
to the best of my ability ; and, in doing so, I was
brought face to face with the problem of land-
ownership and the difficulties which arise out of
the conflicting claims of commoners and owners in
severalty. And I had good reason to know that
mistaken theories on these subjects are very
liable to be translated into illegal actions. I cannot say whether the letters which I wrote in
any degree attained the object (of vastly greater
importance, to my mind, than any personal question) which I had in view. But I was quite
aware, whatever their other results, they would
probably involve me in disagreeable consequences ;
and, among the rest, in the necessity of proving a

variety of statements, which I could only adumbrate within the compass of the space that the "Times" could afford me, liberal as the editor showed himself to be in that respect. What I purpose to do in the course of the present essay is to make good these shortcomings ; to show what Rousseau's doctrines were ; and to inquire into their scientific value—with, I hope, that impartiality which it beseems us to exhibit in inquiries into ancient history. Having done this I propose to leave the application of the conclusions at which I arrive to the intelligence of my readers, as I shall thus escape collision with several of my respected contemporaries.[1]

I have indicated two sources from which our knowledge of Rousseau's system may be derived, and it is not worth while to go any further. But it is needful to observe that the dicta of the author of the "Contrat Social," published in 1762, are not un-

[1] From Mr. Herbert Spencer's letter in the *Times* of the 27th of November, 1889, I gather that he altogether repudiates the doctrines which I am about to criticise. I rejoice to hear it ; in the first place, because they thus lose the shelter of his high authority ; secondly, because, after this repudiation, anything I may say in the course of the following pages against Rousseauism cannot be disagreeable to him ; and, thirdly, because I desire to express my great regret that, in however good company, I should have lacked the intelligence to perceive that Mr. Spencer had previously repudiated the views attributed to him by the land socialists. May I take this opportunity of informing the many correspondents who usually favour me with comments (mostly adverse, I am sorry to say) on what I venture to write, that I have no other answer to give them but Pilate's : "What I have written I have written" ? I have no energy to waste on replies to irresponsible criticism.

frequently very hard—indeed I might say impossible—to reconcile with those of the author of the "Discours," which appeared eight years earlier; and that, if any one should maintain that the older essay was not meant to be taken seriously, or that it has been, in some respects, more or less set aside by the later, he might find strong grounds for his opinion. It is enough for me that the same *à priori* method and the same fallacious assumptions pervade both.

The thesis of the earlier work is that man, in the "state of nature," was a very excellent creature indeed, strong, healthy, good and contented; and that all the evils which have befallen him, such as feebleness, sickness, wickedness, and misery, result from his having forsaken the "state of nature" for the "state of civilisation." And the first step in this downward progress was the setting up of rights of several property. It might seem to a plain man that the argument here turns on a matter of fact: if it is not historically true that men were once in this "state of nature"—what becomes of it all? However, Rousseau tells us, in the preface to the "Discours," not only that the "state of nature" is something which no longer exists, but that "perhaps it never existed, and probably never will exist." Yet it is something "of which it is nevertheless necessary to have accurate notions in order to judge our present condition rightly." After making this singular statement, Rousseau goes on to observe: "Il faudrait même plus de philosophie qu'on ne pense à celui qui entreprendrait de déterminer exactement les précautions à prendre pour faire sur ce sujet de solides observations." And, certainly, the amount of philosophy required to base an argument on that which does not exist, has not existed, and, perhaps, never will exist, may well seem unattainable—at any rate, at first sight. Yet, apart from analogies which might be drawn from the mathematical sciences—where, for example, a straight line is a thing which has not existed, does not exist, and probably never will exist, and yet forms a good ground for reasoning; and the value of which I need not stop to discuss— I take it that Rousseau has a very comprehensible idea at the bottom of this troublesome statement. What I conceive him to mean is that it is possible to form an ideal conception of what ought to be the condition of mankind ;[1] and that, having done so, we are bound to judge the existing state of things by that ideal. That assumption puts us on the " high *priori* road " at once.

[1] Compare *Ancient Law* :—" The Law of Nature confused the Past and the Present. Logically, it implied a state of Nature which had once been regulated by Natural Law ; yet the juris-consults do not speak clearly or confidently of the existence of such a state " (p. 73). "There are some writers on the subject who attempt to evade the fundamental difficulty by contending that the code of Nature exists in the future and is the goal to which all civil laws are moving" (p. 74). The jurisconsults conceived of Natural Law " as a system which ought gradually to absorb Civil Laws" (p. 76). " Its functions were, in short, remedial, not revolutionary or anarchical. And this unfortun-ately is the exact point at which the modern view of a Law of Nature has often ceased to resemble the ancient " (p. 77).

I do not suppose that any one is inclined to doubt the usefulness of a political ideal as a goal towards which social conduct should strive, whether it can ever be completely realised or not ; any more than any one will doubt that it is useful to have a moral ideal towards which personal conduct should tend, even though one may never reach it. Certainly, I am the last person to question this, or to doubt that politics is as susceptible of treatment by scientific method as any other field of natural knowledge.[1] But it will be admitted that, great as are the advantages of having a political ideal, fashioned by an absolute rule of political conduct, it is perhaps better to do without one, rather than to adopt the first phantasm, bred of fallacious reasonings and born of the unscientific imagination, which presents itself. The benighted traveller, lost on a moor, who refuses to follow a man with a lantern is surely not to be commended. But suppose his hesitation arises from a well-grounded doubt as to whether the seeming luminary is anything but a will o' the wisp ? And, unless I fail egregiously in attaining

---

[1] In the course of the correspondence in the *Times* to which I have referred, I was earnestly exhorted to believe that the world of politics does not lie outside of the province of science. My impression is that I was trying to teach the public that great truth, which I had learned from Mill and Comte, thirty-five years ago ; when, if I mistake not, my well-meaning monitor was more occupied with peg-tops than with politics. See a lecture on the "Educational Value of the Natural History Sciences" delivered in 1854 (*Lay Sermons*, p. 97).

my purpose, those who read this paper to the end will, I think, have no doubt that the political lantern of Rousseauism is a mere corpse candle and will plunge those who follow it in the deepest of anarchic bogs.

There is another point which must be carefully borne in mind in any discussion of Rousseau's doctrines; and that is the meaning which he attaches to the word "inequality." A hundred and fifty years ago, as now, political and biological philosophers found they were natural allies.[1] Rousseau is not intelligible without Buffon, with whose earlier works he was evidently acquainted, and whose influence in the following passage is obvious :—

It is easy to see that we must seek the primary cause of the differences by which men are distinguished in these successive changes of the human constitution; since it is universally admitted that they are, naturally, as equal among themselves as were the animals of each species before various physical causes had produced, in some of them, the varieties which we observe. In fact, it is not conceivable that these first changes, by whatever means they were brought about, altered, at once and in the same way, all the individuals of a species; but some having become improved or deteriorated, and having acquired different qualities, good or bad, which were not inherent in their

---

[1] The publication of Buffon's *Histoire Naturelle* began in 1749. Thus Rousseau was indebted to the naturalists; on the other hand, in the case of the elder Darwin, who started what is now usually known as Lamarck's hypothesis, the naturalist was set speculating by the ideas of the philosopher Hartley, transmitted through Priestley. See *Zoonomia*, I. sect. xxxix. p. 483 (ed. 1796). I hope some day to deal at length with this curious fact in scientific history.

nature, the others remained longer in their original state; and such was the first source of inequality among men, which is more easy to prove thus, in a general way, than to assign exactly to its true causes.   (" Discours," Preface.)

In accordance with this conception of the origin of inequality among men, Rousseau distinguishes, at the outset of the "Discours," two kinds of inequality :—

the one which I term *natural*, or *physical*, because it is established by Nature, and which consists in the differences of age, health, bodily strength, and intellectual or spiritual qualities ; the other, which may be called *moral*, or *political*, because it depends on a sort of convention, and is established, or at least authorised, by the consent of mankind.   This last inequality consists in the different privileges which some enjoy, to the prejudice of others, as being richer, more honoured, more powerful than they, or by making themselves obeyed by others.

Of course the question readily suggests itself : Before drawing this sharp line of demarcation between natural and political inequality, might it not be as well to inquire whether they are not intimately connected, in such a manner that the latter is essentially a consequence of the former ? This question is indeed put by Rousseau himself. And, as the only answer he has to give is a piece of silly and insincere rhetoric about its being a question fit only for slaves to discuss in presence of their masters, we may fairly conclude that he knew well enough he dare not grapple with it. The only safe course for him was to go by on the other side and as far as the breadth of the road would permit; and, in the rest of his writings to play fast and loose with the two senses of inequality, as convenience might dictate.

With these preliminary remarks kept well in view, we may proceed to the discussion of those fundamental theses of the "Discourse" and of the "Social Contract" which Rousseau calls the "principes du droit politique." Rousseau defines his object thus :—

Je veux chercher si dans l'ordre civil il peut y avoir quelque règle d'administration légitime et sûre, en prenant les hommes tels qu'ils sont et les lois tels qu'elles peuvent être. Je tâcherai d'allier toujours dans cette recherche ce que le droit permet avec ce que l'intérêt prescrit, afin que la justice et l'utilité ne se trouvent point divisées.[1]

In other words, our philosopher propounds "sure," that is "absolute," principles which are, at once ethically and politically, sufficient rules of conduct, and that I understand to be the precise object of all who have followed in his track. It was said of the Genevese theorist, " Le

---

[1] *Contrat Social*, livre 1er. Compare Hobbes's dedication of *Human Nature* written in 1640 :—" They who have written of justice and policy in general, do all invade each other and themselves with contradictions. To reduce this doctrine to the rules and infallibility of reason there is no way, but, first, put such principles down for a foundation, as passion, not mistrusting, may not seek to displace ; and afterwards to build thereon the truth of cases in the law of Nature (which hitherto have been built in the air) by degrees, till the whole have been inexpugnable." However, it must be recollected that Hobbes does not start from *à priori* principles of ethics, but from the practical necessities of men in society.

genre humain avait perdu ses titres; Jean-Jacques les a retrouvés"; just as his intellectual progeny declare that the nation ought to "resume" the landed property of which it has, unfortunately, lost·the title-deeds.

We are now in a position to consider what the chief of these principles of the gospel according to Jean-Jacques are :—

1. All men are born free, politically equal, and good, and in the "state of nature" remain so; consequently it is their natural right to be free, equal, and (presumably, their duty to be) good.[1]

2. All men being equal by natural right, none can have any right to encroach on another's equal right. Hence no man can appropriate any part of the common means of subsistence—that is to say, the land or anything which the land produces —without the unanimous consent of all other men. Under any other circumstances, property is usurpation, or, in plain terms, robbery.[2]

3. Political rights, therefore, are based upon contract; the so-called right of conquest is no

[1] *Contrat Social*, v. pp. 98, 99. The references here given are to the volumes and pages of Mussay Pathay's edition (1826). *Discours, passim ;* see especially p. 268.

[2] *Discours*, pp. 257, 258–276. How many wild sermons have been preached on this text :—" Ignorez-vous qu'une multitude de vos frères périt ou souffre du besoin de ce que vous avez de trop, et qu'il vous fallait un consentement exprès et unanime du genre humain pour vous approprier sur la subsistance commune tout ce qui alloit audelà de la vôtre ?"

right, and property which has been acquired by force may rightly be taken away by force.[1]

I am bound to confess, at the outset, that, while quite open to conviction, I incline to think that the obvious practical consequences of these propositions are not likely to conduce to the welfare of society, and that they are certain to prove as injurious to the poor as to the rich. Due allowance must be made for the possible influence of such prejudice as may flow from this opinion upon my further conviction that, regarded from a purely theoretical and scientific point of view, they are so plainly and demonstrably false that, except for the gravity of their practical consequences, they would be ridiculous.

What is the meaning of the famous phrase that "all men are born free and equal," which gallicised Americans, who were as much "philosophes" as their inherited common sense and their practical acquaintance with men and with affairs would let them be, put forth as the foundation of the "Declaration of Independence"? I have seen a consid-

---

[1] *Discours*, pp. 276, 280 ; *Contrat*, chap. iii. :—"Telle fut ou dut être" (charming alternative !) "l'origine de la société et des lois, qui donnèrent de nouvelles entraves au foible et de nouvelles forces au riche, détruisirent sans retour la liberté naturelle, fixèrent pour jamais la loi de la propriété et de l'inégalité, d'une adroite usurpation firent un droit irrévocable, et, pour le profit de quelques ambitieux, assujettirent désormais tout le genre humain au travail, à la servitude et à la misère" (*Discours*, p. 278). Behold the quintessence of Rousseauism—method and results—with practical application, legible by the swiftest runner !

erable number of new-born infants. Without wish-
ing to speak of them with the least disrespect—a
thing no man can do, without, as the proverb says,
"fouling his own nest"—I fail to understand how
they can be affirmed to have any political qualities
at all. How can it be said that these poor little
mortals who have not even the capacity to kick
to any definite end, nor indeed to do anything but
vaguely squirm and squall, are equal politically,
except as all zeros may be said to be equal?
How can little creatures be said to be "free" of
whom not one would live for four and twenty
hours if it were not imprisoned by kindly hands
and coerced into applying its foolish wandering
mouth to the breast it could never find for itself?
How is the being whose brain is still too pulpy to
hold an idea of any description to be a moral agent
either good or bad? Surely it must be a joke,
and rather a cynical one too, to talk of the political status of a new-born child? But we may
carry our questions a step further. If it is mere
abracadabra to speak of men being born in a state
of political freedom and equality, thus fallaciously
confusing positive equality—that is to say, the
equality of powers—with the equality of im-
potences ; in what conceivable state of society is
it possible that men should not merely be born,
but pass through childhood and still remain free?
Has a child of fourteen been free to choose its
language and all the connotations with which

words became burdened in their use by generation after generation ? Has it been free to choose
the habits enforced by precept and more surely
driven home by example ? Has it been free to
invent its own standard of right and wrong ? Or
rather, has it not been as much held in bondage
by its surroundings and driven hither and thither
by the scourge of opinion, as a veritable slave,
although the fetters and the whip may be invisible and intangible ?

Surely, Aristotle was much nearer the truth in
this matter than Hobbes or Rousseau. And if
the predicate " born slave" would more nearly
agree with fact than " born free," what is to be
said about " born equal" ? Rousseau, like the
sentimental rhetorician that he was, and half, or
more than half, sham, as all sentimental rhetori-
cians are, sagaciously fought shy, as we have seen,
of the question of the influence of natural upon
political equality. But those of us who do not
care for sentiment and do care for truth may not
evade the consideration of that which is really the
key of the position. If Rousseau, instead of
letting his children go to the *enfants trouvés*, had
taken the trouble to discharge a father's duties
towards them, he would hardly have talked so
fast about men being born equal, even in a political sense. For, if that merely means that all
new-born children are political zeros—it is, as we
have seen, though true enough, nothing to the

purpose ; while, if it means that, in their potentiality of becoming factors in any social organisation—citizens in Rousseau's sense—all men are
born equal, it is probably the most astounding
falsity that ever was put forth by a political
speculator ; and that, as all students of political
speculation will agree, is saying a good deal for it.
In fact, nothing is more remarkable than the
wide inequality which children, even of the same
family, exhibit, as soon as the mental and moral
qualities begin to manifest themselves ; which is
earlier than most people fancy. Every family
spontaneously becomes a polity. Among the
children, there are some who continue to be " more
honoured and more powerful than the rest, and to
make themselves obeyed " (sometimes, indeed, by
their elders) in virtue of nothing but their moral
and mental qualities. Here, " political inequality "
visibly dogs the heels of " natural " inequality
The group of children becomes a political body, a
civitas, with its rights of property, and its practical distinctions of rank and power. And all
this comes about neither by force nor by fraud,
but as the necessary consequence of the innate
inequalities of capability.

Thus men are certainly not born free and equal
in natural qualities ; when they are born, the predicates " free " and " equal " in the political sense
are not applicable to them ; and as they develop
year by year, the differences in the political

potentialities with which they really are born,
become more and more obviously converted into
actual differences—the inequality of political
faculty shows itself to be a necessary consequence of the inequality of natural faculty. It
is probably true that the earliest men were
nomads. But among a body of naked wandering savages, though there may be no verbally
recognised distinctions of rank or office, superior
strength and cunning confer authority of a more
valid kind than that secured by Acts of Parliament; there may be no property in things, but
the witless man will be poverty-stricken in ideas,
the clever man will be a capitalist in that same
commodity, which in the long run buys all other
commodities; one will miss opportunities, the
other will make them; and, proclaim human
equality as loudly as you like, Witless will serve
his brother. So long as men are men and society
is society, human equality will be a dream; and
the assumption that it does exist is as untrue in
fact as it sets the mark of impracticability on every
theory of what ought to be, which starts from it.

And that last remark suggests that there is
another way of regarding Rousseau's speculations.
It may be pointed out that, after all, whatever
estimate we may form of him, the author of works
which have made such a noise in the world could
not have been a mere fool; and that, if, in their
plain and obvious sense, the doctrines which he

advanced are so easily upset, it is probable that he had in his mind something which is different from that sense.

I am a good deal disposed to think that this is the case. There is much to be said in favour of the view that Rousseau, having got hold of a plausible hypothesis, more or less unconsciously made up a clothing of imaginary facts to hide its real nakedness. He was not the first nor the last philosopher to perform this feat.

As soon as men began to think about political problems, it must have struck them that, if the main object of society was the welfare of its members (and until this became clear, political action could not have risen above the level of instinct [1]), there were all sorts of distinctions among men, and burdens laid upon them, which nowise contributed

[1] It is not to be forgotten that what we call rational grounds for our beliefs are often extremely irrational attempts to justify our instincts. I cannot doubt that human society existed before language or any ethical consciousness. Gregarious animals form polities, in which they act according to rules conducive to the welfare of the whole society, although, of course, it would be absurd to say that they obey laws in the juridical sense. The polities of the masterless dogs in Eastern cities are well known. And, in any street of an English town, one may observe a small dog chased by a bigger, who turns round the moment he has entered his own territory and defies the other; while, usually, after various manifestations of anger and contempt, the bigger withdraws. No doubt the small dog has had previous experience of the arrival of assistance under such circumstances, and the big one of the effects of sticks and stones and other odd missiles; no doubt, the associations thus engrained are the prime source of the practical acknowledgment of ownership on both sides. I suspect it has been very much the same among men.

to that end.   Even before the great leveller,
Rome, had actually thrown down innumerable
social and national party-walls, had absorbed all
other forms of citizenship into her own, and brought
the inhabitants of what was then known as the
world under one system of obligations—thoughtful
men were discovering that it was desirable, in the
interests of society, that all men should be as free
as possible, consistently with those interests ; and
that they should all be equally bound by the
ethical and legal obligations which are essential to
social existence.   It will be observed that this
conclusion is one which might be arrived at by
observation and induction from the phenomena of
past and present experience.   My belief is that it
is the conclusion which must be reached by those
means, when they are rightly employed—and
that, in point of fact, the doctrines of freedom and
equality, so far as they were preached by the
Stoics and others, would have had not the least
success, if they had not been so far approved by
experience and so far in harmony with human
instincts, that the Roman jurists found they could
work them up with effect into practical legislation.
For the à *priori* arguments of the philosophers
in the last century of the Republic, and the first
of the Empire, stand examination no better than
those of the philosophers in the centuries before
and after the French Revolution.   As is the
fashion of speculators, they scorned to remain on

the safe, if humble, ground of experience, and preferred to prophesy from the sublime cloudland of
the *à priori;* so that, busied with deduction from
their ideal "ought to be" they overlooked the "what
has been," the " what is," and the " what can be "

It is to them that we owe the idea of living
" according to nature " ; which begot the idea of
the " state of nature " ; which begot the notion
that the " state of nature " was a reality, and that,
once upon a time, " all men were free and equal "
—which again begot the theory, that society ought
to be reformed in such a manner as to bring back
these halcyon days of freedom and equality ; which
begot *laissez faire* and universal suffrage ; which
begot the theory so dear to young men of more
ambition than industry, that, while every other
trade, business, or profession requires theoretical
training and practical skill, and would go to the
dogs if those who carry them on were appointed
by the majority of votes of people who know
nothing about it and very little about them—the
management of the affairs of society will be perfectly successful, if only the people who may be
trusted to know nothing, will vote into office the
people who may be trusted to do nothing.

If this is the political ideal of the modern followers of Rousseau, I, for my part, object to strive
after it, or to do anything but oppose, to the
best of my ability, those who would fain drive us
that way. Freedom, used foolishly, and equality,

asserted in words, but every moment denied by the facts of nature, are things of which, as it seems to me, we have rather too much already. If I mistake not, one thing we need to learn is the necessity of limiting individual freedom for the general good ; and another, that, although decision by a majority of votes may be as good a rough-and-ready way as can be devised to get political questions settled, yet that, theoretically, the des-potism of a majority is as little justifiable and as dangerous as that of one man; and yet another, that voting power, as a means of giving effect to opinion, is more likely to prove a curse than a blessing to the voters, unless that opinion is the result of a sound judgment operating upon sound knowledge. Some experience of sea-life leads me to think that I should be very sorry to find myself on board a ship in which the voices of the cook and the loblolly boys counted for as much as those of the officers, upon a question of steering, or reefing topsails; or where the "great heart" of the crew was called upon to settle the ship's course. And there is no sea more dangerous than the ocean of practical politics—none in which there is more need of good pilotage and of a single, unfaltering purpose when the waves rise high.

The conclusion of the whole matter, then, would seem to be that the doctrine that all men are, in any sense, or have been, at any time, free and equal, is an utterly baseless fiction. Nor does the

21

proposition fare much better if we modify it, so as
to say that all men ought to be free and equal, so
long as the " ought " poses as a command of im-
mutable morality. For, assuredly, it is not intuitively certain " that all men ought to be free and
equal." Therefore, if it is to be justified at all *à
priori*, it must be educible from some proposition
which is intuitively certain ; and unfortunately
none is forthcoming. For the proposition that
men ought to be free to do what they please, so
long as they do not infringe on the equal rights of
other men, assumes that men have equal rights
and cannot be used to prove that assumption.
And if, instead of appealing to philosophy we
turn to revealed religion, I am not aware that
either Judaism or Christianity affirms the political
freedom or the political equality of men in Rousseau's sense. They affirm the equality of men
before God—but that is an equality either of
insignificance or of imperfection.

With the demonstration that men are not all
equal under whatever aspect they are contemplated,
and that the assumption that they ought to be considered equal has no sort of *à priori* foundation—
however much it may, in reference to positive law,
with due limitations, be justifiable by considerations
of practical expediency—the bottom of Rousseau's
argument, from *à priori* ethical assumptions to the
denial of the right of an individual to hold private
property, falls out. For Rousseau, with more

logical consistency than some of those who have
come after him, puts the land and its produce upon
the same footing. "Vous êtes perdus si vous
oubliez que les fruits sont à tous, et que la terre
n'est à personne," says he.[1]

From Rousseau's point of view (and, for the
present, I leave any other aside), this is, in fact,
the only rational conclusion from the premisses.
The attempt to draw a distinction between land,
as a limited commodity, and other things as unlimited, is an obvious fallacy. For, according to
him,[2] the total habitable surface of the earth is the
property of the whole human race in common.
Undoubtedly, the habitable and cultivable land
amounts to a definite number of square miles,
which, by no effort of human ingenuity, at present
known or suspected, can be sensibly increased beyond the area of that part of the globe which is not
covered by water; and therefore its quantity is
limited. But if the land is limited, so is the quantity of the trees that will grow on it; of the cattle
that can be pastured on it; of the crops that can
be raised from it; of the minerals that can be dug
from it; of the wind and of the water-power,
afforded by the limited streams which flow from
the limited heights. And, if the human race were
to go on increasing in number at its present rate,
a time would come when there would not be stand-

[1 Which may be Englished, in brief, "Crops are everybody's
and land is nobody's."]

   [2 As to Hobbes, but on different grounds.

ing ground for any more; if it were not that, long
before that time, they would have eaten up the
limited quantity of food-stuffs and died like the
locusts that have consumed everything eatable in
an oasis of the desert. The attempt to draw a
distinction between land as limited in quantity, in
the sense, I suppose, that it is something that cannot be imported—and other things as unlimited,
because they can be imported—has arisen from
the fact that Rousseau's modern followers entertain
the delusion that, consistently with their principles,
it is possible to suppose that a nation has right of
ownership in the land it occupies. If the island
of Great Britain is the property of the British nation, then, of course, it is true that Britons cannot
have more than somewhere about 90,000 square
miles of land, while the quantity of other things
they can import is (for the present, at any rate), practically, if not strictly, unlimited. But how is the
assumption that the Britons own Britain, to be re-
conciled with the great dictum of Rousseau,
that a man cannot rightfully appropriate any part
of this limited commodity, land, without the unanimous consent of all his fellow men? My strong
impression is that if a parti-coloured plébiscite of
Europeans, Chinese, Hindoos, Negroes, Red Indians,
Maoris, and all the other inhabitants of the terrestrial globe were to decree us to be usurpers, not a
soul would budge; and that, if it came to fighting,
Mr. Morley's late "hecklers" might be safely

depended upon to hold their native soil against all intruders, and in the teeth of the most absolute of ethical politicians, even though he should prove from Rousseau,

> "Exceedingly well
> That such conduct was quite atrocious."

Rousseau's first and second great doctrines having thus collapsed, what is to be said to the third ?

Of course, if there are no rights of property but those based on contract, conquest, that is to say, taking possession by force, of itself can confer no right. But, as the doctrine that there are no rights of property but those based on the consent of the whole human race—that is, that A. B. cannot own anything unless the whole of mankind formally signify their assent to his ownership—turns out to be more than doubtful in theory and decidedly inconvenient in practice, we may inquire if there is any better reason for the assertion that force can confer no right of ownership. Suppose that in the old seafaring days, a pirate attacked an East Indiaman—got soundly beaten and had to surrender. When the pirates had walked the plank or been hanged, had the captain and crew of the East Indiaman no right of property in the prize—I am not speaking of mere legal right, but ethically ? But if they had, what is the difference when nations attack one another; when there is no way out of their quarrel but the appeal to force, and the one that gets the better seizes more or less of the other's territory and demands it as the price of peace? In the latter case, in fact, we have a contract, a price paid for an article—to wit peace—delivered, and certain lands taken in exchange; and there can be no question that the buyer's title is based on contract. Even in the former alternative, I see little difference. When they declared war, the parties knew very well that they referred their case to the arbitrament of force; and if contracts are eternally valid, they are fully bound to abide by the decision of the arbitrator whom they have elected to obey. Therefore, even on Hobbes's or Rousseau's principles, it is not by any means clear to my mind that force, or rather the state of express or tacit contract which follows upon force, successfully applied, may not be plausibly considered to confer ownership.

But if the question is argued, as I think it ought to be, on empirical grounds—if the real question is not one of imagined à priori principle, but of practical expediency—of the conduct which conduces most to human welfare—then it appears to me that there is much to be said for the opinion that force effectually and thoroughly used, so as to render further opposition hopeless, establishes an ownership[1] which should be recog-

---

[1] Submission to the Revolution of 1688 by Jacobites could be advocated ethically on no other ground, though all sorts of pretexts were invented to disguise the fact.

nised as soon as possible. I am greatly disposed to think, that when ownership established by force has endured for many generations, and all sorts of contracts have been entered into on the faith of such ownership, the attempt to disturb it is very much to be deprecated on all grounds. For the welfare of society, as for that of individual men, it is surely essential that there should be a statute of limitations in respect of the consequences of wrong-doing. As there is nothing more fatal to nobility of personal character than the nursing of the feeling of revenge—nothing that more clearly indicates a barbarous state of society than the carrying on of a *vendetta,* generation after generation, so I take it to be a plain maxim of that political ethic which does not profess to have any greater authority than agreeableness to good feeling and good sense can confer, that the evil deeds of former generations—especially if they were in accordance with the practices of a less advanced civilisation, and had the sanction of a less refined morality—should, as speedily as possible, be forgotten and buried under better things.

" Musst immer thun wie neu geboren " is the best of all maxims for the guidance of the life of States, no less than of individuals. However, I express what I personally think, in all humility, in the face of the too patent fact, that there are persons of light and leading—with a political

authority to which I can make not the remotest
pretension, and with a weight of political responsibility which I rejoice to think can never rest on
my shoulders—who by no means share my opinion,
but who, on the contrary, deem it right to fan the
sparks of revenge which linger among the embers
of ancient discords ; and to stand between the dead
past and the living present, not with the healing
purpose of the Jewish leader, but rather to
intensify the plague of political strife, and hold
aloft the brazen image of the father's wrongs,
lest the children might perchance forget and for-
give.

However, the question whether the fact that
property in land was originally acquired by force
invalidates all subsequent dealings in that property
so completely, that no lapse of time, no formal
legalisation, no passing from hand to hand by free
contract through an endless series of owners, can
extinguish the right of the nation to take it away
by force from the latest proprietor, has rather an
academic than a practical interest, so long as the
evidence that landed ownership did so arise is
wanting. Potent an organon as the *à priori*
method may be, its employment in the region of
history has rarely been found to yield satisfactory
results ; and, in this particular case, the confident
assertions that land was originally held in common
by the whole nation, and that it has been con-

verted into severalty by force, as the outcome of
the military spirit rather than by the consent, or
contract, characteristic of industrialism, are singularly ill-founded.

Let us see what genuine history has to say to
these assertions. Perhaps it might have been
pardonable in Rousseau to propound such a statement as that the primitive landowner was either a
robber or a cheat ; but, in the course of the century
and a half which has elapsed since he wrote, and
especially in that of the last fifty years, an
immense amount of information on the subject of
ancient land-tenure has come to light; so that it
is no longer pardonable, in any one, to content
himself with Rousseau's ignorance. Even a superficial glance over the results of modern investigations into anthropology, archæology, ancient law
and ancient religion, suffices to show that there is
not a particle of evidence that men ever existed
in Rousseau's state of nature, and that there are
very strong reasons for thinking that they never
could have done so, and never will do so.

It is, at the least, highly probable that the
nomadic preceded any other social state ; and, as
the needs of a wandering hunter's or pastor's life
are far more simple than any other, it follows that
the inequalities of condition must be less obvious
among nomads than among settled people. Men
who have no costume at all, for example, cannot
be said to be unequally clothed ; they are, doubt-

less, more equal than men some of whom are well clothed and others in rags, though the equality is of the negative sort. But it is a profound mistake to imagine that, in the nomadic condition, any more than in any other which has yet been observed, men are either "free" or "equal" in Rousseau's sense. I can call to mind no nomadic nation in which women are on an equality with men; nor any in which young men are on the same footing as old men; nor any in which family groups, bound together by blood ties, by their mutual responsiblity for bloodshed and by common worship, do not constitute corporate political units, in the sense of the city[1] of the Greeks and Romans. A "state of nature" in which noble and peaceful, but nude and propertyless, savages sit in solitary meditation under trees, unless they are dining or amusing themselves in other ways, without cares or responsibilities of any sort, is simply another figment of the unscientific imagination. The only uncivilised men of whom anything is really known are hampered by superstitions and enslaved by conventions, as strange as those of the most artificial societies, to an almost incredible degree. Furthermore, I think it may be said with much confidence that the primitive " land-

---

[1] I may remind the reader that, in their original senses, πόλις and *civitas* mean, not an aggregation of houses, but a corporation. In this sense, the City of London is formed by the freemen of the City, with their Common Councillors, Aldermen, and Lord Mayor.

grabber " did not either force or cheat his co-proprietors into letting him fence in a bit of the land which hitherto was the property of all.

The truth is we do not know, and, probably, never shall know completely, the nature of all the various processes by which the ownership of land was originally brought about. But there is excellent ground for sundry probable conclusions [1] in the fact that almost all parts of the world, and almost all nations, have yielded evidence that, in the earliest settled condition we can get at, land was held as private or several property, and not as the property of the public, or general body of the nation. Now private or several property may be held in one of two ways. The ownership may be vested in a single individual person, in the ordinary sense of that word ; or it may be vested in two or more individuals forming a corporation or legal person ; that is to say, an entity which has all the duties and responsibilities of an individual person, but is composed of two or more individuals. It is obvious that all the arguments which Rousseau uses against individual land-ownership apply to corporate landownership. If the rights of A, B, and C are individually *nil*, you cannot make any more of your 0 by multiplying it by three. (A B C)—the corporation—must be

---

[1] For the difficulties which attach to the establishment of such probable conclusions, see the remarkable work of M. Fustel de Coulanges—*Recherches sur quelques problèmes d'Histoire : Les Germains.*

an usurper if A, B, and C taken each by himself is so. Moreover, I think I may take it for granted that those who desire to make the State universal landowner, would eject a corporation from its estates with even less hesitation than they would expel an individual.

The particular method of early landholding of which we have the most widespread traces is that in which each of a great number of moderate-sized portions of the whole territory occupied by a nation is held in complete and inalienable ownership[1] by the males of a family, or of a small number of actual or supposed kindred families, mutually responsible in blood feuds, and worshipping the same God or Gods. No female had any share in the ownership of the land. If she married outside the community she might take a share of the moveables; and, as a rule, she went to her husband's community. If, however, the community was short of hands, the husband might be taken into it, and then he acquired all the rights and responsibilities of the other members. Children born in the community became full members of it by domicile, so to speak, not by heredity from their parents. This primitive "city" was lodged in one or more dwellings, each usually standing in a patch of inclosed ground; of arable land in the immediate neighbourhood of the

---

[1] Inalienable, that is, without the consent of the whole owning community.

dwellings ; while pasture and uncleared forest land lay outside all. Each commune was as jealous of its rights of ownership as the touchiest of squires ; but, so long as the population was as scanty in proportion to the occupied territory, as was usually the case in ancient times, the communities got along pretty peaceably with one another. Any notion that all the communities which made up the nation had a sort of corporate overlordship over any one, still more that all the rest of the world had any right to complain of their "appropriation of the means of subsistence," most assuredly never entered the heads of our forefathers. But, alongside this corporate several ownership, there is strong ground for the belief that individual ownership was recognised, to a certain extent, even in these early times. The inclosure around each dwelling was understood to belong to the family inhabiting the dwelling ; and, for all practical purposes, must have been as much owned by the head of it as a modern entailed estate is owned by the possessor for the time being. Moreover, if any member of the community chose to go outside and clear and cultivate some of the waste, the reclaimed land was thenceforth recognised as his, that is to say, the right of ownership, in virtue of labour spent, was admitted.[1]

---

[1] Rousseau himself not only admits, but insists on the validity of this claim in the *Contrat Social*, liv. i. chap. ix.

Thus it is obvious that, though the early land-holders were, to a great extent, collective owners, the imaginary rights of mankind to universal land-ownership, or even of that of the nation at large to the whole territory occupied, were utterly ignored; that, so far from several ownership being the result of force or fraud, it was the system established with universal assent; and that, from the first, in all probability, individual rights of property, under certain conditions, were fully recognised and respected. Rousseau was, there-fore, correct in suspecting that his "state of nature" had never existed—it never did, nor any-thing like it. But it may be said, supposing that all this is true, and supposing that the doctrine that Englishmen have no right to their appro-priation of English soil is nonsense; it must, nevertheless, be admitted that, at one time, the great body of the nation, consisting of these numerous landowning corporations, composed of comparatively poor men, did own the land. And it must also be admitted that now they do not; but that the land is in the hands of a relatively small number of actually or comparatively rich proprietors, who constitute perhaps not one per cent. of the population. What is this but the result of robbery and cheating? The descendants of the robbers and cut-throat soldiers who came over with William of Normandy, have been true to their military instincts, and have "conveyed" the property of the primitive corporations into their own possession. No doubt, that is history made easy ; but here, once more, fact and *à priori* speculations cannot be made to fit.

.Let us look at the case dispassionately, and by the light of real history. No doubt, the early system of land tenure by collective several ownership was excellently adapted to the circumstances in which mankind found themselves. If it had not been so, it would not have endured so long, nor would it have been adopted by all sorts of different races—from the ancient Irish to the Hindoos, and from the Russians to the Kaffirs and Japanese. These circumstances were in the main as follows : That there was plenty of land unoccupied ; that population was very scanty and increased slowly ; that wants were simple ; that people were content to go on living in the same way, generation after generation ; that there was no commerce worth speaking of ; that manufactures were really that which they are etymologically—things made by the hands ; and that there was no need of capital in the shape of money. Moreover, with such methods of warfare as then existed, the system was good for defence, and not bad for offence.

Yet, even if left to itself, to develop undisturbedly, without the intrusion of force, fraud or militarism in any shape, the communal system, like the individual-owner system or the State-

owner system, or any other system that the wit of
man has yet devised, would sooner or later have
had to face the everlasting agrarian difficulty.
And the more the communities enjoyed general
health, peace, and plenty, the sooner would the
pressure of population upon the means of support
make itself felt. The difficulty paraded by the
opponents of individual ownership, that, by the
extension of the private appropriation of the means
of subsistence, the time would arrive when men
would come into the world for whom there was
no place, must needs make its appearance under
any system, unless mankind are prevented from
multiplying indefinitely. For, even if the habitable land is the property of the whole human race
the multiplication of that race must, as we have
seen, sooner or later, bring its numbers up to the
maximum which the produce can support; and
then the interesting problem in casuistry, which
even absolute political ethics may find puzzling,
will arise: Are we, who can just exist, bound to
admit the newcomers who will simply starve themselves and us? If the rule that any one may
exercise his freedom only so far as he does not
interfere with the freedom of others is all-sufficient,
it is clear that the newcomers will have no rights
to exist at all, inasmuch as they will interfere
most seriously with the freedom of their predecessors. The population question is the real riddle
of the sphinx, to which no political Œdipus has as

yet found the answer.   In view of the ravages of
the terrible monster, over-multiplication, all other
riddles sink into insignificance.

But to return to the question of the manner in
which individual several ownership has, in our own
and some other countries, superseded communal
several ownership.   There is an exceedingly instructive chapter in M. de Laveleye's well-known
work on " Primitive Property," entitled " The
Origin of Inequality in Landed Property."   And
I select M. de Laveleye as a witness the more
willingly, because he draws very different conclusions from the facts he so carefully adduces to
those which they appear to me to support.

After enumerating various countries in which,
as M. de Laveleye thinks, inequality and an aristocracy were the result of conquest, he asks very
pertinently—

But how were they developed in such countries as Germany,
which know nothing of conquerors coming to create a privileged
caste above a vanquished and enslaved population ?   Originally
we see in Germany associations of free and independent peasants
like the inhabitants of Uri, Schwyz, and Unterwalden at the
present day.   At the close of the middle ages we find, in the
same country, a feudal aristocracy resting more heavily on the
soil, and a rustic population more completely enslaved than in
England, Italy, or France (p. 222).

The author proceeds to answer the question
which he propounds by showing, in the first place,
that the admission of the right of individuals and
their heirs to the land they had reclaimed, which

22

was so general, if not universal, created hereditary individual property alongside the communal property, so that private estates arose in the waste between the sparse communal estates. Now, it was not every family or member of a community that was enterprising enough to go out and clear waste lands, or that had the courage to defend its possessions when once obtained. The originally small size of the domains thus acquired, and the strong stimulus of personal interest, led to the introduction of better methods of cultivation than those traditional in the communes. And, finally, as the private owner got little or no benefit from the community, he was exempted from the charges and *corvées* laid upon its members. The result, as may be imagined, was that the private proprietors, aided by serf-labour, prospered more than the communities cultivated by their free members, seriously hampered them by occupying fresh waste lands, yielded more produce, and furnished wealth, which, with the help of the *majorat* system, remained concentrated in the hands of owners who, in virtue of their possessions, could maintain retainers; while, freed from the need to labour, they could occupy themselves with war and the chase, and, as nobles, attend the sovereign. On the other hand, their brethren, left behind in the communes, had little chance of growing individually rich or powerful, and had to give themselves up to agricultural toil. The Bishop of Oxford, in his well-known " Constitutional History of England " (vol. i., p. 51), puts the case, as his wont is, concisely and precisely : " As the population increased, and agriculture itself improved, the mark system must have been superseded everywhere." No doubt, when the nobles had once established themselves, they often added force and fraud to their other means of enlarging their borders. But, to begin with, the inequality was the result, not of militarism, but of industrialism. Clearing a piece of land for the purpose of cultivating it and reaping the crops for one's own advantage is surely an industrial operation, if ever there was one.

Secondly, M. de Laveleye points out that the Church was a great devourer of commune lands :—

" We know that a member of the commune could only dispose of his share with the consent of his associates, who had a right of resumption ; but this right could not be exercised against the Church. Accordingly, in these days of religious fervour, the faithful frequently left to the Church all that they possessed, not only their house and its inclosure, but the undivided share in the *mark* attached to it " (p. 225). Thus an abbot, or a bishop, became co-proprietor with the peasants of a commune ; and, with such a cuckoo in the nest, one can conceive that the hedge-sparrows might have a bad time. " Already by the end of the ninth century one-third of the whole soil of Gaul belonged to the clergy" (p. 225). But, if the men who left their property to the Church believed that they got their *quid pro quo* in the shape of masses for their souls, as they certainly did; and if the Churchmen believed as sincerely (and they certainly did) that they gave valuable consideration for the property left them, where does fraud come in? Is it not again a truly industrial operation? Indeed, a keen-witted and eminent Scotch judge once called a huge bequest to a Church "fire insurance," so emphatically commercial did the transaction appear to him.

Thirdly, personal several property was carved out of the corporate communal property in another fashion, to which no objection can be taken by industrialism. Plots of arable land were granted to members of the commune who were skilled artificers, as a salary for their services. The craft transmitting itself from father to son the land went with it and grew into an hereditary benefice.

Fourthly, Sir Henry Maine[1] has proved in a very striking manner, from the collection of the Brehon Laws of ancient Ireland, how the original communal landownership of the sept, with the allotment of an extra allowance of pasture to the chief, as the honorarium for his services of all

[1] See *Early History of Institutions*, especially Lecture vi.

kinds, became modified, in consequence of the power of keeping more cattle than the rest of the sept, thus conferred on the chief. He became a lender of cattle at a high rate of interest to his more needy sept-fellows, who when they borrowed became bound to do him service in other ways and lost status by falling into the position of his debtors. Hence the chief gradually acquired the characteristics of what naturalists have called "synthetic" and "prophetic" types, combining the features of the modern gombeen-man with those of the modern rack-renting landlord, who is commonly supposed to be a purely imported Norman or Saxon product, saturated with the very spirit of industrialism—namely, the determination to get the highest price for an article which is to be had. As a fact, the condition of the native Irish, under their own chiefs, was as bad in Queen Elizabeth's time as it has ever been since. Again, the status of the original commoners of the sept was steadily altered for the worse by the privilege which the chief possessed, and of which he freely availed himself, of settling on the waste land of the commune such broken vagabonds of other tribes as sought his patronage and protection, and who became absolutely dependent upon him. Thus, without war and without any necessity for force or fraud (though doubtless there was an adventitious abundance of both), the communal system was bound to go to pieces, and

to be replaced by individual ownership, in consequence of the operation of purely industrial
causes. That is to say, in consequence of the
many commercial advantages of individual ownership over communal ownership; which became
more and more marked exactly in proportion as
territory became more fully occupied, security of
possession increased, and the chances of the
success of individual enterprise and skill as
against routine, in an industrial occupation,
became greater and greater.

The notion that all individual ownership of
land is the result of force and fraud appears to me
to be on a level with the peculiarly short-sighted
prejudice that all religions are the results of
sacerdotal cunning and imposture. As religions
are the inevitable products of the human mind,
which generates the priest and the prophet as
much as it generates the faithful; so the inequality
of individual ownership has grown out of the
relative equality of communal ownership in virtue
of those natural inequalities of men, which, if
unimpeded by circumstances, cannot fail to give
rise quietly and peaceably to corresponding
political inequalities.

The task I have set myself is completed, as far
as it can be within reasonable limits. I trust
that those who have taken the trouble to follow
the argument, will agree with me that the gospel

of Jean Jacques, in its relation to property, is a very sorry affair—that it is the product of an untrustworthy method, applied to assumptions which are devoid of foundation in fact; and that nothing can be more profoundly true than the saying of the great and truly philosophical English jurist, whose recent death we all deplore, that speculations of this sort are rooted in "impatience of experience and the preference of *à priori* to all other methods of reasoning."

Almost all the multitudinous causes which concurred in bringing about the French Revolution are happily absent in this country; and I have not the slightest fear that the preaching of any amount of political fallacy will involve us in evils of the magnitude of those which accompanied that great drama. But, seeing how great and manifold are the inevitable sufferings of men; how profoundly important it is that all should give their best will and devote their best intelligence to the alleviation of those sufferings which can be diminished, by seeking out, and, as far as lies within human power, removing their causes; it is surely lamentable that they should be drawn away by speculative chimæras from the attempt to find that narrow path which for nations, as for individual men, is the sole road to permanent well-being.

VIII

NATURAL RIGHTS AND POLITICAL RIGHTS

[1890]

In looking through a series of critical notices the other day, my eye was caught by a remark upon my essay "On the Natural Inequality of Men" —to the effect that it was well enough; but why should I have taken all that trouble to slay the slain ?

Evidently, the propounder of the question believes that the doctrines of that school of political philosophers of which Rousseau was the typical representative, are not only killed but dead. But, whatever may hold good of men, doctrines do not necessarily die from being killed. Many a long year ago, I fondly imagined that Hume and Kant and Hamilton having slain the "Absolute," the thing must, in decency, decease. Yet, at the present time, the same hypostatised negation, sometimes thinly disguised under a new name, goes about in broad daylight, in company with the dogmas of absolute ethics, political and other, and seems to be as lively as ever. It would seem to be to no purpose that the history of every branch of physical and historical science teems with examples of the fate which befalls the hasty generaliser who numbers, rather than weighs, supposed facts; and treats the rough approximations to truth obtained by the observation of highly complex phenomena as if they had the precision of geometrical theorems.

There is, unfortunately, abundant evidence that the vicious method of *à priori* political speculation which I have illustrated from the writings of Rousseau is not only in full vigour, but that it is exerting an influence upon the political action of our contemporaries which is extremely serious. No better evidence of the fact need be adduced than the avidity with which the writings of political teachers of this school have been and are being read, especially among the more intelligent of the working classes; and I doubt if any book published during the last ten years has obtained a larger circulation among them, not only in this country but in the United States, than "Progress and Poverty." The other day there was a rumour that some devoted disciple of its author, Mr. Henry George, had bequeathed a large sum of money to him in order to aid in the propagation of his doctrines.

In some respects, the work undoubtedly deserves the success which it has won. Clearly and vigorously written, though sometimes weakened by superfluous rhetorical confectionery, " Progress and Poverty " leaves the reader in no doubt as to Mr. George's meaning, and thus fulfils the primary condition of honest literature. Nor will any one question the author's intense conviction that the adoption of his panacea will cure the ills under which the modern state groans.

Mr. George's political philosophy is, in principle, though by no means in all its details, identical with Rousseauism. It exhibits, in perfection, the same *à priori* method, starting from highly questionable axioms which are assumed to represent absolute truth, and asking us to upset the existing arrangements of society on the faith of deductions from those axioms. The doctrine of "natural rights" is the fulcrum upon which he, like a good many other political philosophers, during the last 130 years, rests the lever wherewith the social world is to be lifted away from its present foundations and deposited upon others. In this respect, he is at one, not only with Rousseau and his conscious or unconscious followers in France and in England; but, I regret to say, may claim the countenance of a far more scientifically minded and practical school of political thinkers—that of the French *Physi-crates* of the eighteenth century.

The founder of this school, Quesnay, the saga-

cious physician of Louis the Fifteenth, whom even
that graceless prince appreciated and called his
"thinker," was an eminently practical man, especially conversant with agriculture.   As the name
taken by his disciples implies, his teaching was,
professedly, based upon careful observation of, and
induction from, the course of nature, as it bears
upon politics.   It would hardly be too much to say
that we owe to the Physiocrates the modern clearness of conviction that the world of human society
is as much the theatre of order and definite
sequence of cause and effect as the world of extra-
human nature ; that there are rules of action, the
observance of which brings about prosperity, while
their neglect entails ruin, which have nothing to
do with the laws of morality or with the ordinances
of religion ; and that the wicked who follow these
rules will not beg their bread, while the pious who
neglect them will.   But Quesnay and his followers
would have been more than mortal if they had
escaped the influence of the spirit of their age ;
and though they never fell into the speculative
monstrosities of Rousseau, yet, about the time
that the latter was occupied with his essay on
" Inequality," Quesnay composed that short work
entitled " Le Droit Naturel," which is all too
largely infected by the à priori method.

Quesnay begins by laying down the proposition
that " Natural Right" may be " vaguely defined "
as " the right which a man has to the things which

are fit for his enjoyment." Truly a vague enough
definition, and one that would need a great deal
more defining before it could be safely turned to
any practical account. Quesnay's friend and
collaborateur, Dupont de Nemours, in the introductory discourse prefixed to the collection entitled
" Physiocratie : ou constitution naturelle du
gouvernement le plus avantageux au genre
humain," published in 1768, has somewhat improved upon it. " Natural Right," he says, is " the
right a man has to do that which is to his
advantage." . He considers that this right is
founded upon the condition that we are " charged
with our own preservation under penalty of
suffering and death." And he adds : " The final
degree of punishment decreed by this sovereign
law is superior to every other interest and to every
arbitrary law." " Natural Right," then, is the
right of a man to do anything necessary for his
own preservation, and to possess himself of any
means of enjoyment. It is possessed to its full
and literal extent by any and every wholly
isolated man. " Natural Right," by this account
of it, must vest in the individual before he has
entered into the social state, and must be antecedent to all forms of relative justice and injustice.
But the contemporaneous and contiguous existence
of many such individuals, all of whom assert their
natural rights, must also necessarily end in the
Hobbesian state of war of each against all, unless

they agree to conventions which shall allow to each his natural right to things enjoyable; or, in other words, his freedom to profit by the advantages which he is competent to obtain from the order of nature.[1]

There seems to me to be a wonderful admixture of wholesome truth and of very unwholesome fiction in these propositions; and, as is not uncommon, the fiction has become popular while the truth is neglected. Indeed, Quesnay himself saw deeper than his disciple, and writes thus in the opening chapter of the treatise I have cited (Daire, p. 41) :—

He who has said that the natural right of man is a nullity has spoken truly.

He who has said that the natural right of man is the right which nature teaches to all animals has spoken truly.[2]

He who has said that the natural right of man is the right which his strength and his intelligence assure him has spoken truly.

He who has said that natural right is limited to the private interest of each man has spoken truly.

---

[1] Daire, *Physiocrates*, Partie première, pp. 19, 20.

[2] In a note Quesnay says: "This is the definition of Justinian." It would be more accurate, I imagine, to say that it is derived from Ulpian : "Jus naturale est, quod natura omnia animalia docuit : nam jus istud non humani generis proprium sed omnium animalium." It is to the same Roman jurist that we owe the maxim that all men, according to the law of Nature, are equal and free : "Quod ad jus naturale attinet, omnes homines æquales sunt." "Quum jure naturali omnes liberi nascerentur." See the exhaustive work of Voigt : *Das jus naturale æquum et bonum und jus gentium der Römer*, Bd. 1, § 56, whence these citations are taken.

He who has said that natural right is a general and sovereign law, which regulates the rights of all men, has spoken truly.

He who has said that the natural right of men is the unlimited right of all to everything has spoken truly.

He who has said that the natural right of men is a right limited by a tacit or explicit convention has spoken truly.

He who has said that natural right has nothing to do with either justice or injustice has spoken truly.[1]

He who has said that natural right is a just, decisive, and fundamental right, has spoken truly.

But none has spoken truly in relation to all cases.

What is one to make of this litany of antinomies? Quesnay himself seems to have been content to leave the riddle unanswered—while his successors do not appear to have understood that there was a riddle to answer. Each proposition may certainly be plausibly justified, and yet contradicts, or is hard to reconcile with, some other. Now, when this is the case, we may be pretty sure that the difficulty arises from some ambiguity of language. If " Natural Right " is susceptible of these opposing predicates, it must be that it stands for two or more widely different ideas. I propose to endeavour to show that this solution of the difficulty is correct.

Some time ago I fell in with an Indian tiger story of a peculiarly gruesome sort, and I repeat the substance of it, not from any especial love for

---

[1] In a note Quesnay observes that this is the case of a man alone in a desert island, whose natural right to the products of the island involves neither justice nor injustice, inasmuch as these terms express the relations of two or more persons.

horrible stories, but because the tale led me, and therefore may easily lead my readers, into a train of fruitful reflections upon this very question of "Natural Rights."

A tigress carried off an unfortunate Indian villager—as a cat may carry off a mouse—without doing the man any mortal injury. Tracked to her lair in the jungle, the brute was seen to set down the half-disabled captive before her cubs, who commenced mumbling and mauling him to the best of their infantine ability, while the tender mother complacently watched their clumsy efforts to deal with the big game she had brought home. But, if the man, driven desperate, succeeded for a moment in beating off his small tormentors and crawling away a few yards, a judiciously administered grip with the thoughtful parent's strong jaws, or a cuff from her heavy and sharp-clawed paw, at once reduced the victim to a state in which the cubs could safely resume their worrying and scratching.

I suppose that no one in whose imagination these words suffice to body forth a vision of the thing will fail to be horrified at the apparently wanton infliction of such grievous mental and bodily torture upon a harmless peasant ; nor think, without satisfaction, of the justice done by the rifle-shots that eventually laid the tigress and her ferocious progeny low. The assertion that the tigress had a "natural right" to do what she did, or that she and her cubs were justified by the " Law of Nature " in their course of action, will perhaps seem to most a monstrous, if not a wicked, doctrine. Yet this very doctrine is implicitly inculcated in one of the most familiar works of an author from whom the youthful mind· half a century ago derived its earliest impressions of ethics; and also, unfortunately, of poetry. The young people of that day were taught to repeat:

> " Let dogs delight to bark and bite,
>   For 'tis their nature to ;
> Let bears and lions growl and fight,
>   For God hath made them so."

As poetry, this pious doggerel is undoubtedly nought. But, as moral philosophy, ripe, nay even aged reflection must, I think, satisfy us that it is not only sound, but has the merit of putting the case in a nutshell. For, whatever tigers and tigresses may be and do, it is quite clear, if we adopt the creative hypothesis and believe that God made them, that He " made them so." The acts which we are pleased to denounce as wantonly cruel are, therefore, necessary and intentional consequences of the divine creative operation. In fact, if there is evidence of intention anywhere in the fabric of things, the study of the structure of one of the cats, great or small, will prove it to be a machine most admirably adapted to slay and tear to pieces other living quadrupeds; and will demonstrate that, if it was intended to do anything, it must have been intended to perform exactly that butcher's work which it executes so well.

On the other hand, if we prefer to say no more than there is good evidence for saying, it is unquestionably true that the "nature" or innate tendency of the whole race of tigers is to prey on other large animals, men included, inasmuch as not only is their bodily and mental constitution especially fitted for that operation, but since they must perish if they fail to perform it. Tigers (as M. Dupont says of men) are charged with their own preservation under penalty of death. Moreover, when we inquire into the past history of these predaceous animals, we find that the cats, great and small, are but the last term of a long series of species of animals most of which are now extinct; which have succeeded one another through the tertiary epoch, therefore, for many thousands, or more probably millions, of years; and which, in their capacity of butchering machines, have undergone a steady though slow and gradual improvement, every step of which has been effected at the expense of an enormous total of suffering to the animals butchered. If, then, we deny that tigers have a natural right to torment and devour men, we really impeach, not the conduct of the tigers, but the order of nature. And if we ourselves, with our notions of right and

23

wrong, are, like the tigers, products of that order, whence comes our competence to deny the exercise of their natural rights to those beings who stand upon the same foundation of natural right as ourselves ? To say that a thing exists in nature and to say that it has a natural right to existence are, in fact, merely two ways of stating the same truth; which is that, in nature, fact and justification of the fact, or, in other words, might and right, are coextensive. To be and to have a natural right to be, to possess a faculty and to have the natural right to exert it, are all one. Thus, it really must be admitted that the hymnologist of my childish days has reason on his side. Whether children's little hands " were made to tear each other's eyes " or not, it does not lie with us to object to tigers, any more than to dogs, or bears, or lions, growling and fighting as their natures dictate. Beyond a doubt, by the " Law of Nature," which is the foundation of " natural right," the cats and their carnivorous allies are justified.

Having thus established the " rights of tigers " to the exercise and enjoyment of the faculties with which nature has endowed them, it will be interesting to follow out the logical development of the doctrine, such as might be expected from a thoroughgoing advocate of those rights. It is admitted that a tiger has a natural right to eat a man; but if he may eat one man he may eat another, so that a tiger has a right of property in all men, as potential tiger-meat. Men are as much the "gratuitous offering" of nature to tigers for their subsistence, or part subsistence, as fruits are to men. But any one tiger has no more natural right of property in men than any other tiger. All tigers are free to eat any man they can seize : and, if two tigers are sneaking along through the jungle on opposite sides of a foot-path, their rights to the villager, who, travelling thereby, fondly imagines he is going home, are equal. So that we may safely enunciate the conclusion that all tigers have an equal natural right to eat all men.

I think it would be difficult to object to this argument on purely logical grounds ; and the conclusions to which we are forced appear startling enough ; but here we stop. If the advocate of the "rights of tigers" attempts to drive us into the further admission that, as tigers have a right to eat men, it is wrong of men to put obstacles in the way of their having their rights by refusing to be eaten, we protest against the doctrine, not on the low and selfish ground of mere personal interest, but because, however plausible, it is a patent fallacy. The champion of the "rights of tigers" has, in fact, made a convenient, though unwarrantable, jump from one sense of the word "right" to another—from "natural right" to "moral right." No doubt, he who hinders or refuses to admit a moral right is morally wrong—unjust, or, if you

will, wicked. But very little consideration will
show that hindrance or denial of "natural rights"
may not only be far from wrong, but is, in fact, a
necessary consequence of the existence of such
"natural rights." Grant that the tiger kills and
eats men in the exercise of his natural right to
preserve his own existence, and to do that for
which nature has expressly fitted him; it is no less
true that men kill tigers in the exercise of their
equal natural right to preserve their existence.
If the tiger is entitled by the law of nature to use
his claws and teeth and soft-footed stealthy
cleverness for the purpose of his self-preservation,
the man may employ his hands and the weapons
they are so admirably adapted to fabricate and
wield, and use his still greater cunning, in tracking
and stalking tigers to the like end.

Thus the natural rights of tigers and the
natural rights of men, though quite indisputable and alike safely founded on the "Law of
Nature," are diametrically opposed to one another.
It follows, therefore, that they are rights to which
no correlative duties correspond—rights of which
the exercise may be impeded, or prevented, without
the perpetration of wrong. And that is just the
difference between "natural laws and rights," on
the one hand, and "moral and civil laws and
rights" on the other. Moral laws and civil laws
are commands of an authority which may be dis-
obeyed; but the sanctioning authority threatens

and visits with penalties those who disobey. "Thou shalt not steal," the negative form of the recognition of rights of property, is both a moral and a civil law. It rests on the authority either of a Deity, or on that of conscience, or on that of some civil person whose dominion is recognised; and its sanction, or penalty, incurred by disobedience, is hell, or remorse, or imprisonment, or all three.

The proper object and effect of moral and civil laws are to benefit all who are subjected to them by bringing about a state of peace and mutual confidence—the laws restraining each individual from acts which are hurtful and encouraging those which are beneficial to the polity of which he is a member. On the contrary, the "Law of Nature" is not a command to do, or to refrain from doing, anything. It contains, in reality, nothing but a statement of that which a given being tends to do under the circumstances of its existence; and which, in the case of a living and sensitive being, it is necessitated to do, if it is to escape certain kinds of disability, pain, and ultimate dissolution. The natural right deduced from such a law of nature is simply a way of stating the fact; and there is, in the nature of things, no reason why a being possessing such and such tendencies to action should not carry them into effect. Confused with moral and civil laws and translated into the language of command, the

law of nature would bid the individual : " Do
what you will, so far as you can." But it is only
inexactly and by way of metaphor, that we can
speak of disobedience to a law of nature or of
penalties for such disobedience. If, by impossibility, a tiger were to have an attack of the
philozoic and vegetarian fanaticism which is going
about, and to declare that he would neither kill,
nor eat flesh, any more, he would undoubtedly
undergo a lingering and painful death by starvation. But there is neither disobedience nor penalty
here. The laws of nature are statements of tendencies, and if one law expresses the truth, that
tigers which kill and eat will live and wax fat,
another expresses the converse truth, that if tigers
do not kill and eat, they will wax lean and die.
The results are consequences of two modes of
action, both of which are in accordance with
natural law (or they could not occur) and not
rewards or penalties. Indeed, that they cannot
be the latter is clear from the further truth, that
the tiger who has grown old in doing his best to
fulfil the first " law of nature," as with age his
limbs grow stiff and his tusks wear down, falls,
very much against his will, under the second
" law " and dies as miserably of starvation as if
he had refused to kill and eat on the loftiest of
antivivisection and vegetarian principles.

The crown of the differences between the " law
of nature " with its consequent " natural rights "

and moral or civil laws lies in this : that consistent and thoroughgoing action, based upon the
law of nature and the natural rights which flow
from it, tends to benefit the individual at the
expense of all other individuals whose needs and
desires are of the same kind ; and, so far from
bringing about a state of peace among such individuals, necessitates a state of war—that is to
say of either conscious or unconscious competition
among them. The ceaseless and pitiless " struggle
for existence" which obtains throughout the whole
world of living things is, in truth, the inevitable
consequence of the circumstance that each living
being strives knowingly, or ignorantly, to exert
all its powers for the satisfaction of its needs ;
and asserts a tacit claim to possess (to the exclusion of other beings) all the space on the
earth's surface which it can occupy and to appropriate all the subsistence which it can utilise.[1]
The state of sentient nature, at any given time,
is the resultant of the momentarily balanced
oppositions of millions upon millions of individuals, each doing its best to get all it can and
to keep what it gets; each, in short, zealously

[1] Sixteen centuries ago, Ulpian drew the conclusion that,
according to the "jus naturale," the elements "mare," "aer,"
and, at any rate, "litora," are the common property of all
living things.   Isidore of Seville (see *Voigt*, i. 576), probably
founding himself on Ulpian, reckons "communis omnium
possessio et omnium una libertas, acquisitio eorum quæ cœlo,
terra marique capiuntur," as among the natural rights of men.

obeying the law of nature and fighting tooth and nail for its natural rights. This is the *ne plus ultra* of individualism; and, wherever individualism has unchecked sway, a polity can no more exist than it can among the tigers who inhabit the same jungle. It is, in fact, the sum of all possible anti-social and anarchic tendencies.

Even among tigers (or at any rate tigresses), however, pure individualism does not always dominate. When the tigress has brought forth her cubs, and while she is nourishing, protecting, and training them, she and they enter into an association, formed of individuals held together by the attraction of the instincts which constitute the animal basis of sympathy, and thus constitute a polity, however small its scale and short its duration. And it will be observed that this most rudimentary of polities, the *family*, could not exist without the renouncement, on the part of the tigress at least, of some of the "Rights of Tigers." The tigress no longer acts upon her natural right of eating all she kills, for example; she acts as if she were conscious of duties towards her cubs. The cubs, on the other hand, are fond and more or less obedient, acting as if they had correlative duties towards their parent. It will not be supposed, I hope, that I suggest that either tigress or cubs are capable of entertaining moral ideas; all that I desire to point out is that, partly by instinct, partly by the effects of very simple experiences, both sides perform acts which a more developed intelligence symbolises by these moral ideas.

I have pointed out in the course of this discussion that among the jurists of old Rome, who first systematically developed the conceptions of the "Law of Nature" and "Natural Rights," Ulpian rightly judged that brutes came under such law and had such rights, no less than men. It is obvious that, without recurrence to that "state of nature" of mankind, of which so very much is said and so very little known, an individual man, isolated from his fellows and removed from all social relations, comes under the same law of nature; and has "natural rights" in exactly the same sense as the individual tiger possesses them. Before the advent of man Friday, Robinson Crusoe's right and might were coextensive, except in so far as he might be influenced by remembrance of the moral and civil laws of his former social existence. There was no reason why he should abstain from doing anything it pleased him to do, and which lay within the scope of his natural faculties. No one would deny that he had a natural right to take possession of his cave; to cut down the trees that suited his purpose; to gather fruits; to kill any of the wild goats for his subsistence; to shoot any number of the cannibal visitors, who would otherwise kill him for their subsistence. Crusoe's "natural rights" thus potentially extended over the whole island and everything in it. According to the law of nature as defined by Quesnay, he was owner of everything therein which he desired and was able to appropriate. Suppose, however, that another wreck had simultaneously cast Will Atkins upon the opposite shore, and that Atkins had established himself there in Crusoe's fashion; then it is plain that the law of nature would confer upon him rights no less extensive. Crusoe and Atkins, stalking the same goat from opposite sides, would have been in a position identical with that of two tigers in the jungle, slinking after the same Hindoo, so far as the law of nature is concerned. And if each insisted upon exerting the whole of his natural rights, it is clear that there would be nothing for it but to fight for the goat. In the case of the men, as in that of the brutes, extreme and logical individualism means isolation and the state of war; it is plainly incompatible with the peace and co-operation which are the essentials of even temporary association. On the other hand, if the two men followed the dictates of the commonest common sense, not less than those of natural sympathy, they would at once agree to unite in peaceful co-operation with each other, for their mutual comfort and protection. And that would be possible only if each agreed to limit the exercise of his natural rights so far as they might involve any more damage to the other than to himself. This is to say, the two men would, in reality, renounce the law of nature, and put themselves under a moral and civil law, replacing natural rights, which have no wrongs, for moral and civil rights, each of which has its correlative wrong. This, I take it, is the root of truth which saves the saying of Paul of Tarsus that "sin came by the law" from being a paradox. The solitary, individual man, living merely under the so-called law of nature, which cannot be violated, and having rights the contradictions of which are not wrongs, cannot sin. Wrong-doing becomes possible only when, by associating with another man, or other men, for peace and co-operation, the individual becomes implicitly, or explicitly, bound to observe certain rules of conduct in relation to him or them; any violation of these rules is a wrong.

Probably none of the political delusions which have sprung from the "natural rights" doctrine has been more mischievous than the assertion that all men have a natural right to freedom, and that those who willingly submit to any restriction of this freedom, beyond the point determined by the deductions of *à priori* philosophers, deserve the title of slave. But to my mind, this delusion is incomprehensible except as the result of the error of confounding natural with moral rights. It is undoubtedly true that a man, like a tiger or any other animal, has a natural right to freedom, if by that phrase we merely mean that, so far as he is a mere individual being, there is no reason why he should not do what he pleases. But that is a very harmless proposition, and neither despot nor slave-owner need boggle at it. If, on the other hand, the champion of freedom means, as he usually does, that the natural right to freedom affords, in itself, a ground for objecting to this or that restraint upon the liberties of men who form a polity, the argument appears to me to be as sophistical as it is mischievous. For, as we have seen, it is a necessary condition of social existence that men should renounce some of their freedom of action; and the question of how much is one that can by no possibility be determined à *priori*. That which it would be tyranny to prevent in some states of society it would be madness to permit in others. The existence of a polity depends upon the adjustment of the two sets of forces which its component units, the individual men, obey—the repulsive of natural right, and the attractive and coactive of individual sympathy and corporate dominion. Which of them ought to predominate at any given time must surely depend upon external and internal circumstances and upon the degree of development of the polity. The Duke of Wellington is said to have defined martial law as " the will of the Commander-in-Chief for the time being "—that is to say, it is the sweeping away of all " rights," natural, civil, and moral, except so far as they are sanctioned by the commander. Yet, surely, no one but a lunatic can maintain that, in case of invasion, or rebellion, threatening the social person—the polity—with destruction, that composite man has not as much natural right to take any measure essential to self-preservation, as an individual man has under the law of nature. And from this extreme case, to the petty question, as to whether the depositary of dominion in a polity has or has not the right to infringe the " natural right" of a man to leave the path in front of his house unswept of snow, there is an endless gradation in the importance of the problems, all of which can be solved only by the application of the same principles. Is it, or is it not, for the welfare of society at that time and under those circumstances—looking at the question all round and taking fully into account the disadvantages of restraint of liberty— that its members should be compelled to do this, or be restrained from doing that ?

The political delusions which spring from the ' natural rights' doctrine are multitudinous; but I think there is only one more which is worth attention at present. That is the extraordinary notion that the logical consequence of the " natural right " of all men to any given thing is the sharing of the rights of property in that thing equally among all the claimants. Let us suppose two boys, John and Peter. I take an apple out of my pocket, and I say, " This apple is entirely yours, John; and, Peter, it is also entirely yours. The whole apple belongs to each of you, and you have each a right to eat the whole of it. Now, my boys, you may eat it, so long as neither of you gives up any fraction of the right I have given him nor infringes the other's right." The boys, I take it, would be somewhat puzzled. If their common sense, *plus* their appetites, were stronger than their logical faculty, they would probably suggest that they should divide the apple and each eat half. But I should have to say "No. You are violating my conditions —which were that you should neither of you give up any portion of his right to the whole. The arrangement you propose necessitates that John should give up his right to one half, and Peter his right to the other." Not improbably, my young f.iends, if of English extraction, might propose another way out of the difficulty; namely, the wager of battle. But again I should have to refuse. The trial by battle would unfortunately involve the infringement of the natural rights of the vanquished by the victor, which is, once more, contrary to my stipulation. In fact, under the conditions stated, the apple would have to remain uneaten.

Thus we see once more, that the absolute "natural rights" theory—that is to say individualism pure and simple—if carried out logically, is merely reasoned savagery, utter and unmitigated selfishness, incompatible with social existence.

And this would be obvious to every one, were it not that the ambiguous sense of the word " rights " gives a moral colour to human relations which are neither moral nor immoral, but, as Quesnay rightly says, antecedent to morality.

My readers may imagine that I have forgotten " Progress and Poverty." By no means ; the preceding pages must, in fact, be regarded as a sort of " Prolegomena " to that work and especially to the first chapter of the seventh book, which contains the theoretical foundation of the practical measure which its author advocates.

According to Mr. George, society is very ill ; and he proposes a method of treatment professedly based upon strict deduction from the principles of absolute political physiology. Whether the remedy is calculated to achieve the results predicted, or not, is a question I shall not now discuss ; but it will be admitted that it is drastic, consisting as it does in neither more nor less than the eviction of all several landowners and the confiscation of that which is, and, for many centuries has been, regarded as their undoubted property. The measure is of exactly the same order as would be the confiscation of the interest of all money belonging to working-men in savings banks, on the ground that interest, as usury, is contrary to the principles of absolute ethics—an opinion which it must be remembered has been (perhaps still is) supported by papal infallibility ; which is, at least, equal in weight to the philosophical species of that commodity.   Surely the medicine is a strong medicine.   Now I humbly submit, that while one might take Epsom salts, on the recommendation of the first old woman who proposed that remedy for a sick headache, a rational man would like to have clearly intelligible reasons, or extremely trustworthy authority, before he ventured with an equally light heart, upon croton oil or tartar emetic. The latter might certainly put an end to his sick headache—but what if at the same time it put an end to him ?   So, it is at any rate possible, that the expropriation of landowners, while it might put an end to a state of things inconsistent with the principles of absolute political ethics, might also destroy the society it strove to heal.   Therefore, I think we are bound to see that Mr. George's " absolute " principles are " absolutely " true before we act upon even the most logical of deductions from them. Without presumption, it may be said to be just possible that the principles may be unsound and the deductions fallacious.

In the chapter to which I have referred, the author sets out by putting the question, What constitutes the rightful basis of property ?   And I have conscientiously endeavoured to set forth, accurately, the essentials of his answer in the following abstract of it.

I. All men have equal rights :

The laws of nature are the decrees of the Creator. There is written in them no recognition of any right save that of labour ; and in them is written broadly and clearly the equal right of all men to the use and enjoyment of Nature : to apply to her by their exertions and to receive and possess her reward. Hence, as Nature gives only to labour, the exertion of labour in production is the only title to exclusive possession. ("Progress and Poverty," 1889, p. 237.)

II. There is no foundation for any rightful title to ownership except this : That a man has a right to himself ; to the use of his own powers ; to the enjoyment of the fruit of his own exertions (p. 236) ; therefore, to whatsoever he makes or produces.

III. The right to that which is produced is "vested" in the producer by natural law (p. 236). It is also a "fundamental law of Nature that her enjoyment by man shall be consequent upon his exertion" (p. 241).

IV. Land is a gratuitous offering of Nature, not a thing produced by labour (p. 238) ; all men therefore have equal rights to it (p. 239). These rights are inalienable, as existing men cannot contract away the rights of their successors (p. 240). Every infant who comes into the world has as good a right to landed estates as their present possessors, by whom he is, in fact, robbed of his share (p. 240).

This, I believe, is a complete, if a succinct, statement of Mr. George's case. And I, for one, am quite prepared to admit that, if it can be

24

sustained, the sooner the foundations of our
present polity are broken up and replaced by
something less open to objection, the better. But
even Mr. George, I imagine, will admit that the
enterprise is grave, and by no means to be undertaken with a light heart, still less with that
superficial intellectual apprehension which comes
of a light head. The political philosopher who
uses his *à priori* lever, knowing that it may stir
up social discord, without the most conclusive
justification, to my mind comes perilously near
the boundary which divides blunders from
crimes.

The several elements of the proposition which
I have quoted under I. might have been taken
almost *verbatim* from the writings of the
Rousseauites and the Physiocrats. But it is
one of the most interesting features of *à priori*
speculation, that different philosophers, starting
from verbally identical propositions, arrive at
contradictory conclusions. And the Physiocrats
deduced the right and the necessity of maintaining several ownership of land from the principles
common to them and Mr. George, as confidently
as, and, in my judgment, with much better reason
than, Mr. George deduces its hideous wrongfulness
and the paramount necessity of abolishing it. The
equality of men question has already been sufficiently discussed. If, as I maintain, there is no such
thing as natural equality among men, then of

course any argument based upon it is necessarily worthless. From the fact that men are unequal it cannot well be concluded that they have "equal rights to the use and enjoyment of nature."

Passing from this point, we are met by the broad assertion that "the exertion of labour in production is the only title to exclusive possession." So far Mr. George is at one with the Physiocrats, who also rest the claim to ownership on labour bestowed. Let us consider the grounds upon which Mr. George rests this assertion. We need not trouble ourselves whether they are the same or different from those set forth by his predecessors.

The following questions and answers enlighten us on this head.

What constitutes the rightful basis of property ? What is it that enables a man to say justly of a thing, "It is mine" ? Is it not, primarily, the right of a man to himself, to the use of his own powers, to the enjoyment of the fruits of his own exertions ? ("Progress and Poverty," p. 236.)

And, on the same page, we are told that the title to everything produced by human exertions "descends from the original producer, in whom it is vested by natural law." Here we are back again on the ground of the "law of nature" and "natural rights," according to which, as we have seen, a man has a right to keep anything he is strong enough to keep, whether he has produced it or not. But the law of nature affords not the least reason why another man who is stronger should not take his possession away from him.

As I have already fully shown, there is not the least connection between the natural rights of the solitary individual and the moral or civil rights of the man who has entered into association with others. A man may justly say that it is no more than the " use of his own powers," to knock another down and rob him of his dinner ; and that it is no more than " the enjoyment of the fruits of his own exertions " to proceed to eat that dinner. Is it pretended that the man who has entered into association with others retains those " natural rights " ?

But let us assume, for the sake of argument, not only that labour is the " only " title to exclusive possession, but that the foundation of this title lies in the right of a man to himself ; and in which is, somewhat sophistically, included the right to the use of his own powers and the enjoyment of the fruits of his own exertions. If we try to believe both these propositions at once, surely we fall into perplexities worse than any that have yet befallen us. If labour is the only title to exclusive possession ; if, for example, there can be no exclusive possession of cultivated land simply and solely because, according to Mr. George, it is not a product of labour—propositions on the axiomatic certainty of which the whole fabric of " Progress and Poverty " rests—how in the world does a man

come by the " right to himself " ?   I have paid a
good deal of attention to those branches of natural
history which treat more especially of man, but
never yet have I come across even the smallest
grounds for believing that a man has ever been
known to make himself, or to endow himself by
his own labour with the powers he exerts.   I
have heard often enough of men who were said to
be self-made.   Indeed, I have known some cases
in which the fact was alleged in justification of
the ways of Providence, and for the purpose of
shifting the responsibility for the existence of
some people on to the right shoulders.   But I
have always taken this phrase about " self-
making " to be a metaphor, and a very foolish
one, inasmuch as the men said to be self-made
are usually those whom nature has especially
favoured with costly gifts and exceptional opportunities.   No doubt it may be said, with justice,
that a man who learns diligently and strives hard
to do right, really bestows labour on himself, and
does so far fulfil the necessary conditions of self-
ownership laid down in " Progress and Poverty."
But, on the other hand, might not his teachers, on
the very same ground, claim possession of the
fruits of their labours in him ?   Might not the
mother, who not only bore him, but bore with
him, day and night, for half-a-dozen years, fed
him, clothed him, nursed him in sickness, taught
him the rudiments of civilisation—might not she

rightfully appeal to this wonderful labour-test of ownership ?

Is there any logical way out of the following argumentation, the like of which is perhaps to be found only in " Alice in Wonderland " ? The exertion of labour in production is the only title to exclusive possession. No gratuitous offering of Nature can be the subject of such private ownership. Therefore a man can have no exclusive possession of himself, except in so far as he is the product of the exertion of his own labour and not a gratuitous offering of Nature. But it is only a very small part of him which can in any sense be said to be the product of his own labour. The man's physical and mental tendencies and capacities, dependent to a very large extent on heredity, are certainly the " gratuitous offering of Nature ; " if they belong to anybody, therefore, they must belong to the whole of mankind, who must be, so to speak, a kind of collective slaveowners, all of each. So much of the man as depends on the care taken of him in infancy and childhood is the property of his mother, or of those who took her place. Another smaller portion belongs to the people who educated him. What remains is his own. So that the man's right to himself and to all his powers and to all the fruits of his labour, which the writer of " Progress and Poverty " makes the foundation of his system, turns out, if we follow another fundamental proposition of the same author to its logical consequences, to be a right to a mere fraction of himself and to the exercise of the powers which exclusively belong to that fraction. Surely it would take a greater sage than Solomon to settle the respective claims of mankind in general, the mother and the educators, to the ownership of a child; and when these were satisfied, what might remain in the shape of a right to himself would be hardly big enough to form a safe basis for anything, let alone property.

Unless my readers can see their way better than I can through this logic-chopping maze, we must give up the attempt to reconcile the two fundamental propositions of the system we are discussing : the first, that labour is the "only" title to exclusive possession, and the second, that the foundation of this title lies in the right of a man to himself—that is to say to the exclusive possession of himself. What our political philosopher appears to me to mean is this. A man is the exclusive possessor of himself and of the powers with which he is endowed by Nature ; therefore he is the exclusive possessor of whatever is brought into existence by the exertion of those powers in the form of labour. On the other hand, a man possesses, exclusively, nothing else than these powers, therefore he cannot be the exclusive possessor of anything but that which they produce. Substantially, as I have said, it is the position taken up by the Physiocrats, and, right or wrong, it is, at any rate, intelligible. But I do not quite see how it is to be proved by any one who disputes it. The statement that a man is the exclusive possessor of himself, even in the sense of bare ownership, is most assuredly not known to be true by intuition—as, for example, the proposition that two straight lines will not enclose a space is said to be. The whole ancient Roman world would have cried out against it. For them, a man's children, grown up or not, no less than his slaves, were so far from being exclusive possessors of themselves that their father could dispose of them as he thought fit. Nor, as far as I know, is there any part of the modern world in which a legal "infant" has the full ownership of himself and the absolute right to the usufruct of his own powers. Again, to the best of my knowledge, there is no country or nation in which an adult man has, or ever had, in any sense, the exclusive possession of himself. On the contrary, the state invariably lays claim to him for the discharge of various military or civil offices, and to more or less of the fruits of his exertions in the shape of rates and taxes for the support of the machinery of external defence and internal protection. In truth, as I have already pointed out, the very existence of society depends on the fact that every member of it tacitly admits that he is not the exclusive possessor of himself, and that he admits the claim of the polity of which he forms a part, to act, to some extent, as his master. I do not think we need discuss, any further, propositions which, as they are stated, are contradictory; and which, when they are remodelled so as to escape such contradiction, fall into the no less fatal difficulty of contradicting plain facts. The axiom that a man has a right to himself, in the sense in which it is used in " Progress and Poverty," is a baseless assumption of exactly the same order as that other that all men are free and equal.

However, there is no greater mistake than the hasty conclusion that opinions are worthless because they are badly argued. The principle that " the exertion of labour in production is the only title to exclusive possession " has a great deal to say for itself if we only substitute " may be usefully considered to be a " for " is the only." And, besides this, it will be interesting to trace out its logical consequences, even without such alteration. For we shall find our result to be wonderfully different from that set forth in " Progress and Poverty." It is there declared to be irreconcilable with exclusive (or several) owner-ship of land. I think that it will become apparent that it authorises the several ownership of land to exactly the same extent as it does the several ownership of anything else.[1]

[1] See the clear recognition of this fact in L'Abbé Baudeau's *Première Introduction à la Philosophie Économique*, 1771, in

Let us consider what " Progress and Poverty " has to say about this question.

What most prevents the realisation of the injustice of private property in land is the habit of including all the things that are made the subject of ownership in one category, as property. . . . The real and natural distinction is between things which are the produce of labour and things which are the gratuitous offerings of Nature ; or, to adopt the terms of political economy, between wealth and land. These two things are in essence and relations widely different, and to class them together as property is to confuse all thought when we come to consider the justice, or the injustice, the right or wrong of property. . . .

The essential character of the one class of things is that they embody labour, are brought into being by human exertion, their existence or non-existence, their increase or diminution, depending on man. The essential character of the other class of things is that they do not embody labour, and exist irrespective of human exertion and irrespective of man ; they are the field or environment in which man finds himself ; the storehouse from which his needs must be supplied ; the raw material upon which and the forces with which his labour alone can act.— (" Progress and Poverty," pp. 238—239.)

The latter kind of property is land, the former all other commodities which constitute men's possessions ; and the latter are said, it will be observed, to be " brought into being by human exertion, their existence or non-existence, their increase or diminution depending on man." Surely this is an assertion which, though pardonable enough as a common manner of speaking,

Daire's collection (p. 657). All *biens* or commodities, including land, are, in the long run, more or less fashioned natural products ; " présents de la nature, mais aussi effets de l'art."

becomes a glaring fallacy the moment it is regarded as a scientific statement from which the
most serious practical consequences are deducible.
Can anything whatever, in strict truth, be said to
be " brought into being by human exertion " ?
Let us consider one of the earliest and simplest
products of human industry, a flint implement.
Probably, its earliest condition was a natural flint
nodule, such as one may find on any chalk down,
rounded at one end, roughly sharp at the other,
and thus convenient to the hand of the savage
who picked it up.   Now did he thus acquire any
right of property in his find or not ?   He certainly spent no labour upon it, beyond that of
taking possession.   It was emphatically " a gratuitous offering of Nature," just as much as the
land on which it lay.   The existence or the
non-existence of flints, their increase or diminution, nowise depends on man ; they exist irrespect-
ively of him, their quantity is strictly limited, and
no man, by taking thought, can add a flint to
those which already exist.   If taking possession
could give a title to the one thing, why not to the
other ?   But suppose it did not.   Let it occur to
our forefather that a few knocks with another
stone would chip the thin end of his flint to a
sharper edge and make it a handier tool or weapon.
Let him give those half-dozen blows ; then, forsooth, it " embodies labour " and may be said to
have been " brought into being by human exer-

tion." By the sacramental operation of these half-dozen taps, that which previously was the common property of all men has now become several property vested " by natural law " absolutely in one man.

With the gradual improvement of the art of flint chipping, the implement advanced from the rough, hardly modified, natural nodule to the exquisitely symmetrical and delicate axe, or spear, or arrow head, of a subsequent epoch, or to the still more finished ground axes of yet later date. The quantity of labour invested in each implement, therefore, steadily increased, as time went on, in proportion to the quantity of the raw flint. But the latter was always there. The assertion that the most perfected and artificial of these implements is " brought into being by human exertion," becomes a gross error if it leads us to forget that, without the peculiar physical properties of the flint, which are emphatically "the gratuitous offering of nature," any amount of human exertion would be thrown away.

What is true in this extremely simple case, is true of everything which is said to be produced by human industry. In all such things there is something—a bundle of natural qualities and powers which exists irrespective of human exertion—and something, a shaping and modification of the bundle, which is the effect of human exertion. It is only the relative proportion of the

two which varies.[1]   A man who hurls a stone
loads it with a dose of labour which evaporates
when the missile strikes its object, and the stone
returns to its previous condition of a mere offering
of Nature.   A man who slices the same stone and
cuts a cameo out of the slice, permanently incor-
porates an enormous amount of labour with it.

In the one case, the " gratuitous offering " is at a
maximum, in the other at a minimum ; but the
foundation in each case is a gift of Nature.

" Progress and Poverty " sets before us the case of
a steel pen with much elaboration (p. 236).   But
the author fails to notice the patent fact that the
iron ore, the existence of which is the *conditio sine
quâ non* of that of the pen, is a gratuitous offering
of Nature.   The well-known case of the chronometer balance-wheel spring would have still
better exemplified the maximum incorporation of
labour with the minimum of " the gratuitous
offering."

Now is there any real difference between land
and other things in this respect?   In Upper
Egypt, I have stood with one foot on soil bearing
a rich green crop, and the other on the stony
desert, as barren as a brick floor, which extended
for hundreds of miles to the westward without
supporting so much as a blade of grass.   The
green crop, in fact, reached exactly as far as the

[1] I have long since argued all this out in my *Introductory
Primer of Science.*

muddy water of the Nile had been carried by the labour of the irrigator. Surely, in this case, the cultivable land " embodied labour" and had no more existence independently of human exertion than the pen or the watch spring.

In the state of nature, I doubt if ten square miles of the surface of the chalk downs of Sussex would yield pickings enough to keep one savage for a year. But, thanks to the human labour bestowed upon it, the same area actually yields, one way or another, to the agriculturist the means of supporting many men. If labour is the foundation of the claim to several ownership, on what pretext can the land, in this case also, be put upon a different footing from the steel pen ? The same argument holds good for even the richest soil in the west of North America or in the south of Russia. In the natural state of such land, the savage hunter needs access to a vast area in order to make even a precarious livelihood. The labour spent upon it is an important factor in bringing about its rich harvests.

If we keep these simple and obvious truths in mind, the value of the following argument will be readily appraised :—

The right to exclusive ownership of anything of human production is clear. No matter how many the hands through which
it has passed, there was at the beginning of the line, human
labour—some one who, having procured or produced it by his
exertions, had to it a clear title as against all the rest of

mankind, and which could justly pass from one to another by sale or gift.[1]

Suppose, however, that we let this go and proceed to the next sentence :—

But at the end of what string of conveyances or grants can be shown or supposed a like title to any part of the material universe ?

Well, but surely all " human productions," from the roughest flint implement to the most exquisite chronometer, are " parts of the material universe " ? We have seen that man cannot make flints ; nor can he make the iron, or gold, or sodium, or silicon, which enters into the structure of the watch or the pen. His most consummate art is but a moving into certain places of the parts of the material universe with which Nature supplies him at least as gratuitously as she supplies land.

What then becomes of the next part of the argument ?

To improvements such an original title can be shown, but it is a title only to the improvements and not to the land itself. If I clear a forest, drain a swamp, or fill a morass, all I can justly claim is the value given by these exertions. They give me no right to the land itself, no claim other than to my equal share with every other member of the community in the value which is added to it by the growth of the community.

By a parity of reasoning, it would seem that I might say to a chronometer maker : " The gold and the iron of this timepiece, and, in fact, all the

[1] *Progress and Poverty*, p. 242.

substances out of which it is constructed, are parts of the material universe, therefore the property of mankind at large. It is very true that your skill and labour have made a wonderful piece of mechanism out of them; but these are only improvements. Now you are quite entitled to claim the improvements, but you have no right to the gold and the iron—these belong to mankind."

The watchmaker might reasonably think the task set before him as difficult as that imposed upon Shylock, when he was told that he was entitled to have his pound of flesh, but that he must shed no blood in the cutting it out. He might urge that for all practical purposes the "improvements" are the chronometer, while the gratuitous offering of Nature in the shape of raw material is relatively insignificant. To the ordinary mind there seems to be a great deal of sanity in this contention : not so to our political philosopher.

But it will be said : "There are improvements which in time become indistinguishable from the land itself !" Very well ; then the title to the improvements becomes blended with the title to the land : the individual right is lost in the common right. It is the greater that swallows up the less, not the less that swallows up the greater. Nature does not proceed from man, but man from Nature, and it is unto the bosom of Nature that he and all his works must return again. (p. 243.)

What answer is appropriate to such stuff as this but Mr. Burchell's famous, if unpolite, monosyllable "Fudge"?

It is one of the special characteristics of the *à priori* school to assume the exact truth of any currently received proposition which is convenient for the business of deductive brain-spinning. But every one who is conversant with things, and not merely with what is more or less properly said about things, is aware that most widely received propositions, even in many branches of physical science, may be only approximately true; and that if a chain of deductions of unusual weight is to be suspended from any of them, it is highly needful to examine it afresh, in order to see whether it will bear the strain—whether, in fact, it is accurate enough for the new purpose to which it is to be put. For ordinary purposes, a foot rule is an accurate measure, but it does not follow that it will suffice for ascertaining the exact length of the base line of a trigonometrical survey.

In this very case of the ownership of land, Mr. George essentially agrees with the Physiocrats who declared agriculture to be the only really productive industry, because land alone produces the food-stuffs by which men maintain their existence. In a rough and ready sense this is true, and it would be pedantic to object to it. But when such a statement is taken as the peg on which to hang deductions which end in grave practical consequences, it is needful to re-examine it thoroughly. And an elementary knowledge of the realities of the case enables one to see that, in

25

any but a popular sense, the proposition is untrue. In a strictly scientific sense, the soil is no more a producer than air and water and sunshine are; indeed, is altogether less important than they as a condition of production. For food-plants, which are the producers and the only producers of food-stuffs properly so called, could not possibly get on without air, water, and sunshine, though they might do without soil. It would be possible to grow a crop of food-plants, no part of which had ever been in contact with the soil. On the other hand, the richest of soils may be as barren as the desert in regard to economic production—for the simple reason that it is occupied by a luxuriant growth of plants that are not producers of food-stuffs adapted to human needs.

The "gratuitous offering of Nature" in the shape of a hundred acres of tropical forest would be of not much more use to a savage than the like area of a gorse common.

We have all this time been occupied with the eleven pages—not very large pages either—which make up the first chapter of the seventh book of "Progress and Poverty"; but there are more fallacies than pages, and I have not yet done with them. Indeed, like a careful entertainer, I have saved some of the best for the last. Here is a very fine one :—

The Almighty, who created the earth for man, and man for

the earth, has entailed it upon all the generations of the children of men by a decree written upon the constitution of things—a decree which no human action can bar and no prescription determine. (p. 240.)

One would think that the utterer of these "prave 'ords" had been the conveyancer who effected the entail of which he speaks thus confidently. Big-sounding but empty phrases may be the making of a stump-orator; but what is to be said of them in the mouth of a professed thinker? And what is the practical outcome of this tall talk?

Though his titles have been acquiesced in by generation after generation, to the landed estates of the Duke of Westminster, the poorest child that is born in London to-day has as much right as his eldest son. Though the sovereign people of the State of New York consent to the landed possessions of the Astors, the puniest infant that comes wailing into the world in the squalidest room of the most miserable tenement house, becomes at that moment seized of an equal right with the millionaires. And it is robbed if the right is denied. (p. 240.)

Landowners can make no just claim to compensation if society choose to resume its right. ("Progress and Poverty," Preface, p. vii.)

Who would not be proud to be able to orate in this fashion? Whose heart would not beat high at the tempest of cheers which would follow stirring words like these addressed to needy and ignorant men? How should the impassioned speaker's ear be able to catch a tone as of the howl of hungry wolves among the cheers? Why should he care that his stirring words might stir up the plain enough conclusion: Well, if these things are all ours as much as theirs, and we are the stronger, why do we not take our own, and that at once? What harm in robbing robbers?

Well, whether exhortations in this style are legitimate or not, this much is certain—that, as I hinted before, it is desirable to make very sure of your ground before proceeding to such extremities. Many years ago I heard of an Englishman who had gone to see the Coliseum at Rome by moonlight. He had been warned that the place was haunted by thieves, and was on the alert. Sure enough, a man brushed hastily past him, and the Englishman, looking back, saw a watch in his hand. Without more ado, our countryman, being a prompt sort of person, knocks the fellow down, captures the watch, and makes off to his hotel, lest there should be accomplices about. And, lo! when he is safe in his room he finds he has two watches.

I am disposed to think that the communities who follow out Mr. George's suggestions will find themselves, on Mr. George's own principles, in the position of our too ready-fisted Briton. For, according to Mr. George, that deed of entail which he should have somewhere in a tin box in his office, confers the land upon " all the generations of the children of men." Hence it follows that the London infant has no more title to the Duke of Westminster's land, and the New York baby no more to Messrs. Astor's land, than the child of a North American squaw, of a native Australian, or of a Hottentot. Property of the community, forsooth! What right has any community, from a village to a nation, to several property in land more than an individual man has?

Natural justice can recognise no right in one [*body of men*] to the possession and enjoyment of land that is not equally the right of all [*their*] fellows.   (p. 240.)

Does it make any difference to the validity of this proposition if I substitute the words in italics for the actual words " man " and " his " ? So the splendid prospect held out to the poor and needy is a mere rhetorical mirage ; and they have been cheated out of their cheers by mere " bunkum." Consider the effect of a sober and truthful statement of what the orating person really meant or, according to his own principles, ought to mean ; say of such a speech as this :—

My free and equal fellow countrymen, there is not the slightest doubt that not only the Duke of Westminster and the Messrs. Astor, but everybody who holds land from the area of a thousand square miles to that of a tablecloth, and who, against all equity, denies that every pauper child has an equal right to it, is a ROBBER. (Loud and long-continued cheers ; the audience, especially the paupers, standing up and waving hats.) But, my friends, I am also bound to tell you that neither the pauper child, nor Messrs. Astor, nor the Duke of Westminster, have any more right to the land than the first nigger you may meet, or the Esquimaux at the north end of this great continent, or

the Fuegians at the south end of it. Therefore, before you
proceed to use your strength in claiming your rights and take
the land away from these usurping Dukes and robbing Astors,
you must recollect that you will have to go shares in the produce
of the operation with the four hundred and odd millions of
Chinamen, the hundred and fifty millions who inhabit Hindo-
stan, the—— (loud and long-continued hisses ; the audience,
especially the paupers, standing up and projecting handy
movables at the orator).

IX

GOVERNMENT: ANARCHY OR
REGIMENTATION

[1890]

As a problem of political philosophy, Government presents three principal aspects. We may ask in whom is the sovereign authority vested? Or by what machinery should that authority be exercised? Or in respect of what matters is its exercise legitimate?

The first two of these questions have been discussed by philosophers and fought over by factions from the earliest times. Innumerable battles have been waged about the rival claims of kings, nobles and popular leaders to the "right divine to govern wrong;" and for, or against, the excellence of this or that legislative and administrative apparatus. The third question, on the other hand, has come to the front only in comparatively recent times. But its importance has increased and is increasing rapidly; indeed, at present, it completely overshadows the others.　The great problem of modern political philosophy is to determine the province of government.　Is there, or is there not, any region of human action over which the individual himself alone has jurisdiction and into which other men have no business to intrude ?

In the ancient polities of Greece and Rome hardly any part of human life, except a man's family religious practices, was thus sacred from the intrusion of the State.　Beyond the limits of this primary social group even religious liberty ceased.　The ancient States permitted no acts which manifested want of respect, still less such as savoured of active opposition, to the cults authorised by the community.　Any "infidels" who ventured to give open expression to their lack of faith in the gods of the city were quickly taught that they had better keep their opinions to themselves ; and no mercy was shown to those foreign religions the practices of which were judged to be inconsistent with the public welfare.　But the old pagan religions had no propaganda; and as persecution is usually a correlate of proselytism, they were fairly tolerant in practice, until the progress of Christianity opened the eyes of the Roman authorities to the fact that civil existence, as they understood it, was incompatible with religious existence, as the Christians understood it.　Pagan Rome, therefore, systematically persecuted Christianity with the intention of averting a political catastrophe of the gravest character. The Christian Church was the "International" of the emperors of the second and third centuries.

It is commonly supposed that the result of the intermittent, if internecine warfare thus waged was the victory of the Church, and that, in the words of Julian, the Galilean conquered. But those who compare the Christianity of Paul with that of Constantine's prelates may be permitted to doubt whether, as in so many other cases, the vanquished did not in effect subdue the victor; whether there is not much more of Greek philosophy and of Roman organisation and ritual, than of primitive Christianity, in the triumphant Catholicism of the fourth and later centuries. One heritage of old Roman statecraft, at any rate, passed bodily over to Catholic churchcraft. As soon as the church was strong enough, it began to persecute with a vigour and consistency which the Empire never attained. In the ages of faith, Christian ecclesiasticism raged against freedom of thought, as such, and compelled the State to punish religious dissidence as a criminal offence of the worst description. The ingenuity of pagan persecutors failed to reach the shameful level of that of the Christian inventors of the Holy Office; nor did the civil governors of pagan antiquity ever degrade themselves so far as to play the executioner for a camarilla of priests. The doctrine that the authority of the State extends to men's beliefs as well as to their actions, and, consequently, is conterminous with the whole of human life; and that the power of the State ought to be used for the promotion of orthodoxy and the extermination of heterodoxy is, in fact, a necessary corollary of Romanism, which, however disguised by prudence when the Papacy is weak, is sure to reappear when it is strong enough to dispense with hypocrisy. In the sixteenth century, the theory and practice of a thousand years had so thoroughly incorporated intolerance with Christianity, that even the great reformers held firmly by this precious heirloom of the ages of faith, whatever other shards of ecclesiastical corruption they might cast aside. Happily, the pretensions to infallibility of sects, who differed only in the higher or lower positions of the points at which they held on to the slope between Romanism and Rationalism, were so absurd, that political Gallios have been able to establish a *modus vivendi* among them. In this country, at any rate, the State is approaching, if it has not quite reached, a position of non-intervention (inclining perhaps to malevolent neutrality) in theological quarrels.

The prolonged intellectual and physical struggles which have thus tended to the more and more complete exclusion of a great group of human interests and activities from the legitimate sphere of governmental interference, have exerted a powerful influence on the general theory of

Government. Two centuries have elapsed since this influence, having for some time made itself felt among political philosophers, prompted that systematic inquiry into the proper limits of governmental action in general, which is contained in John Locke's two "Treatises on Government," published in 1689.

The Revolution of 1688 marks one of the acute stages of that contest between Liberalism and Absolutism in these islands which began to manifest itself in a remote period of our history. Liberalism, represented by Parliamentary politicians and Protestant theologians, had prevailed over Absolutism, represented by the Stuarts in the political sphere, and by Papistry, open or disguised, in that of religion. The two "Treatises" form an apology for the victors. A theoretical justification for the accomplished fact was much needed; and Locke would have been unworthy of his reputation as a speculative philosopher, if he had failed to discover, or to invent, a theory sufficiently plausible to satisfy those who desired nothing better than to be persuaded of the justice of acts, by which, in any case, they meant to stand. The first essay is ostensibly directed at poor dead and gone Sir Robert Filmer, with his Adamic mythology (which, by the way, Locke treats as if it were serious history); but the controversial shots are intended to pass through their ostensible object and to slay the defenders of divine right, who lay behind the Filmerian outpost. In the second essay, " On Civil Government," which alone has any interest to us at the present day, the theory of State omnipotence propounded by Hobbes (and supposed, though wrongfully, to have been invented in the interests of monarchy) is vigorously assaulted.

Hobbes was a thinker and writer of marvellous power, and, take him altogether, is probably the greatest of English philosophers; but it was given to him, as little as to Locke, to escape from entanglement in the *à priori* speculations which had come down mainly from the Roman jurists.[1] Setting out from the assumption of the

---

[1] Hobbes's conception of the State may be sufficiently gathered from the following passages extracted from the *Philosophical Rudiments concerning Government and Society* (1651): "All men, therefore, among themselves are by nature equal; the inequality we now discern hath its spring from the civil law" (chap. i. 3). "Nature hath given to every one a right to all" (*ibid.* 10). "The natural state of men before they entered into society was . . . . a war of all men against all men" (*ibid.* 12). In whatever man or body of men dominion or governmental authority is vested, "each citizen has conveyed all his strength and power to that man or council" (chap. v. 11). The supreme power is *absolute* (chap. vi. 13), and comparable to the soul of the city as its will (*ibid.* 19). "The will of every citizen is in all things comprehended in the will of the city, and the city is not tied to the civil laws," and the will of the depository of dominion is the will of the city (chap. vi. 14). Judging of good and evil does not belong to private citizens (chap. xii. 1), nor do they possess any rights or liberties except such as the sovereign grants. All power, temporal and spiritual, is united (under Christ) in the sovereign authority of a Christian city, and absolute obedience is due to it. When the sovereign is not Christian, and his commands are contrary to those of the Church, the subject must, disobeying but not resisting, "go to Christ by martyrdom" (chap. xviii. 13).

natural equality of men, and of a primary " state
of nature " in which every man strove for the full
exercise of his "natural rights," and which was,
therefore, a state of war of each against all ;
Hobbes further assumed that, in order to obtain
the blessings of peace, men entered into a contract
with one another, by which each surrendered the
whole of his natural rights to the person or persons appointed, by common consent, to exercise
supreme dominion, or sovereignty, over each and
all of the members of the commonwealth constituted by the contract. The authority of the
sovereign (whether one man or many, monarch or
people [1]) to whom this complete surrender of
natural rights was made, was thus absolute and
unquestionable. From the time of the surrender,
the individual member of the Commonwealth—
the citizen—possessed no natural rights at all ;
but, in exchange for them he acquired such civil
rights as the sovereign despot thought fit to grant
and to guarantee by the exercise of the whole
power of the State, if necessary. Civil law, sanctioned by the force of the community, took the
place of "natural right," backed only by the force
of the individual. It follows that no limit is, or
can be, theoretically set to State interference. The
citizen of the " Leviathan " is simply a member
of a composite organism controlled by the State
will ; he has no more freedom in religious matters

---

[1] See *Philosophical Rudiments*, chapters vi. and vii.

than in any others; but is to perform the practices of the State religion, and to profess the creed of its theology, whether he likes the one and believes the other, or not. The ideal of the State is a sternly disciplined regiment, in which the citizens are privates, the State functionaries officers, and every action in life is regulated and settled by the sovereign's "Regulations and Instructions." Disobedience is worse than mutiny. For those who disobey need not even be tried by court-martial. By the very act of insubordination they revoke the social contract, and, falling back into the state of nature—that is to say, of the war of each against all—they become aliens, who may be dealt with, summarily, as enemies.

Thus, there are three fundamental points in Hobbes's theory of a polity: First, the primitive state of nature, conceived as a state of war, or unrestricted struggle for existence, among men. Second, the contract, by the execution of which men entered into commonwealths or polities. Third, the complete surrender of all natural rights to the sovereign, and the conferring of absolute and despotic authority upon him, or them, by that contract.

Now, Locke also assumes a primitive state of nature, though its characters are different; he also assumes the contractual origin of the polity; and thus, on these two points, is in general agreement with Hobbes. But, with respect to the third article, he diametrically opposes Hobbes, and declares that the surrender of natural rights which took place when the social compact was made was not complete, but, on the contrary, most strictly and carefully limited.

The difference is of great importance. It marks the point of separation of two schools of *à priori* political philosophy, which have continued to be represented, with constantly increasing divergence, down to the present time, when the ultimate stages of their respective series confront one another as *Anarchy* on the one hand, and *Regimentation* on the other.

But it is necessary to define these epithets with care, before going further. Anarchy, as a term of political philosophy, must be taken only in its proper sense, which has nothing to do with disorder or with crime ; but denotes a state of society, in which the rule of each individual by himself is the only government the legitimacy of which is recognised. In this sense, strict anarchy may be the highest conceivable grade of perfection of social existence ; for, if all men spontaneously did justice and loved mercy, it is plain that all swords might be advantageously turned into ploughshares, and that the occupation of judges and police would be gone.[1] Anarchy, as

---

[1] "For if men could rule themselves, every man by his own command, that is to say, could they live according to the laws of nature, there would be no need at all of a city, nor of a

thus defined, is the logical outcome of that form of political theory, which for the last half-century and more has been known under the name of *Individualism*.[1]

I have, unfortunately, no such long established prescription to offer for the term *Regimentation*; but I hope it will be accepted until some one discovers a better denomination for the opposite view, the essence of which is the doctrine of State omnipotence. "Socialism," which at first suggests itself, is unfortunately susceptible of being used in widely different senses. As a general rule, no doubt, socialistic political philosophy is eminently regimental. But there is no necessary connection between socialism and regimentation. Persons, who, of their own free will, should think fit to imitate the primitive Christians depicted by the Acts, and to have all things in common, would be Socialists; and yet they might be none the less Individualists, so long as they refused to compel any one to join them. The only true contradictory of Individualism is that more common kind of

common coercive power."—Hobbes, *Philosophical Elements*, chap. vi. 13, *note*.

[1] It is employed as an already familiar appellative by Louis Blanc in the first volume of his *Histoire de la Révolution Française*, published in 1847, which contains a very interesting attempt to trace the influence of the principles of authority, of individualism, and of fraternity, through French history. The first volume of the elaborate work of Marlo (Winkelblech), *Organization der Arbeit*, published in 1850, gives a very complete exposition of the theory of Individualism under the name of *Liberalismus*.

Socialism which proposes to use the power of the State in order, as the phrase goes, to "organise" society, or some part of it. That is to say, this "regimental" Socialism proposes to interfere with the freedom of the individual to whatever extent the sovereign may dictate, for the purpose of more or less completely neutralising the effects of the innate inequalities of men. It is militarism in a new shape, requiring the implicit obedience of the individual to a governmental commander-in-chief, whose business is to wage war against natural inequality, and to set artificial equality in its place.

I propose now to give an outline of the progress, first of Regimentation and then of Individualism since the seventeenth century.

In France Regimentation was strongly advocated by Morelly and by Mably before Rousseau's essay on the Social Contract made its appearance; and, to my mind, except in point of literary form, the works of the ormer two writers are much better worth reading. But, while the immense popularity of Rousseau made him the apparent leader of the movement in favour of social regimentation, the comparative vagueness of his demands for equality commended him to practical politicians. His works became the gospel of the political—one might almost say the religious—sect of which Robespierre and St. Just were the chiefs ;[1] and the famous conspiracy of their would-be continuator, Babœuf, was an attempt to bring about the millennium of eighteenth century socialism by sanguinary violence.

According to Rousseau, the social contract is " the foundation of all rights " (chap. ix.) ; though the sovereign is not bound by it (chap. vii.), inasmuch as he can enter into no contract with himself. This sovereign is the totality of the citizens. Each, in assenting to the social contract, gives himself and all he possesses to the sovereign (vi.), " lui et toutes ses forces dont les biens qu'il possède font partie " (chap. ix.). He loses his natural liberty, and the State becomes master of him and of his goods (chap. ix.). As nature gives a man absolute power over all his members, the social compact gives the polity an absolute power over its citizens. The State, however, does not really despoil him. He gets back civil liberty (that is, such amount of liberty as the State

[1] As Mr. Lecky justly says : "That which distinguishes the French Revolution from other political movements is, that it was directed by men who had adopted certain speculative *à priori* conceptions of political right, with the fanaticism and proselytising fervour of a religious belief, and the Bible of their creed was the *Contrat Social* of Rousseau " (*History of England in the Eighteenth Century*, vol. v. p. 345). I have not undertaken a criticism of Rousseau's various and not unfrequently inconsistent political opinions, as a whole. It was not needful for my purpose to do so ; and, if it had been, I could not have improved upon the comprehensive and impartial judgment of our historian of the eighteenth century.

decrees) and a right of property in that which he possesses (chap. viii.). His previous possession, which was bare usurpation, is thus changed into right. In this way members of the community become mere depositaries of the public property, the private right of ownership being subordinate to the supreme right of the community (chap. ix.). The general will is the source of authority; whoever refuses to obey its behests is to be coerced into obedience by the whole body—"which means nothing more than that he shall be forced to be free" (chap. vii.). As will be seen on turning to the extracts from the "Philosophical Rudiments" given above (p. 388, *note*), most of this is Hobbism pure and simple. The fundamental principle of the Rousseauite, as of the Hobbist, polity is the omnipotence of the State; its boasted liberty is a grant from the sovereign despot, whose absolutism is sugared over by the suggestion that each man has an infinitesimal share in it. And, if any one of the sovereign people should be as blind to the benefits of this sort of free bondsmanship and coerced brotherly love as the "Needy knifegrinder" was, his "incivism" is to be cured by physical treatment: "On le forcera d'être libre."

The despotism of the "general will" (*volonte générale*) being thus established, how is the sovereign to make his commands known? This is a point about which it is surely necessary to be very

clear. Unfortunately, Rousseau leaves it not a
little obscure. He commences the second chapter
of his second book by declaring that the general
will is that of the body of the people; that, as
such, the declaration of it is an act of sovereignty,
while the declaration of the will of a part of the
people is merely an act of administration. Yet, in
a note, we are told that for the "will" to be
"general" it need not be unanimous, only all the
votes must be taken. How the expression of will
which is not unanimous can be other than that of
a part of the people, does not appear. But full
light is thrown upon Rousseau's real meaning in
the second chapter of the fourth book. Following
Locke's dictum that nothing can make a man a
member of a commonwealth "but his actually
entering into it by positive engagement and express promise and compact " (" Civil Government,"
§ 122) he tells us that

the only law which, by its nature, requires unanimous assent,
is the social compact : for civil association is the most voluntary
of all acts : every man being born free and master of himself, no
one, under any pretext whatever, can subject himself without
avowal of the act.

Those who do not assent when the social contract is made remain strangers among the citizens;
but after the State is constituted, residence within its bounds is to be taken as assent to the
contract.

Outside this primitive contract, the vote of the majority obliges the test ; that is a consequence of the contract itself.

In the Rousseauite State, then, sovereignty means neither more nor less than the omnipotence of a bare majority of voices of all the members of the State collected together in general meetings (chaps. xii.—xiv.).

During the sittings of this sovereign multitude, which are to take place at fixed intervals,

the jurisdiction of the government ceases, the executive power is suspended, and the person of the lowliest citizen is as sacred and inviolable as that of the highest magistrate ; for where the represented is present the representative ceases to exist.

In fact, in each of these periodical meetings, the polity potentially returns to the state of nature, and its members, if they please, may dissolve the social contract altogether : if they do not so please, they reappoint office-bearers to do the work assigned to them, whatever that may be (iii. chap. xvii.), until the next assembly. Society is thus a sort of joint-stock company, whose officers vacate their posts at every general meeting, and whose shareholders can wind up the concern, or go on, as the assembly may resolve, with such articles of association as a bare majority of the shareholders may determine shall be binding until the next meeting. An industrial company organised in this way would probably soon resign sovereignty to a liquidator. But then the members of industrial associations certainly do not undergo that transfiguration which, according to Rousseau, is worked by entrance into the social contract. "The general will," says he, "is always upright and always tends towards the general good" (liv. ii. chap. iii.); "the people are never corrupted" (*ibid.*); "all constantly desire the happiness of each" (liv. ii. chap. iv.).

Unfortunately, the intellect and the information of the sovereign are not always quite up to the standard of his morality :—

The general will is always just; but the judgment which guides it is not always enlightened (liv. ii. chap. vi.).

It would seem that flattery of the sovereign is not peculiar to monarchies. Notoriously, kings can do no wrong, and always spend their lives in sighing for the welfare of their subjects. If they seem to err, it is only because they are misled and misinformed. That has been the great make-believe of apologists for despotism from all time.

A properly enlightened sovereign people, with its incorruptible altruism, can never lose sight of the true end of legislation, the greatest good of all; and if we seek to know what that is, Rousseau tells us that it embraces two things, Liberty and Equality (liv. ii. chap. xi.). Liberty, he says, is "obedience to the law which one has laid down for oneself" (liv. i. chap. viii.); a well-sounding definition. But to my mind it is somewhat hard to reconcile with the obligation to submit to laws laid down by other people who happen to be in a majority. Unless, indeed, this " law which one has laid down for oneself" simply inculcates obedience to the majority. But, if that be liberty, then liberty is no less possessed by the man who makes it a law to himself to obey any master; and liberty is as fully possessed by the slave who makes up his mind to be a slave, as by the freest of free men.

With respect to the other aim of government, the maintenance of equality, Rousseau makes an instructive statement in answering the objection that the attempt is chimerical.

It is precisely because the nature of things (*force des choses*) continually tends to the destruction of equality, that the power of legislation ought always to tend to maintain it.[1]

---

[1] In spite of all his sentimentalism, Rousseau occasionally sees straight into the realities of things. *A prendre le terme dans la rigueur de l'acception, il n'a jamais existé de véritable démocratie, et il n'en existera jamais. Il est contre l'ordre naturel que le grand nombre gouverne, et que le petit soit gouverné. . . . . S'il y avait un peuple de dieux il se gouvernerait démocratiquement. Un gouvernement si parfait ne convient pas à des hommes* (liv. iii. chap. iv..). " A second Daniel come to judgment!" For it would not be far from the truth to say that the only form of government which has ever permanently existed is *oligarchy.* A very strong despot, or a furious multitude, may, for a brief space, work their single or collective will ; but the power of an absolute monarch is, as a rule, as much in the hands of a ring of ministers, mistresses, and priests, as that of Demos is, in reality, wielded by a ring of orators and wire-pullers. As Hobbes has pithily put the case, " A democracy in effect is no more than an aristocracy of orators, interrupted sometimes with

Absolute equality of power and wealth is not required, but neither opulence nor beggary is to be permitted ; and it is to depend upon the legislators' view of the circumstances whether the community shall devote itself to agriculture or to manufactures and commerce (liv. ii. chap. xi.). Thus the State is to control distribution no less than production. Moreover, the sovereign people is to settle the articles of a State religion, not exactly as religious dogmas, but as " sentiments of sociability without which a man can neither be a good citizen nor a faithful subject " :—

Without being able to oblige any one to believe them, he may banish from the State whoever does not believe them ; he may banish them, not for impiety, but for unsociability—as persons incapable of sincerely loving the laws or justice, and of sacrificing themselves to duty if needful. . . . If any one, after having acknowledged these same dogmas, conducts himself as if he did not believe them, let him be punished with death : he has committed the greatest of crimes, he has lied before the law (liv. iv. chap. viii.).

The articles of the State creed are : the existence of a powerful, intelligent, beneficent, foreseeing and provident Deity ; the life to come, the happiness of the just, the punishment of the

the temporary monarchy of one orator " (*De Corpore Politico*, chap. ii. 5). The alternative of dominion does not lie between a sovereign individual and a sovereign multitude, but between an aristarchy and a demarchy, that is to say, between an aristocratic and a democratic oligarchy. The chief business of the aristarchy is to persuade the king, emperor, or czar, that he wants to go the way they wish him to go ; that of the demarchy is to do the like with the mob.

wicked, the sanctity of the social contract and of the laws. These are the positive doctrines of the Rousseauite creed. Of negative dogmas there is only one, and the reader may be surprised to learn that it enjoins the repression of intolerance. Having banished unbelievers in the State creed and put to death lapsed believers, Rousseau thanks God that he is not as those publicans, the devotees of " les cultes que nous avons exclus "—intolerant. Does he not proclaim that all religions which tolerate others should themselves be tolerated ? Yet the qualificatory provision, " so far as their dogmas are in no way contrary to the duties of the citizen," would seem to effect a considerable reduction in the State toleration of the tolerators ; since, as we have just seen, it is obligatory on the citizen to profess the State creed.

Whether Rousseau used the works of Morelly and of Mably, as he did those of Hobbes and Locke, and whether his reputation for political originality is not of that cheap and easy sort which is won by sedulously ignoring those who have been unmannerly enough to anticipate us, need not be discussed. At any rate, important works of both these authors, in which the principles to be found in the essay on the " Social Contract " are made the foundation of complete schemes of regimental socialism, with community of goods, were published earlier than that essay. Robespierre and St. Just went as far as Rousseau in the direction of enforcing equality, but they left it to Babœuf to try to go as far as Mably. In their methods of endeavouring (by the help of the guillotine) to "force men to be free," they supplied the works naturally brought forth by the Rousseauite faith. And still more were they obedient to the master in insisting on a State religion, and in certifying the existence of God by a governmental decree.

The regimental Socialists of our own time appear to believe that, in their hands, political regimentation has taken a new departure, and substantially differs from that of the older apostles of their creed. Certainly they diverge from the views of Owen or of Fourier; but I can find nothing of importance in the serious writings of the modern school, nor even in their romances, which may not be discovered in the works of Morelly and of Mably, whose advocacy of the doctrines that several ownership is the root of all the evils of society; that the golden age would return if only the State directed production and regulated consumption; and that the love of approbation affords a stimulus to industry, sufficient to replace all those furnished by the love of power, of wealth and of sensual gratification, in our present imperfect state, is as powerful as that of any later writers.

We may now turn to the other line of development of political philosophy based upon *à priori* arguments, which is represented by individualism in various shades of intensity. I have already said that the founder and father of political individualism, as it is held by its more moderate adherents at the present day, is John Locke; and that his primary assumptions—the state of nature and the contractual basis of society—are the same as those of his predecessor Hobbes, and of his successors Rousseau and Mably. But I have also remarked that the condition of men in the state of nature, imagined by Locke, is different from that assumed by either Hobbes or Rousseau. For these last philosophers, primitive man was a savage; lawless and ferocious according to the older, good and stupid, according to the younger, theorist. Locke's fancy picture of primitive men, on the other hand, represents them under the guise of highly intelligent and respectable persons, "living together according to reason, without a common superior on earth, with authority to judge between them" ("Civil Government," § 19).

The Law of Nature [1] is, in fact, the law dictated by reason, which "teaches all mankind who will but consult it, that, being all equal and independent, no one ought to harm another in his life,

[1] This view of the law of nature comes from the jurists. Hobbes defines it in the same way, but he says that, in the state of nature, the Law of Nature is silent. In speaking of Locke as the founder and father of Individualism, I do not forget that Hooker (to whom Locke often refers), and still earlier writers, have expressed individualistic opinions. Nevertheless, I believe that modern individualism is essentially Locke's work.

liberty, or possessions." Elsewhere (§ 4), the state of nature is defined as a state of "perfect freedom," in which men "dispose of their possessions and persons as they think fit"; and further as a state of equality,

wherein all the power and jurisdiction is reciprocal, no one having more than another; there being nothing more evident than that creatures of the same species and rank, promiscuously born to all the same advantages of nature,[1] and the use of the same faculties, should also be equal one amongst another without subordination or subjection.

Again (§ 7), since the law of nature "willeth the peace and preservation of all mankind," every man has a "right to punish the transgressors of

[1] Yet Locke, of course, knows well enough that children are not born equal and that adults are extremely unequal. All that he really means is that men have an "equal right to natural freedom," and that is a mere *à priori* dictum (§ 54-87). The sceptics as to the reality of the state of nature are treated with some contempt (§ 14). "It is often asked as a weighty objection, Where are, or ever were there, any such men in a state of nature? To which it may suffice as an answer at present, that since all princes and rulers of independent governments, all through the world, are in a state of nature, it is plain that the world never was, or ever will be, without numbers of men in that state. I have named all governors of independent communities, whether they are or are not in league with others, for it is not every compact that puts an end to the state of nature between men, but only this one of agreeing together mutually to enter into one community and make one body politic; other promises and compacts men may make with one another, and yet still be in the state of nature. The promises and bargains for truck, &c., between the two men in the desert island mentioned by Garcilasso de la Vega, in his *History of Peru*, or between a Swiss and an Indian, in the woods of America, are binding to them though they are perfectly in a state of nature, in reference to one another: for truth and keeping of faith belongs to men as men, and not as members of society."

that law "; that is to say, those who invade the rights of others. Moreover, truth and the keeping of faith are commands of the Law of Nature, and belong "to men as men," and not as members of society (§ 14). Locke uses the term Law of Nature, therefore, in the sense in which it was often (perhaps generally) employed by the jurists, to denote a system of equity based on purely rational considerations.

There is no connection between this law of nature and "natural rights," properly so called. The state of nature imagined by Locke is, in fact, the individualistic golden age of philosophical anarchy, in which all men voluntarily rendering *suum cuique*, there is no need of any agency for the enforcement of justice. While Hobbes supposes that, in the state of nature, the Law of Nature was silent, Locke seems to imagine that it spoke loudly enough, but that men grew deaf to it. It was only in consequence of the failure of some of them to maintain the original standard of ethical elevation that those inconveniences arose which drove the rest to combine into commonwealths ; to choose rulers ; and to endow them, as delegates of all, with the sum of the right to punish transgressors inherent in each.

In taking this important step, however, our forefathers exhibited that caution and prudence which might be expected from persons who dwelt upon the ethical heights which they had reached in the state of nature. Instead of making a complete surrender of all the rights and powers which they possessed in that state, to the Sovereign, and thus creating State omnipotence by the social contract, as Hobbes wrongfully declared them to have done, they gave up only just so much of them as was absolutely necessary for the purposes of an executive with strictly limited powers. With the Stuarts recognised by France, and hosts of Jacobite pamphleteers on the look-out for every coign of vantage, it would never do to admit the Hobbesian doctrine of complete surrender. So Locke is careful to assert that when men entered into commonwealths they must have stipulated (and, therefore, on approved *à priori* principles, did stipulate) that the power of the Sovereign was strictly limited to the performance of acts needful " to secure every one's property."

§ 131. But though men, when they enter into society, give up the equality, liberty, and executive power they had in the state of nature, into the hands of the society to be so far disposed of by the legislative, as the good of society shall require ; yet it being only with an intention in every one the better to preserve himself, his liberty and property ; (for no rational creature can be supposed to change his condition with an intention to be worse), the power of the society, or legislative constituted by them, can never be supposed to extend farther, than the common good ; but is obliged to secure every one's property by providing against those three defects above mentioned, that made the state of nature so unsafe and uneasy.[1]

[1] The following passages complete the expression of Locke's meaning: " Political power, then, I take to be a right of making

To listen to Locke, one would imagine that a general meeting of men living in the state of nature having been called to consider the " defects " of their condition, and somebody being voted to the tree (in the presumable absence of chairs), this earliest example of a constituent assembly resolved to form a governmental company, with strictly limited liability, for the purpose of defending liberty and property ; and that they elected a director or body of directors, to be known as the Sovereign, for the purpose of carrying on that business and no other whatsoever. Thus we are a long way from the absolute Sovereign of Hobbes. Here is the point, in fact, at which Locke diverged from the older philosopher ; and at which Rousseau and Mably; after profiting as much as they could by Locke's " Essay," left him and laid the theoretical foundations of regimental socialism.

The physiocrats of the eighteenth century, struggling against the effects of that " fureur de gouverner," which one of their leaders, the elder Mirabeau, called the worst malady of modern states, and which had nearly succeeded in strang-

laws with penalties of death, and consequently of all less penalties, for the regulating and preserving of property, and of employing the force of the community in the execution of such laws and in the defence of the commonwealth from foreign injury ; and all this only for the public good," (§ 3). " Government has no other end than the preservation of property " (§ 94). " The great and chief end, therefore, of men's uniting into commonwealths and putting themselves under government is the preservation of their property " (§ 124).

ling every branch of French industry and starving the French people, necessarily welcomed and adopted Locke's individualistic formula. Their favourite maxim of "Laissez faire" was a corollary of the application of that formula in the sphere of economy; and it was a great thing for them to be able to add to the arguments based on practical expediency, which could be properly appreciated only by those who took pains to learn something about the facts of the case, the authority of a deduction from one of those *à priori* truths, the just appreciation of which is supposed to come by nature to all men. The axiom of absolute ethics in question has been stated in many ways. It is laid down that every man has a right to do as he pleases, so long as he does no harm to others; or that he is free to do anything he pleases, so long as he does not interfere with the same freedom in others. Daire, in the introduction to his "Physiocrates" (p. 16), goes so far as to call the rule thus enunciated a "law of nature."

La loi naturelle qui permet à chacun de faire tout ce qui lui est avantageux sous la seule condition de ne pas nuire à autrui. [1]

---

[1] The oldest recorded form of the rule, and that which has the most positive character, is contained in the command of the Jewish law, "Thou shalt love thy neighbour as thyself," (Leviticus xix. 18), (neighbour including "stranger that dwelleth with you," v. 34), which stands in the same relation to the individualistic maxim as Fraternity to Equity. The strength of Judaism as a social organisation has resided in its unflinching

The physiocrats accepted the dogma of human equality, and they further agreed with Locke in considering that the restriction of the functions of the Government to the protection of liberty and property was in nowise inconsistent with further- ance of education by the State. On the contrary, they considered education to be an essential condition of the only equality which is consistent with liberty. Moreover, they laid great stress on the proposition that justice is inseparably con- nected with property and liberty. Nothing can be stronger than the words of Quesnay on this point :—

Là où les lois et la puissance tutelaire n'assurent point la propriété et la liberté, il n'y a ni gouvernement ni société profit- ables ; il n'y a que domination et anarchie sous les apparences d'un gouvernement; les lois positives et la domination y protègent et assurent les usurpations des forts, et anéantissent la pro- priété et la liberté des faibles.[1]

That is to say, the absolute political ethics of the individualist leave as little doubt in his mind that private property and the right to deal freely with it are essential to the protection of the weak against the strong, as the absolute political ethics

advocacy of freedom, within the law ; equality, before the law ; and fraternity, outside the law. I am not sure that, from the purely philosophical point of view, the form in which that great Jew, Spinoza, has stated the rule is not the best : "Desire nothing for yourself which you do not desire for others," (*nihil sibi appetere quod reliquis hominibus non cupiant*). (*Ethices*, IV. xviii.)

[1] *Droit Naturel*, chap. 5.

of the regimental socialist assure him that private
property and freedom of contract involve the
tyranny of the strong over the weak.

Through the widespread influence of the "Wealth
of Nations," individualism became a potent factor
in practical politics. Wherever the principles of
free-trade prevailed and were followed by industrial prosperity, individualism acquired a solid
fulcrum from which to move the political world.
Liberalism tended to the adoption of Locke's
definition of the limits of State action, and to
consider persistence in letting alone as a definition
of the whole duty of the statesman. But in the
hands of even the most liberal governments, these
limits proved pretty elastic ; and, however objec-
tionable State interference might be, it was found
hard to set bounds to it, if indirect as well as
direct interference were permissible. So long ago
as the end of the eighteenth century, the distinguished scholar and statesman Wilhelm von
Humboldt[1] attempted to meet this difficulty. He
wrote a special treatise, which remained unpub-
lished till sixty years later, for the purpose of
showing that the legitimate functions of the State

[1] Von Humboldt's essay was written in 1791 ; but views so
little likely to be relished by the German governments of that
day needed cautious enunciation, and only fragments appeared
(under the auspices of Schiller) until 1852, when the treatise
formed part of the posthumous edition of Von Humboldt's
works. A translation, under the title of *The Sphere and Duties
of Government*, was published in 1854, by Dr. Chapman (then,
as now, the editor of the *Westminster Review*), and became very
well known in this country.

are negative ; and that governments have no right to take any positive steps for the promotion of the welfare of the governed. Von Humboldt does not encumber himself with Locke's " limited contract," but starts an *à priori* axiom of his own, namely :—

That reason cannot desire for any man any other condition than that in which each individual not only enjoys the most absolute freedom of developing himself by his own energies in his perfect individuality, but in which external nature even is left unfashioned by any human agency, but only receives the impress given to it by each individual by himself and his own free will, according to the measure of his wants and instincts, and restricted only by the limits of his powers and rights. (p. 18).

From this very considerable assumption (which I must say does not appear to me to possess the quality of intuitive certainty) the conclusion is deduced that

the State is to abstain from all solicitude for the positive welfare of the citizens and not to proceed a step farther than is necessary for their mutual security and protection against foreign enemies ; for with no other object should it impose restrictions on freedom.

This conclusion differs but little from that of Locke, verbally. Nevertheless in its practical application, Von Humboldt excludes not only all and every matter of religion, of morals, and of education, but the relations of the sexes, and all private actions not injurious to other citizens, from the interference of the State. However, he permits governmental regulation of the power of testamentary devolution; and (though somewhat unwillingly) interference with acts which are not immediately hurtful to one's neighbours, yet the obvious tendencies of which are to damage them or to restrict their liberties.

By far the best and fullest exposition known to me of the individualism which, in principle, goes no further than Locke's formula, is Dunoyer's " Liberté du Travail " of which the first volume was published in 1825, and the whole work in 1845. One great merit of the author is the resolute casting aside all the *à priori* figments of his predecessors ; and another lies in his careful and elaborate discussion of the historical growth of Individualism, which goes a long way towards the establishment of the conclusion, that advance in civilisation and restriction of the sphere of Government interference have gone hand in hand. J. S. Mill has referred to Dunoyer's work ; but later expositors of Individualism ignore him completely, although they have produced nothing comparable to the weighty case for the restriction of the sphere of government, presented with a force which is not weakened by fanaticism, in the seventh chapter of the ninth book of Dunoyer's work.

The year 1845 is further marked in the annals of Individualism by the appearance of Stirner's

" The Individual and his Property,[1] " in which the author, going back to first principles, after a ruthless criticism of both limited Individualism and regimental Socialism, declares himself for unlimited Individualism; that is to say, Anarchy. Stirner justly points out that " natural right " is nothing but natural might. Man, in the state of nature, could know of no reason why he should not freely use his powers to satisfy his desires. When men entered into society they were impelled by self-interest. Each thought he could procure some good for himself by that proceeding; and his natural right to make the most out of the situation remained intact. The theory of an express contract, with either complete or incomplete surrender of natural rights, is an empty figment, nor was there any understanding, except perhaps that each would grasp as much as he could reasonably expect to keep. According to this development of Individualism, therefore, the state of nature is not really put an end to by the formation of a polity; the struggle for existence is as severe as ever though its conditions are somewhat different. It is a state of war; but instead of the methods of the savage, who sticks at no treachery, and revels in wanton destruction, we have those of modern warfare, with its Red Cross ambulances, flags of truce strictly respected, and extermination con-

---

[1] *Der Einzige und sein Eigenthum,* by Max Stirner. I follow the account of the contents of the book given by Meyer, *Der Emancipationskampf des vierten Standes* (Ed. 2, 1882, pp. 36—44).

ducted with all the delicate courtesies of chivalry.
The rules of this refined militancy are called laws,
and prudence dictates respect for them because, as
it is to the advantage of the majority that they
should be observed, the many have agreed to fall
upon any one who breaks them ; and the many are
stronger than the one. . Thus the sole sanction of
law being the will of the majority, which is a mere
name for a draft upon physical force, certain to be
honoured in case of necessity; and "absolute
political ethics" teaching us that force can confer
no rights; it is plain that state-compulsion
involves the citizen in slavery, as completely as if
any other master were the compeller.   Wherever
and whenever the individual man is forced to submit to any rules, except those which he himself
spontaneously recognises to be worthy of observance, there liberty is absent.   And thus we
arrive at the position of the great apostle of
anarchy, Bakounine, according to whom the
liberty of man consists solely in this : that " he
pays obedience to natural laws, because *he himself*
admits them to be such, and not because they
have been imposed upon him from without by any
other will, whether divine or human, collective or
individual." [1]   Hence it fellows that the "sovereign
people" worshipped by the great champions of
liberty and equality, when it dares to impose the
"general will" upon the individual, even if that

---

[1] *Dieu et l'Etat*, 1881.

person be in a minority of one, is as brutal a usurper as ever exercised monarchical tyranny; and, whether a man shall so much as recognise the right of another to the freedom which he himself exercises, is to be left to his private judgment. As all property is robbery, so is all government from without, tyranny.

In this country, where the influence of the pedantry of the Absolute is so much trammelled by common sense and more or less experience of the difference between the nature of things and *à priori* assumptions, Individualism has, usually, stopped short of the conclusions of Stirner and of Bakounine, beyond which, so far as I can see, the *à priori* method can hardly carry its most hardened practitioner. Nevertheless, the "party of Individual Liberty," of which Mr. Auberon Herbert is the spokesman, must, I think, be classified as Anarchist;[1] though the definition of their conception of the relations of the individual to government looks, at first sight, as if it meant no more than limited Individualism.

Each man and woman are to be free to direct their faculties and their energies according to their own sense of what is right

---

[1] Let me remind the reader that I use "anarchy" in its philosophical sense. Heaven forbid that I should be supposed to suggest that Mr. Herbert and his friends have the remotest connection with those too "absolute" political philosophers who desire to add the force of dynamite to that of persuasion. It would be as reasonable to connect Monarchists with murder, on the strength of the proceedings of a Philip the Second, or a Lewis the Fourteenth.

and wise, in every direction except one.　They are not to use their faculties for the purpose of forcibly restraining their neighbour from the same free use of his faculties. [1]

And as to Governments—

They must simply defend the person and property of all persons by whomsoever they are assailed. [2]

This, it will be observed, is the dictum of Locke and nothing more.

But, in the application of the theory to practice, Mr. Herbert goes a good deal further than even Humboldt or Dunoyer.　He would do away with all enforced taxation and levying of duties, and trust to voluntary payments for the revenue of the State.　The relations of the sexes and the disposition of property by will are to be quite free; traffic of all kinds is to be released from restrictions; state inspection is to be abolished, no less than all hygienic regulations; state education goes, as a matter of course, and with it all state-aided museums, libraries, galleries of art, parks, and pleasure grounds.　In fact, the functions of government within the State are rigidly restricted to the administration of civil and criminal justice.

But this is not all.　Mr. Herbert oversteps the bounds of limited Individualism and enters the region of Anarchy, when he says he is not quite sure that even this pittance of administrative power is strictly justifiable.

[1] *The Right and Wrong of Compulsion by the State*, 1885.
[2] *Ibid.* p. 33.

I do not think that it is possible to find a perfect moral foundation for the authority of any Government, be it the Government of an emperor or a Republic. They are all of the nature of an usurpation, though I think, when *confined within certain exact limits*, of a justifiable usurpation.[1]

A "justifiable usurpation" is something which I can no more conceive than I can imagine a round square ; it being the nature of usurpation, as I imagine, to be unjustifiable. But I presume that what is meant is, that, though government has no moral authority, it is practically expedient that it should be permitted to exist, if confined within very narrow limits. Absolute ethics, in Mr. Herbert's opinion, refuses to acknowledge the right of any government except the government of the individual by himself. Therefore I am unable to discern any logical boundary between Mr. Herbert's position and that of Bakounine.

The fact that Individualism, pushed to its logical extreme, must end in philosophical anarchy, has not escaped that acute thinker and vigorous writer, Mr. Donisthorpe, whose work on "Individualism"[2] is at once piquant, learned, and thoroughgoing—qualities in which the writings of speculative philosophers do not always abound. I commend Mr. Donisthorpe's eighth chapter, entitled "A Word for Anarchy," to those who

[1] *The Right and Wrong of Compulsion by the State*, 1885, p. 22.
[2] *Individualism : a System of Politics*, 1889.

desire to understand whither the Individualist
principle, stripped bare of *à priori* fogs and for-
mulas, and followed out to its consequences, lands
its supporters.

Starting from assumptions about the equality
of men, their natural rights and the social contract, common to so many political philosophers
of the *à priori* school, we have been offered the
choice of two alternative routes. Taking that
indicated by Hobbes, Rousseau, Mably, and their
successors, we have found ourselves committed to
the further *à priori* assumption that, when men
entered into society, they surrendered all their
natural rights; and, acknowledging the omnipotence of the general will, received back such
legal and moral obligations and permissions as the
Sovereign might be pleased to sanction. Absolute
political ethics thus arrived, by a plausible logical
process, at *Regimentation ;* that is, a quasi-military
organisation of society, for the purpose of conquer-
ing the general welfare by means of that enforced
apparent equality which brings about the hugest
of real inequalities.

On the other hand, when we took the path
pointed out by Locke and followed by Liberalism,
we made an *à priori* assumption of a diametrically
opposite character. We said that men entering
into the social contract reserved all their natural
rights, except such as it was absolutely necessary

to yield to government, in order that it should exercise its only legitimate function, the defence of the liberty and property of the individual. According to this limited individualist view, the business of government (except in relation to external enemies) is negative; it is to interfere only for the purpose of preventing any one citizen from using his liberty in such a way as to interfere with the equal liberty of another citizen. According to the regimentalist view, on the contrary, the business of government is not only negative, but also and eminently positive. It is the duty of the State to interfere for the purpose of promoting the welfare of society (of which equality is supposed to be a necessary condition), however much such interference may restrict individual liberty. The final outcome of Regimentation is seen in those extreme forms of regimental Socialism which undertake to regulate not only production and consumption, but every detail of human life; that of Individualism is Anarchy, which abolishes collective government and trusts to the struggle for existence, modified by such ethical and intellectual considerations as may be freely recognised by the individual, for the establishment of a social *modus vivendi*, in which freedom remains intact, except so far as it may be voluntarily limited.

Granting the premisses, I am unable to see that one of these lines of argument is any better than the other ; and they are mutually destructive. But suppose that, not being blinded by any *à priori* cataracts, we use our eyes upon these premisses— what utter shams and delusions they show themselves to be ! I hope that no more need be said about natural rights and the equality of men. But there is just as little foundation in fact for the social contract and either the limited, or the unlimited, devolution of rights and powers which is supposed to have been effected by it. We have sadly little definite knowledge of the manner in which polities arose, but, if anything is certain, it is that the notion of a contract, whether expressed or implied, is by no means an adequate expression of the process.

The most archaic polities of which we have any definite record are either families, or federations of families ; and the most doctrinaire of political philosophers will hardly be prepared to maintain that the family polity was based upon contract between the *paterfamilias* and his wife and children, and arose out of the expressed desire of the latter to have their liberty and property protected by their governor ; or that even any tacit understanding on that subject influenced the formation of the family group. In truth, the more primitive the condition of a polity, the less is there of a contract, either expressed or implied, between its members—the more common is it to find that neither wife nor child possessed either liberty, or property, worth speaking of. The *pater-familias* of the Aryan stock, at any rate, could say " L'état c'est moi " with more truth than any later monarch. So far from the preservation of liberty and property and the securing of equal rights being the chief and most conspicuous objects aimed at by the archaic polities of which we know anything, it would be a good deal nearer the truth to say that they were federated absolute monarchies, the chief purpose of which was the maintenance of an established Church for the worship of the family ancestors.

Philosophers, proud of living according to reason, are too apt to forget that people who do not profess themselves to be more than ordinary men mostly live according to unreason; or what seems such to the philosophers. Moderns, who make to themselves metaphysical teraphim out of the Absolute, the Unknowable, the Unconscious, and the other verbal abstractions whose apotheosis is indicated by initial capitals, may find it difficult to imagine that it seemed good to ancient men to perform the same theurgic operation upon their very concrete but deceased forefathers ; and to believe that, unless the Manes were regularly propitiated with a supply of such commodities as ghosts can enjoy, they would not only withdraw their benevolent protection, but would make things very unpleasant for their descendants and their fellow countrymen. Yet there can be little question that this theory lies at the foundation of the ancient polity ; and that the dominant purpose of its organisation was not the preservation of liberty or property, by taking order that no man used his freedom in a way to interfere with others' freedom, but the performance of those religious obligations by which the good will of the ancestral gods might be secured. Archaic society aims, not at the freest possible exercise of rights, but at the exactest possible discharge of duties. The most marked inequalities and seeming iniquities of ancient law, such as succession in the male line, the acknowledgment of agnate blood relationship only, adoption, divorce for barrenness, are direct consequences of the religious foundation of ancient society. Thus the whole fabric of *à priori* political speculation which we have had under consideration is built upon the quicksand of fictitious history. So far as this method of establishing their claims is concerned, *Regimentation* and *Individualism*—enforced Socialism and Anarchy—are alike out of court.

The comments upon the preceding essays which have come under my notice, lead me to suspect that my purpose in writing them has been somewhat misunderstood.

They appear to have been regarded by the regimental socialists as an onslaught specially directed against their position ; and as an attempt to justify those who, content with the present, are opposed to all endeavours to bring about any fundamental change in our social arrangements.

Those who have had the patience to follow me to the end will, I trust, have become aware that my aim has been altogether different. Even the best of modern civilisations appears to me to exhibit a condition of mankind which neither embodies any worthy ideal nor even possesses the merit of stability. I do not hesitate to express the opinion, that, if there is no hope of a large improvement of the condition of the greater part of the human family; if it is true that the increase of knowledge, the winning of a greater dominion over Nature which is its consequence, and the wealth which follows upon that dominion, are to make no difference in the extent and the intensity of Want, with its concomitant physical and moral degradation, among the masses of the people, I should hail the advent of some kindly comet, which would sweep the whole affair away, as a desirable consummation. What profits it to the human Prometheus that he has stolen the fire of heaven to be his servant, and that the spirits of the earth and of the air obey him, if the vulture of pauperism is eternally to tear his very vitals and keep him on the brink of destruction?

Assuredly, if I believed that any of the schemes hitherto proposed for bringing about social amelio-

ration were likely to attain their end, I should
think what remains to me of life well spent in
furthering it. But my interest in these questions
did not begin the day before yesterday; and,
whether right or wrong, it is no hasty conclusion
of mine that we have small chance of doing wisely
in this matter (or indeed in any other), unless we
think rightly. Further, that we shall never
think rightly in politics until we have cleared our
minds of delusions; and, more especially, of the
philosophical delusions which, as I have endeavoured to show, have infested political thought
for centuries. My main purpose has been to contri-
bute my mite towards this essential preliminary
operation. Ground must be cleared and levelled
before a building can be properly commenced;
the labour of the navvy is as necessary as that of
the architect, however much less honoured; and
it has been my humble endeavour to grub up
those old stumps of the *à priori*, which stand in
the way of the very foundations of a sane political
philosophy. To those who think that questions
of the kind I have been discussing have merely
an academic interest, let me suggest, once more,
that a century ago Robespierre and St. Just
proved that the way of answering them may have
extremely practical consequences.

The task which I set before myself, then, was
simply a destructive criticism of *à priori* political
philosophy, whether regimental or individualistic.

But I am aware that the modesty of the purely
critical attitude is not appreciated as it ought to
be. There is a prevalent idea that the constructive genius is in itself something grander than the
critical, even though the former turns out to
have merely made a symmetrical rubbish heap in
the middle of the road of science, which the
latter has to clear away before anybody can get
forward. The critic is told : It is all very well to
show that this, that, or the other is wrong; what
we want to know is, what is right ?

Now, I submit that it is unjust to require a
crossing sweeper in Piccadilly to tell you the road
to Highgate; he has earned his copper if he has
done all he professes to do and cleaned up your
immediate path. So I do not think any one has
a claim upon me to make any positive suggestions,
still less to commit myself to any ambitious
schemes of social regeneration such as are now as
common as blackberries. Reading and experience
have led me to believe that the results of political
changes are hardly ever those which their friends
hope or their foes fear; and, if I were offered a
free hand by Almighty power, I should, like
Hamlet, shudderingly object to the responsibility
of attempting to set right a world out of joint.
But I may perhaps, without presumption, set
forth some reflections, germane to the subject,
which have now and again crossed my mind.

About this question of government, for example ;

28

perhaps it is the prejudice of scientific habit, which leads me to think that it might be as well to proceed from the known to the unknown. Most of us, I hope, have tried their hands at self-government; and those who have met with any measure of success in that difficult art will, I believe, agree with me that safety lies neither in the regimentation of asceticism nor in the anarchy of reckless self-seeking, but in a middle course. Surely there is a time to submit to guidance and a time to take one's own way at all hazards.

A good many of us, again, have had practical experience of the government of that elementary polity, a family. In this business, the people who fail utterly are, on the one hand, the martinet regimentalists and, on the other, the parents whose theory of education appears to be that expounded by the elder Mr. Weller, when, if I remember rightly, he enlarged upon the advantages which Sam had enjoyed by being allowed to roam at will about Covent Garden Market, from babyhood upwards. Individualism, pushed to anarchy, in the family is as ill-founded theoretically and as mischievous practically as it is in the State; while extreme regimentation is a certain means of either destroying self-reliance or of maddening to rebellion.

When we turn from the family to the aggregation of families which constitutes the State, I do not see that the case is substantially altered. The problem of government may be stated to be, What ought to be done and what to be left undone by society, as a whole, in order to bring about as much welfare of its members as is compatible with the natural order of things? and I do not think men will ever solve this problem unless they clear their minds, not merely of the notion that it can be solved *à priori;* but unless they face the fact that the natural order of things '—the order, that is to say, as unmodified by human effort—does not tend to bring about what we understand as welfare. On the contrary, the natural order tends to the maintenance, in one shape or another, of the war of each against all, the result of which is not the survival of the morally or even the physically highest, but of that form of humanity, the mortality of which is least under the conditions. The pressure of a constant increase of population upon the means of support must keep up the struggle for existence, whatever form of social organisation may be adopted. In fact, it is hard to say whether the state of anarchy or that of extreme regimentation would be the more rapidly effective in bringing any society which multiplies without limit to a crisis.

The cardinal defect of all socialistic schemes appears to me to be, that they either ignore this difficulty or try to evade it by nonsensical suppositions about increasing the production of vital capital[1] *ad libitum*. Individualism, on the other hand, admitting the inevitability of the struggle, is too apt to try to persuade us that it is all for our good, as an essential condition of progress to higher things. But that is not necessarily true ; the creature that survives a free-fight only demonstrates his superior fitness for coping with free-fighters—not any other kind of superiority.

The political problem of problems is how to deal with over-population, and it faces us on all sides. I have heard a great deal about the tyranny of capital. No doubt it is true that labour is dependent on capital. No doubt if, out of a thousand men, one holds and can keep all the capital,[2] the rest are bound to serve him or die. But if, on this ground, labour may be said to be the slave of capital, it would be equally just to say that capital is the slave of labour. A naked millionaire, with a chest full of specie, might be set down in the middle of the best agricultural estate in England ; but unless somebody would work for him, he would probably soon perish from cold and hunger, having previously lost everything for lack of protection. The state of things attributed to the tyranny of the capitalist might be far more properly ascribed to the self-enslavement

---

[1] The term "vital capital" is defined in an essay on "Capital and Labour" published in *The Nineteenth Century* (1890), which could not conveniently be included in this volume.

[2] Using the term in its more restricted sense.

of the wage earners. It is their competition with one another which makes his strength.

Over-population has two sources: one internal by generation, one external by immigration. Theoretically, the elimination of Want is possible by the arrest of both, in such a manner as to restrict the population of any area to the number capable of being fed by the agricultural produce of that area ; the manufacturing and professional population being kept down to a number equal to the difference between the necessary agricultural and the total permissible population. A polity of this kind might be self-supporting, and there need be no poverty in it, except such as arose from moral delinquencies or unavoidable calamities.

This is, substantially, the plan of the " Closed Industrial State "[1] set forth by Fichte ; and, so far as I can see, there is no other social arrangement by which Want can be permanently eliminated. For if either unrestricted generation or unrestricted immigration is permitted ; or if any considerable proportion of the industrial population is allowed to depend for its food upon foreign sources, pauperism becomes imminent—in the first case, by the competition of the native and the imported workers with one another ; in the second case, by the competition in the market of foreign industries of the same nature.

I offer no opinion whether Fichte's Utopia is

[1] *Der geschlossene Handelsstaat*, 1800.

practically realisable or not. That about which I have a very strong opinion is, that political speculators who, while ignoring these conditions, promise a millennium of equality and fraternity, are reckoning sadly without their host, or rather hostess, Dame Nature.

END OF VOL. I